IQ
BRAINBENDERS

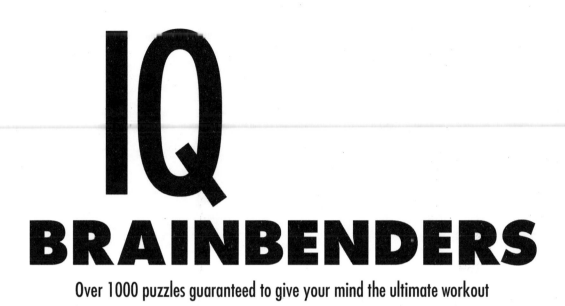

IQ
BRAINBENDERS

Over 1000 puzzles guaranteed to give your mind the ultimate workout

ARCTURUS

ARCTURUS

This edition published in 2009 by Arcturus Publishing Limited
26/27 Bickels Yard, 151–153 Bermondsey Street,
London SE1 3HA

Copyright © 2009 Arcturus Publishing Limited

ISBN: 978-1-84837-169-9

Printed in Malaysia

IQ
BRAINBENDERS

Stand by for the ultimate test: over 1000 IQ puzzles specially designed to stretch your logical and lateral thinking abilities to the limit. Some will require keen mathematical skill, others an ability to recognize patterns and sequences or spot similarities and differences, but all are supremely logical and can be solved if you have the right approach.

Some of the answers will jump straight out at you. However, others will require a bit more thought. Try not to rush for an answer – have faith in your abilities and all will become clear – and don't feel tempted to have a peek at the answer page too soon. If you feel completely stumped by one particular puzzle, then move on and come back to it later – finding the solution to a later puzzle just might give you the inspiration you need!

But the idea of this book is not about right and wrong answers, it's about exercising your mind, flexing your mental muscles and, ultimately, helping you to fulfil your IQ potential.

Multiplication Table

×	1	2	3	4	5	6	7	8	9	10	11	12
1	1	2	3	4	5	6	7	8	9	10	11	12
2	2	4	6	8	10	12	14	16	18	20	22	24
3	3	6	9	12	15	18	21	24	27	30	33	36
4	4	8	12	16	20	24	28	32	36	40	44	48
5	5	10	15	20	25	30	35	40	45	50	55	60
6	6	12	18	24	30	36	42	48	54	60	66	72
7	7	14	21	28	35	42	49	56	63	70	77	84
8	8	16	24	32	40	48	56	64	72	80	88	96
9	9	18	27	36	45	54	63	72	81	90	99	108
10	10	20	30	40	50	60	70	80	90	100	110	120
11	11	22	33	44	55	66	77	88	99	110	121	132
12	12	24	36	48	60	72	84	96	108	120	132	144

Cube Numbers		Square Numbers		Numerical Values			Prime Numbers
1	1	1	1	A	26	2
2	8	4	2	B	25	
3	27	9	3	C	24	3
4	64	16	4	D	23	
5	125	25	5	E	22	
6	216	36	6	F	21	5
7	343	49	7	G	20	
8	512	64	8	H	19	
9	729	81	9	I	18	7
10	1000	100	10	J	17	
11	1331	121	11	K	16	
12	1728	144	12	L	15	11
13	2197	169	13	M	14	
14	2744	196	14	N	13	13
15	3375	225	15	O	12	
16	4096	256	16	P	11	
17	4913	289	17	Q	10	17
18	5832	324	18	R	9	
19	6859	361	19	S	8	
20	8000	400	20	T	7	19
			21	U	6	
			22	V	5	23
			23	W	4	
			24	X	3	
			25	Y	2	29
			26	Z	1	

PUZZLE 1

What is missing in the last grid?

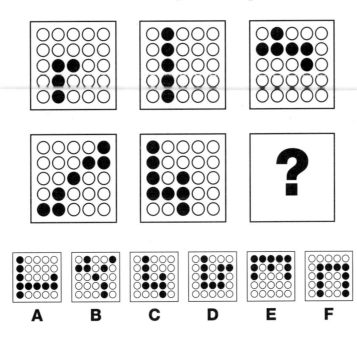

A   B   C   D   E   F

PUZZLE 2

What time should the missing watch read?

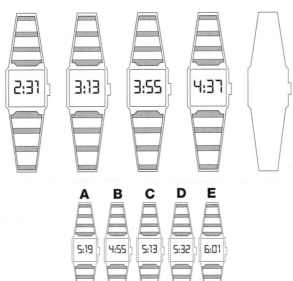

A   B   C   D   E

PUZZLE 3

What number is missing?

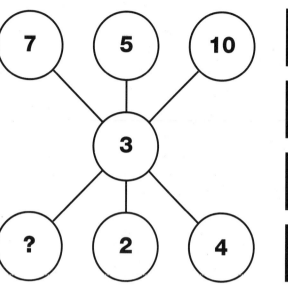

PUZZLE 4

Which number completes the puzzle?

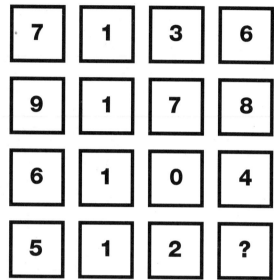

PUZZLE 5

Which number completes this sequence?

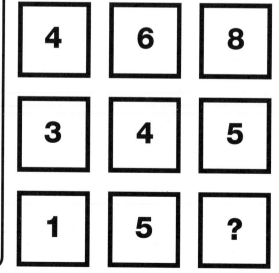

PUZZLE 6

Following a logical sequence, can you complete this puzzle?

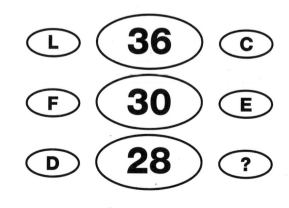

PUZZLE 7

Which circle replaces the question mark?

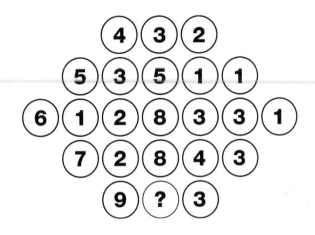

PUZZLE 8

Which number replaces the question mark and completes the puzzle?

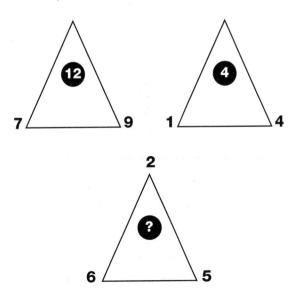

9
PUZZLE

Following a logical sequence, which number needs to be added to complete the puzzle?

6
7
2   4

10
9
5   7

12
?
3   4

10
PUZZLE

What number is missing?

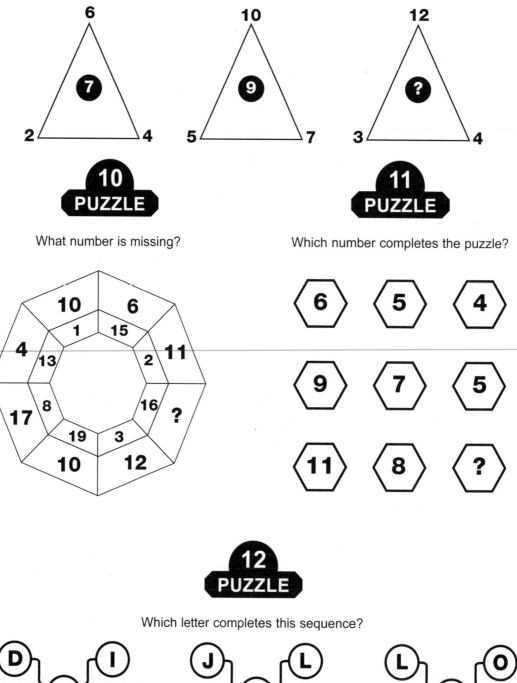

10   6
1   15
4
13   2   11
17   8   16
19   3   ?
10   12

11
PUZZLE

Which number completes the puzzle?

6   5   4

9   7   5

11   8   ?

12
PUZZLE

Which letter completes this sequence?

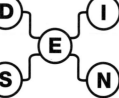

D   I
E
S   N

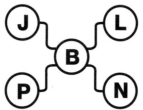

J   L
B
P   N

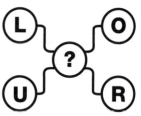

L   O
?
U   R

PUZZLE 13

Which letter replaces the question mark to complete this circle?

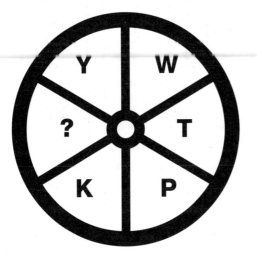

PUZZLE 14

Which number completes the puzzle?

PUZZLE 15

Which letter replaces the question mark and completes the puzzle?

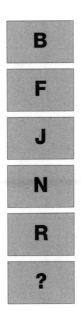

PUZZLE 16

Which number replaces the question mark and completes the puzzle?

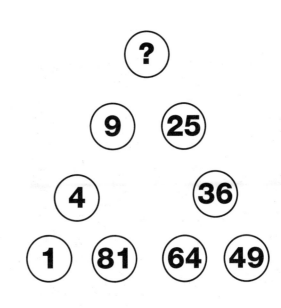

PUZZLE 17

What number is missing?

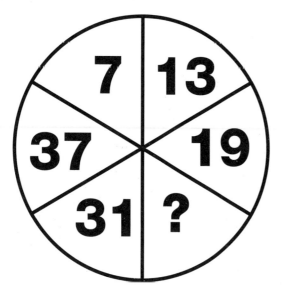

PUZZLE 18

Which letter completes the puzzle?

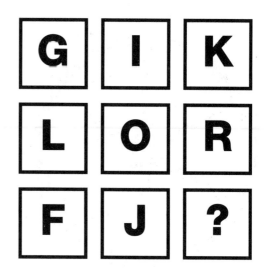

PUZZLE 19

Which number completes this sequence?

PUZZLE 20

Following a logical sequence, can you complete this puzzle?

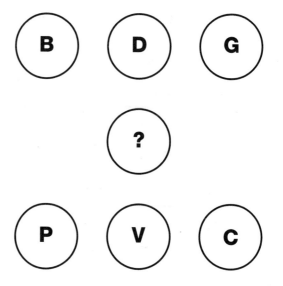

21 PUZZLE

Which letter is missing from the lower middle hexagon?

22 PUZZLE

Which letter completes the puzzle?

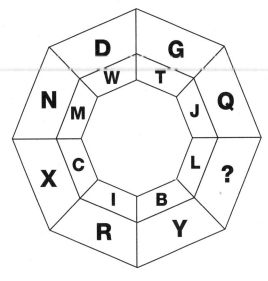

23 PUZZLE

Which number is missing from the bottom triangle?

24 PUZZLE

Which number replaces the question mark and completes the puzzle?

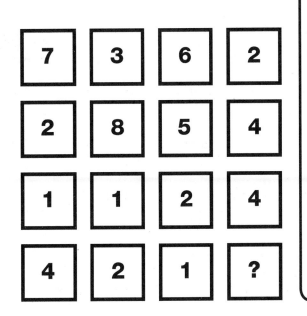

PUZZLE 25

Which watch completes the sequence?

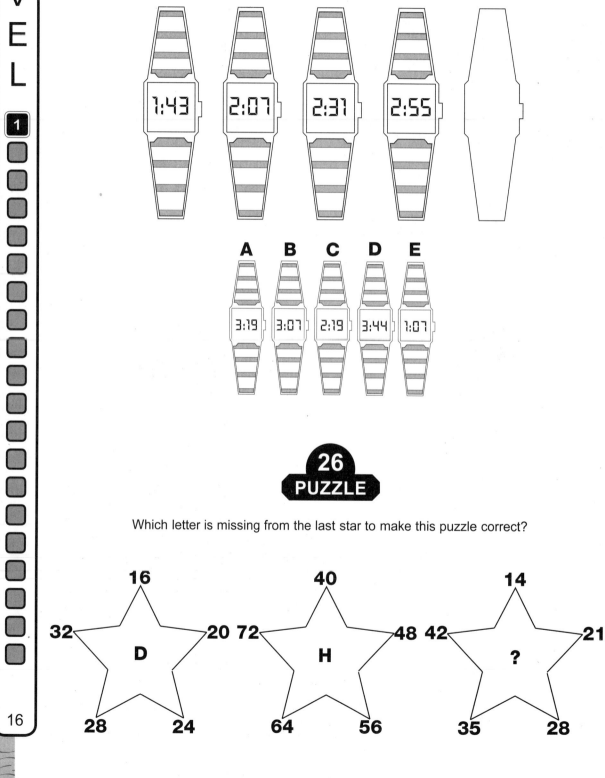

1:43   2:07   2:31   2:55

A   **B**   **C**   **D**   **E**

3:19   3:07   2:19   3:44   1:07

PUZZLE 26

Which letter is missing from the last star to make this puzzle correct?

16
32   20   D   28   24

40
72   48   H   64   56

14
42   21   ?   35   28

PUZZLE 27

Which letter completes this puzzle?

PUZZLE 28

Which letter replaces the question mark to make this puzzle work?

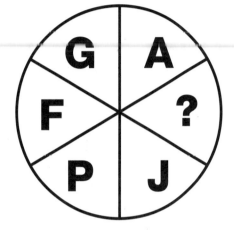

PUZZLE 29

Which number replaces the question mark and completes the puzzle?

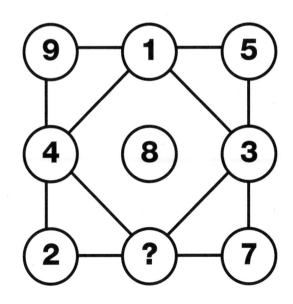

PUZZLE 30

Where should the minute hand be put on the bottom clock?

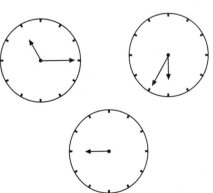

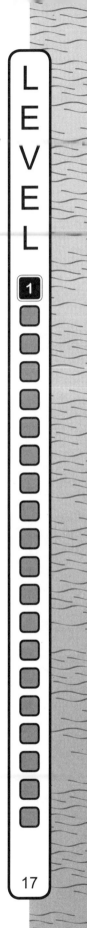

PUZZLE 31

Which number completes this sequence?

4	6	3
7	11	5
13	21	?

PUZZLE 32

Which number completes this sequence?

5   8   14   26   ?

PUZZLE 33

Which letter needs to be added to continue the sequence?

E   H   L   Q   ?

PUZZLE 34

What number needs to be added to the last triangle to complete the puzzle?

3
6
10
15
21
?

PUZZLE 35

Which number should be added to complete the sequence?

25
36
49
64
?

What is missing from the last hexagon?

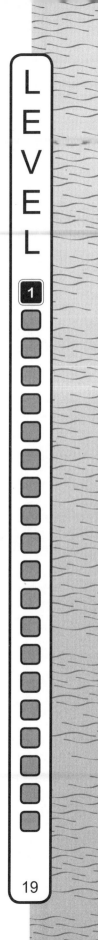

37 PUZZLE

Which letter completes the puzzle?

B

C

E

G

?

38 PUZZLE

Which number replaces the question mark and completes the puzzle?

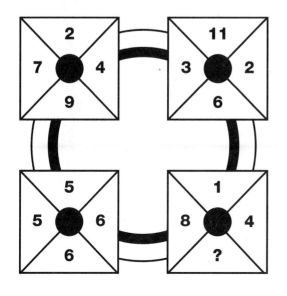

39 PUZZLE

Which number replaces the question mark and completes the puzzle?

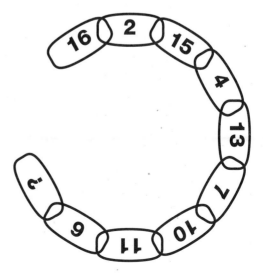

40 PUZZLE

Which pattern completes the line?

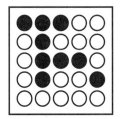

A   B   C   D   E

41 PUZZLE

Which of the lower six patterns completes the puzzle?

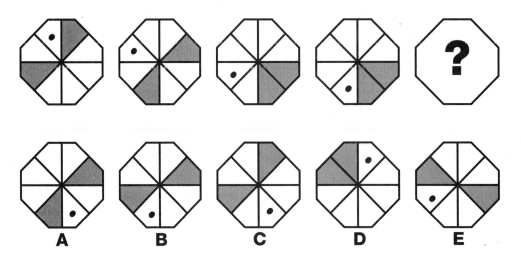

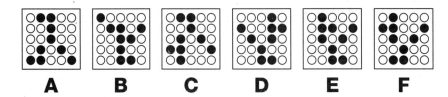

A   B   C   D   E   F

PUZZLE 42

What is missing from the last circle?

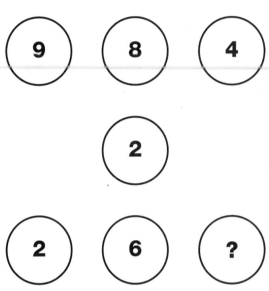

9   8   4

2

2   6   ?

PUZZLE 43

Which letter completes the puzzle?

I   F

?   E   C

E   G

PUZZLE 44

Which number replaces the question mark and completes the puzzle?

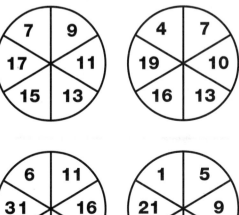

PUZZLE 45

Which letter replaces the question mark and completes the puzzle?

L E V E L

1

PUZZLE 46

Which playing card goes in the empty space?

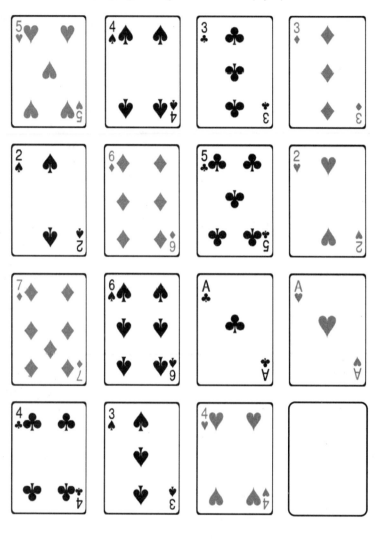

PUZZLE 47

Which number completes the puzzle?

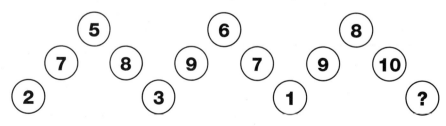

PUZZLE 48

Which letter is missing from the lower right hand circle?

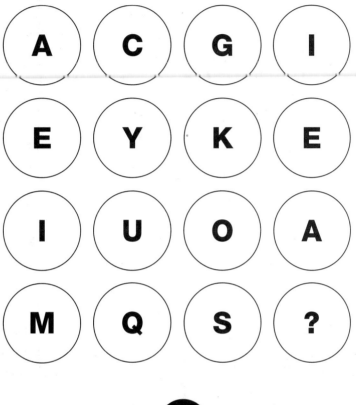

A	C	G	I
E	Y	K	E
I	U	O	A
M	Q	S	?

PUZZLE 49

Which number replaces the question mark and completes the puzzle?

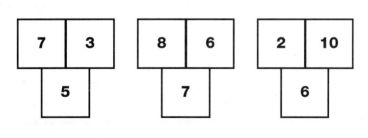

7	3
	5

8	6
	7

2	10
	6

4	2
	?

LEVEL 1

PUZZLE 50

What is missing from the last circle?

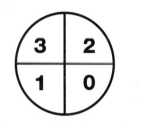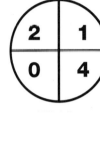

PUZZLE 51

Which letter completes the puzzle?

A　C　E

O　Q　G

M　K　?

PUZZLE 52

This arrangement of 8 coins produces a square, with 3 coins per side. Can you move 4 of the coins to give a square with 4 coins per side?

PUZZLE 53

Which number replaces the question mark and completes the puzzle?

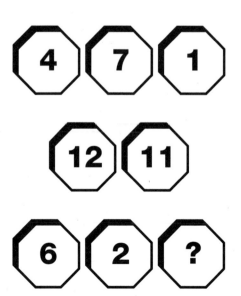

24

What is missing from the last square?

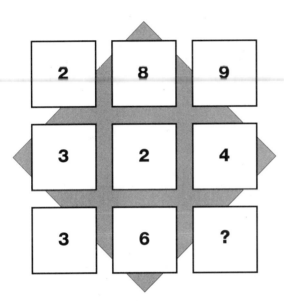

Which numbers complete the puzzle?

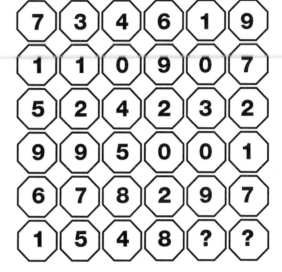

Which number is the odd one out in each oval?

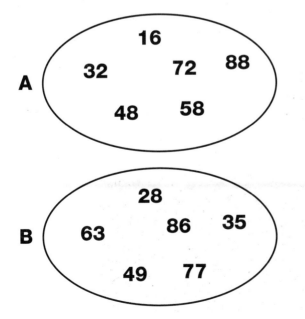

Which letter replaces the question mark and completes the puzzle?

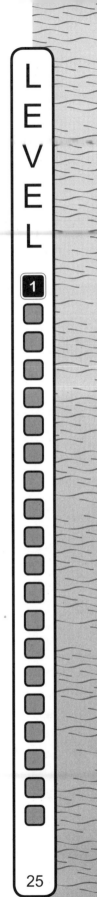

58 PUZZLE

What is the missing arrangement?

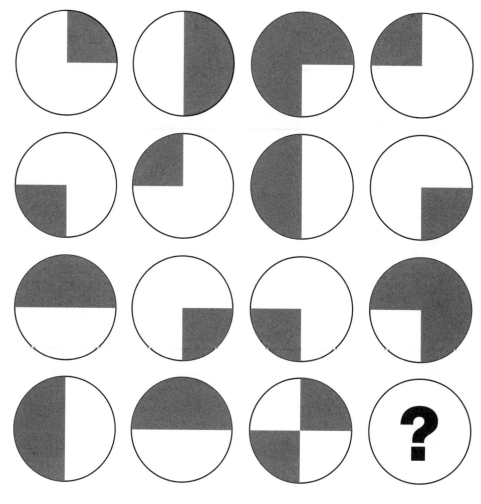

59 PUZZLE

Which domino completes the puzzle?

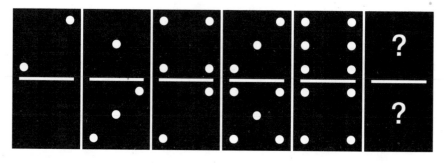

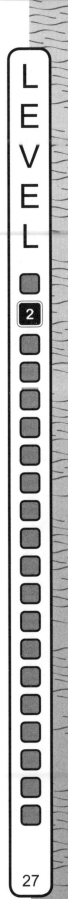

1 PUZZLE

What is missing from the last segment?

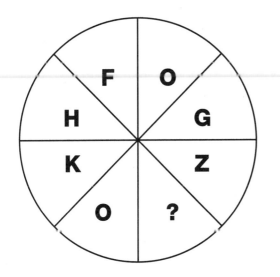

2 PUZZLE

Which letter completes the puzzle?

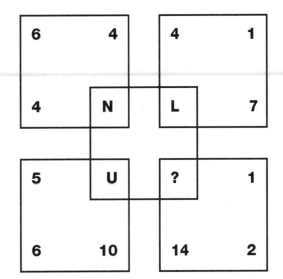

3 PUZZLE

Which tool will make the last scale balance?

4 PUZZLE

Which number replaces the question mark and completes the puzzle?

27

PUZZLE 5

Which number goes in the empty circle?

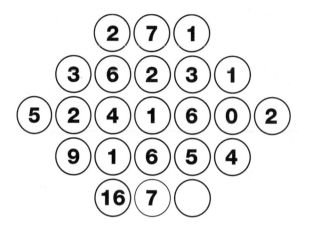

PUZZLE 6

Which of the smaller boxes follows the same rule as these six?

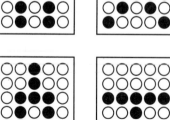

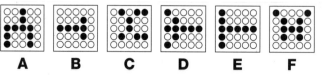

A   B   C   D   E   F

What is missing from the lower middle circle?

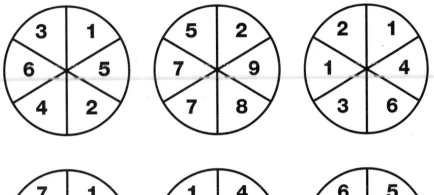

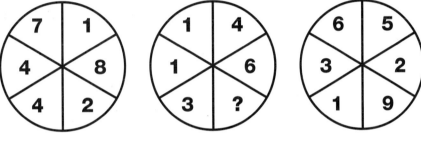

8
PUZZLE

Which letter replaces the question mark and completes the puzzle?

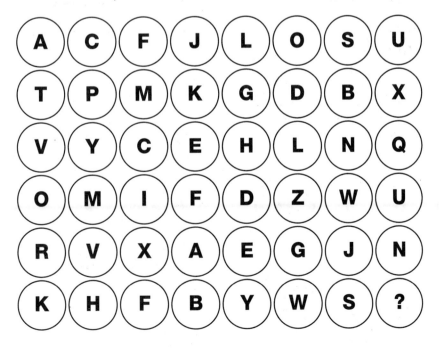

PUZZLE 9

Where does the missing hand go?

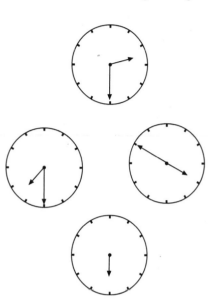

PUZZLE 10

What is missing from the last circle?

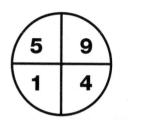

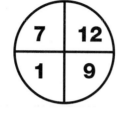

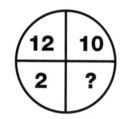

PUZZLE 11

Which letter completes the puzzle?

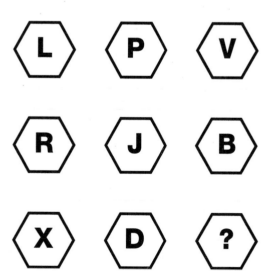

L   P   V

R   J   B

X   D   ?

PUZZLE 12

Which number completes the puzzle?

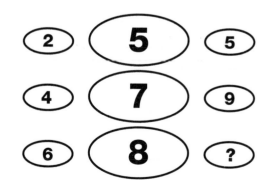

2   5   5

4   7   9

6   8   ?

13 PUZZLE

What is missing from the bottom right hand circle?

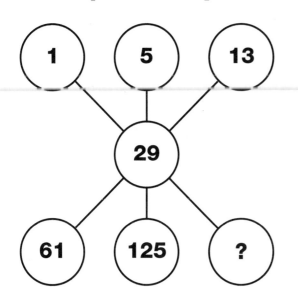

14 PUZZLE

Which letter completes the puzzle?

15 PUZZLE

Which number replaces the question mark and completes the puzzle?

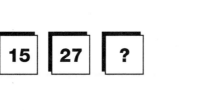

16 PUZZLE

Which number replaces the question mark and completes the puzzle?

10	
8	13
16	6
4	19
22	?

LEVEL

2

17 PUZZLE

What is missing from the last star?

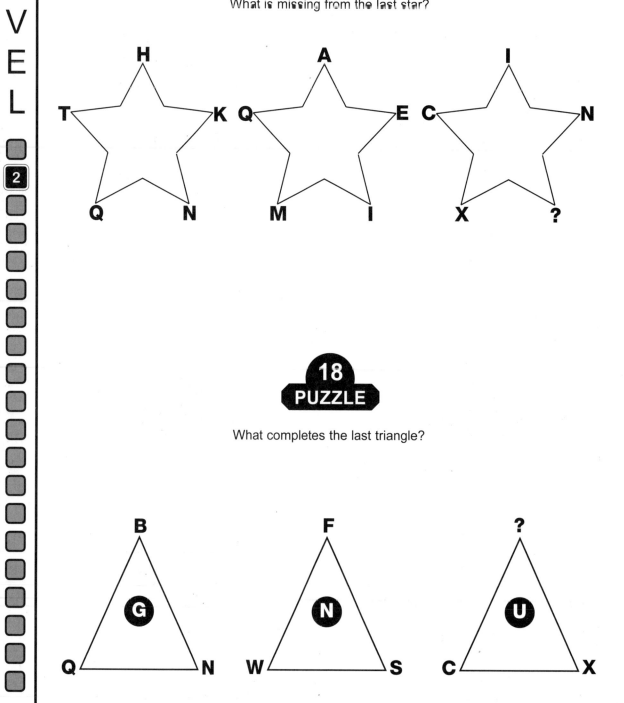

18 PUZZLE

What completes the last triangle?

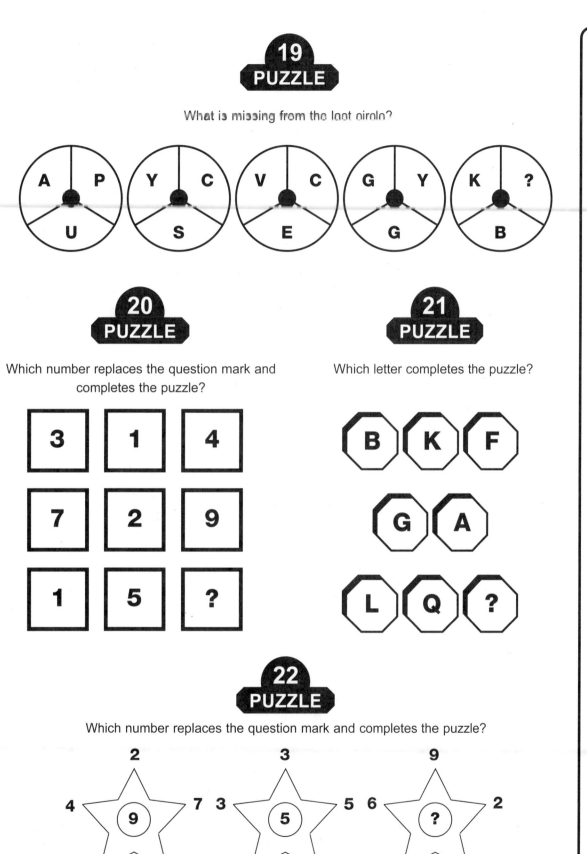

19 PUZZLE

What is missing from the last circle?

A | P
U

Y | C
S

V | C
E

G | Y
G

K | ?
B

20 PUZZLE

Which number replaces the question mark and completes the puzzle?

3 | 1 | 4
7 | 2 | 9
1 | 5 | ?

21 PUZZLE

Which letter completes the puzzle?

B K F

G A

L Q ?

22 PUZZLE

Which number replaces the question mark and completes the puzzle?

2
4   9   7
3   1

3
3   5   5
4   2

9
6   ?   2
4   3

33

PUZZLE 23

Which letter goes in the lower right hand square to complete the puzzle?

B	K	E
G	M	E
I	X	?

PUZZLE 24

Which number completes the puzzle?

5   11   6

3

8   14   ?

PUZZLE 25

In this circle which letter goes in the empty segment?

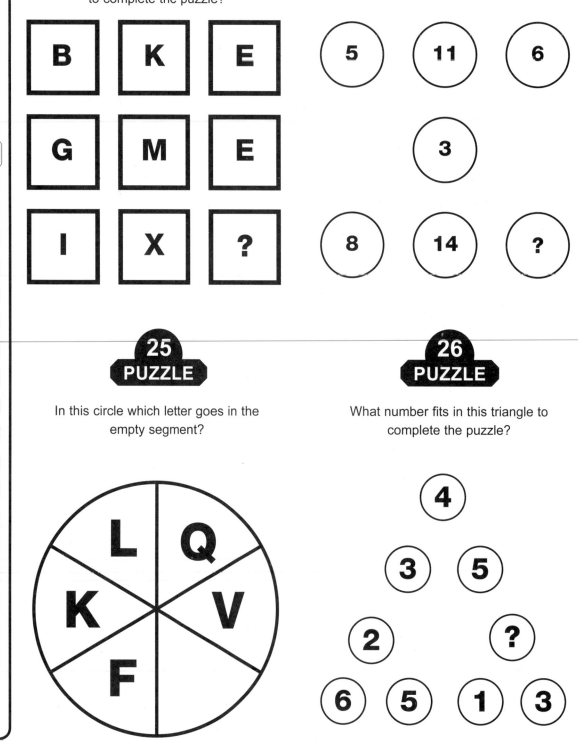

PUZZLE 26

What number fits in this triangle to complete the puzzle?

4

3   5

2   ?

6   5   1   3

PUZZLE 27

What is missing from the last circle?

(2)	(7)	(17)
(3)	(11)	(19)
(5)	(13)	(?)

PUZZLE 28

Which number completes the puzzle?

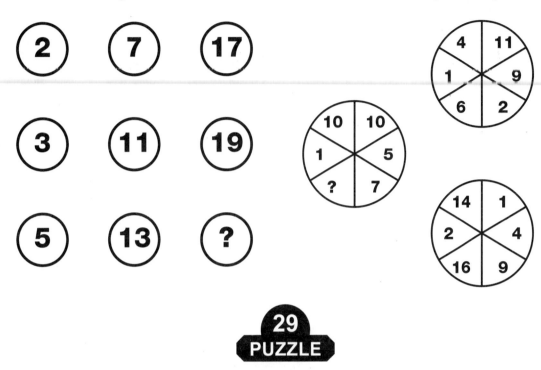

Top circle: 4, 11, 1, 9, 6, 2

Middle circle: 10, 10, 1, 5, ?, 7

Bottom circle: 14, 1, 2, 4, 16, 9

PUZZLE 29

Which letter replaces the question mark and completes the puzzle?

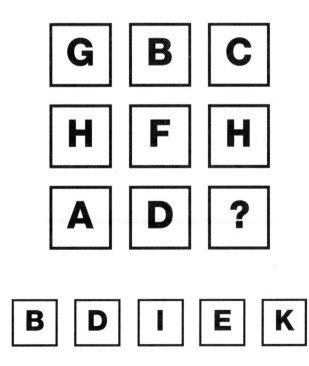

G	B	C
H	F	H
A	D	?

B	D	I	E	K

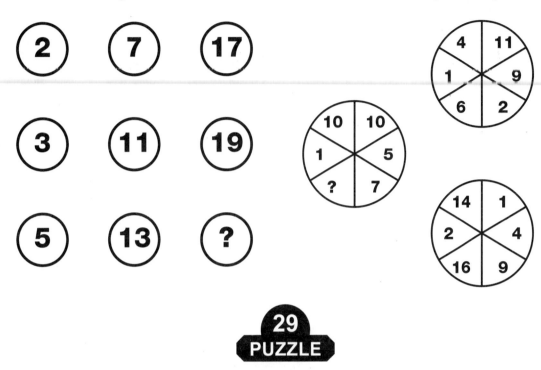

Which number goes in the bottom square to complete the sequence?

2

6

14

30

?

Which number replaces the question mark and completes the puzzle?

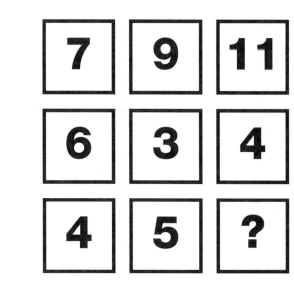

7	9	11
6	3	4
4	5	?

Which watch will complete the sequence?

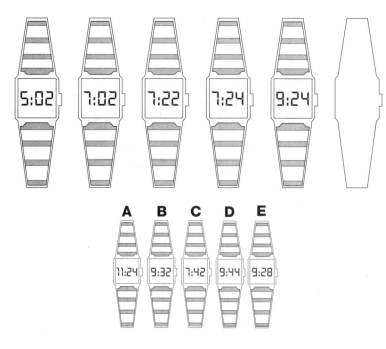

5:02 7:02 7:22 7:24 9:24

A 11:24 B 9:32 C 7:42 D 9:44 E 9:28

Which four digit number is missing from the last oval?

195

383

575

763

955

?

Which number completes the puzzle?

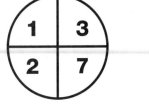

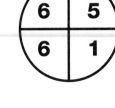

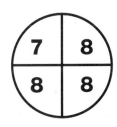

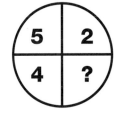

35 PUZZLE

Which letter replaces the question mark and completes the puzzle?

B	Y

C	X

E	V

G	T

K	P

M	?

36
PUZZLE

Which pattern completes the puzzle?

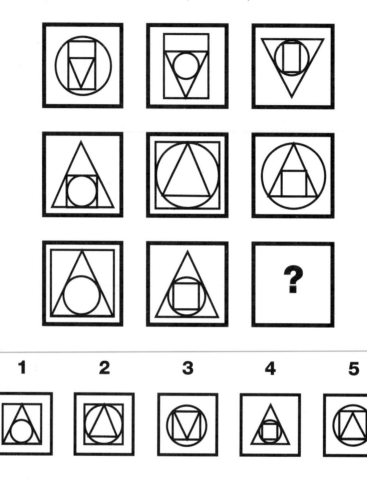

37
PUZZLE

What is missing from the last grid?

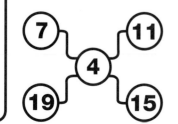

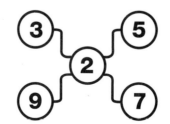

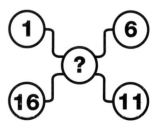

PUZZLE 38

Which of the lower circles replaces the question mark?

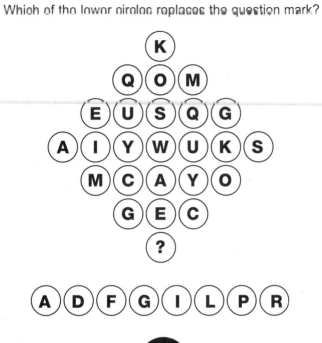

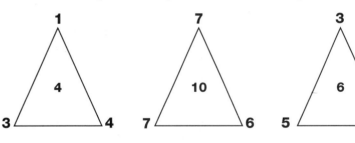

A D F G I L P R

PUZZLE 39

Which number replaces the question mark and completes the puzzle?

PUZZLE 40

Which letter completes the puzzle?

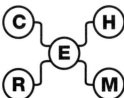
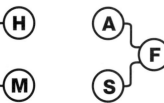
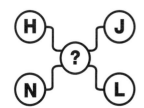

PUZZLE 41

In this sequence of letters what needs to be added to make the puzzle correct?

P	N
T	R
X	V
B	Z
F	D
J	?

PUZZLE 42

Which number replaces the question mark and completes the puzzle?

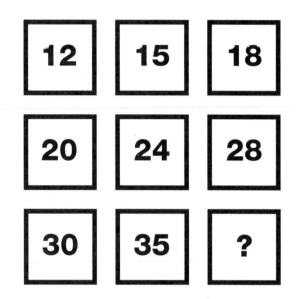

12	15	18
20	24	28
30	35	?

PUZZLE 43

Which number completes this sequence?

21	28	35	42	?

PUZZLE 44

What number goes in the bottom right circle?

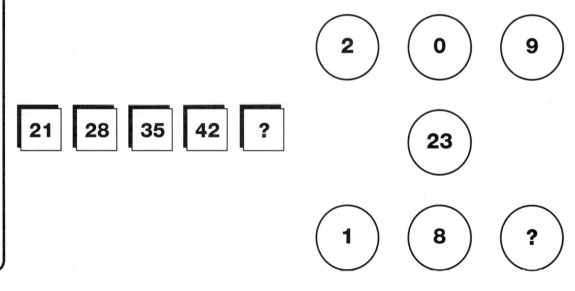

2	0	9
	23	
1	8	?

PUZZLE 45

What is missing from the last star?

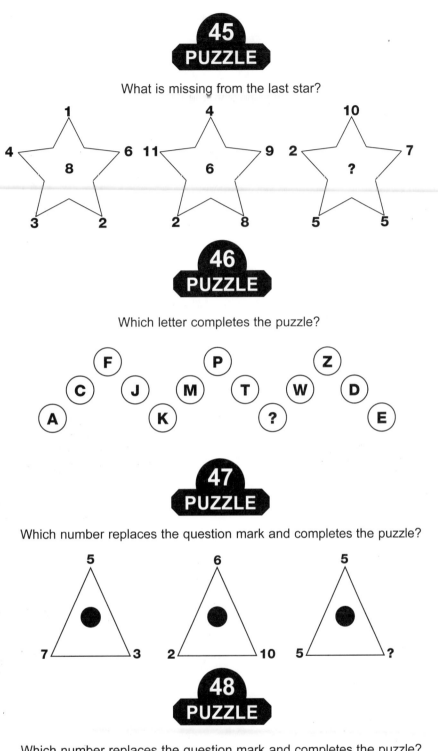

PUZZLE 46

Which letter completes the puzzle?

PUZZLE 47

Which number replaces the question mark and completes the puzzle?

PUZZLE 48

Which number replaces the question mark and completes the puzzle?

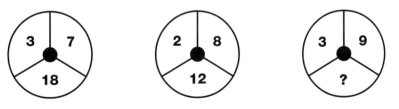

49 PUZZLE

What is missing from the last triangle?

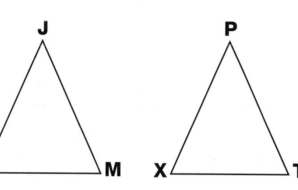
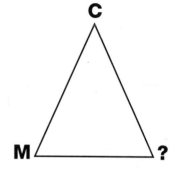

J

P   M

P

X   T

C

M   ?

50 PUZZLE

Where does the missing hand go?

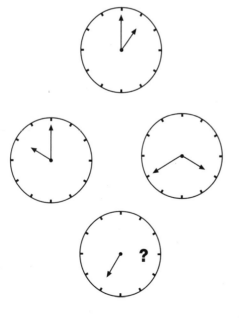

51 PUZZLE

Which letter replaces the question mark
and completes the puzzle?

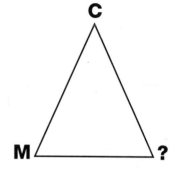

A	H
K	T

C	J
M	V

G	N
Q	Z

E	L
O	?

52 PUZZLE

Which segment completes the puzzle?

```
C L F U J C L F U J        1  F U        2  K H
N V Q R A N V Q R A           V Q R A       T E P Y
W X G S M W X G S M           W X G S       U J C L
H B O D █ █ B O D K       3   B O           A N
P Y I █ █ █ I T E            A N
C L F █ █ █ F U J           S M W X
N V Q R █ █ V Q R A         D K H B
W X G S M W X G S M     4   E P           5  G S
H B O D K H B O D K       Y I               B O D K
P Y I T E P Y I T E       C L F U           I T E P
                          N V Q R           J C
                          X G
```

53 PUZZLE

Which letter replaces the question mark and completes the puzzle?

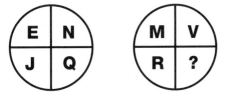

54 PUZZLE

Which letter follows the sequence to complete the puzzle?

A H F M K R P ?

Which number completes this sequence?

Which letter is missing from this circle?

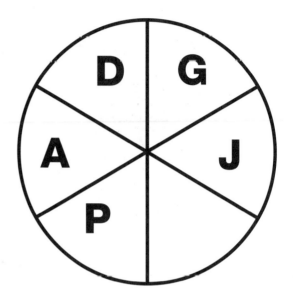

Can you move just 2 matches to create 7 squares?

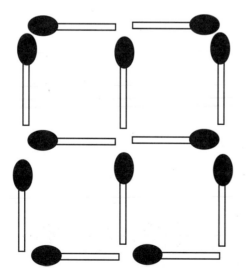

What is missing from this pyramid of numbers?

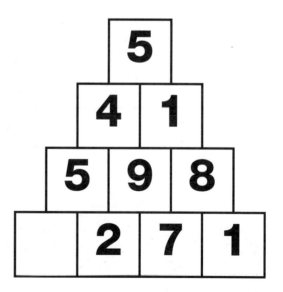

PUZZLE 1

Which number replaces the question mark and completes the sequence?

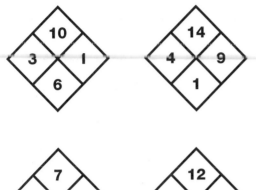

Diamonds:
- 10 / 3 · 1 / 6
- 14 / 4 · 9 / 1
- 7 / 2 · 1 / 4
- 12 / 5 · 3 / ?

PUZZLE 2

Which number replaces the question mark and completes the sequence?

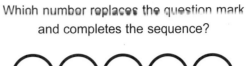

4	1	11	11	3
3	3	1	6	5
9	2	9	4	2
6	4	8	9	3
5	1	?	1	4

PUZZLE 3

Which number replaces the question mark and completes the sequence?

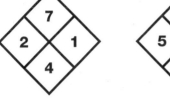

Wheel numbers: 1, 3, 5, 3, 3, 9, 4, 7, 3, 5, 8, 9, 1, 4, 16, 6, 4, 2, 4, 6, 6, 3, 1, ?, 3, 2

PUZZLE 4

Which letter replaces the question mark and completes the sequence?

13	INC	2
6	QRG	7
4	DOM	8
7	SUI	7
8	AD?	2

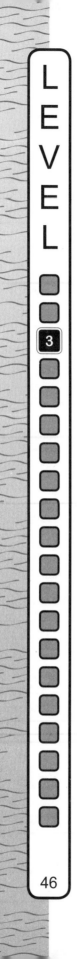

5 PUZZLE

What time should be displayed on the bottom clock face?

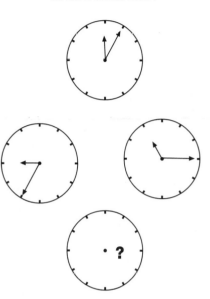

6 PUZZLE

Which four letters complete this puzzle?

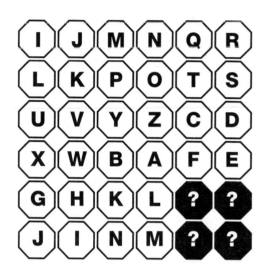

7 PUZZLE

What should be added to the bottom right circle to complete the puzzle?

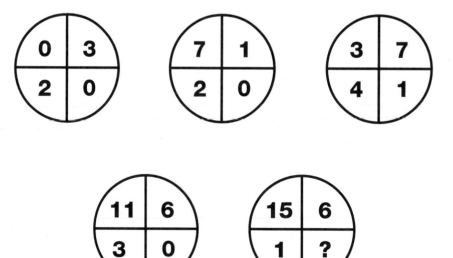

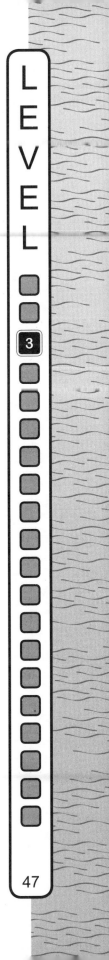

8

PUZZLE

Which letter replaces the question mark and completes the sequence?

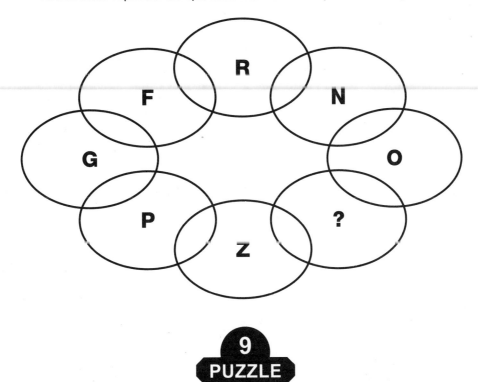

R

F

N

G

O

P

?

Z

9

PUZZLE

Which number replaces the question mark and completes the sequence?

4	2	8	7
6	3	6	6
5	1	5	3

1	0	8	8
7	1	4	2
8	7	2	9

3	2	4	8
2	1	8	9
7	4	9	7

3	0	6	2
4	1	6	4
6	3	?	5

PUZZLE 10

What completes this sequence?

3
4
7
11
?

PUZZLE 11

Which number completes this pyramid?

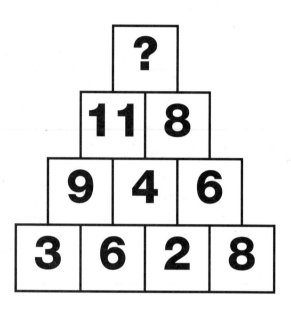

PUZZLE 12

What number is missing from the bottom right circle?

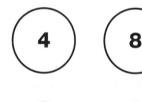

4	8	9
9	2	1
5	6	?

PUZZLE 13

Which number replaces the question mark and completes the puzzle?

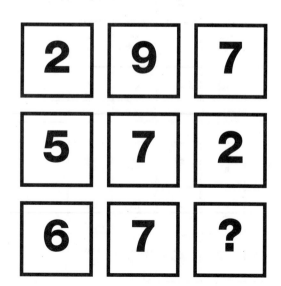

2	9	7
5	7	2
6	7	?

48

PUZZLE 14

Which letter replaces the question mark and completes the puzzle?

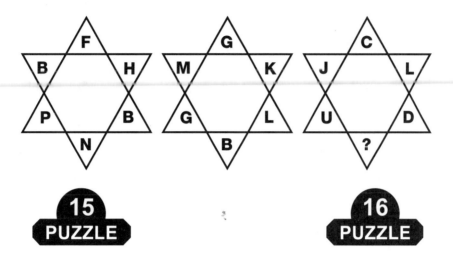

PUZZLE 15

Which number replaces the question mark and completes the puzzle?

PUZZLE 16

Which letter replaces the question mark and completes the puzzle?

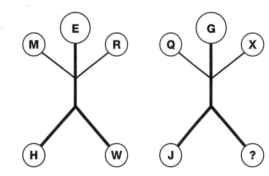

PUZZLE 17

Which letter replaces the question mark and completes the puzzle?

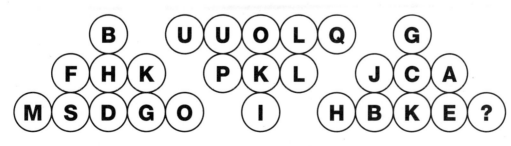

LEVEL

3

49

18 PUZZLE

Which of the bottom six grids completes this pattern?

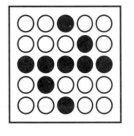 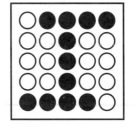 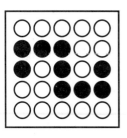

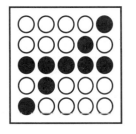 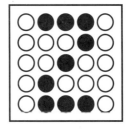 

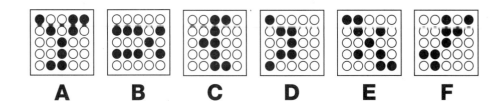

A **B** **C** **D** **E** **F**

19 PUZZLE

What is missing from the last shape?

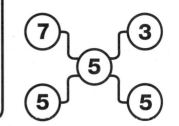  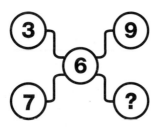

PUZZLE 20

Which number replaces the question mark and completes the puzzle?

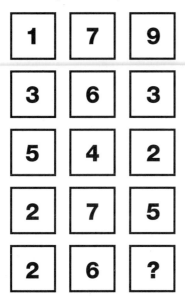

1	7	9
3	6	3
5	4	2
2	7	5
2	6	?

PUZZLE 21

Which letter replaces the question mark and completes the puzzle?

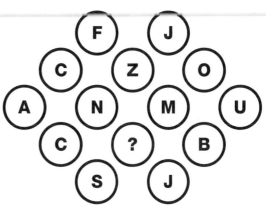

PUZZLE 22

Which number replaces the question mark and completes the puzzle?

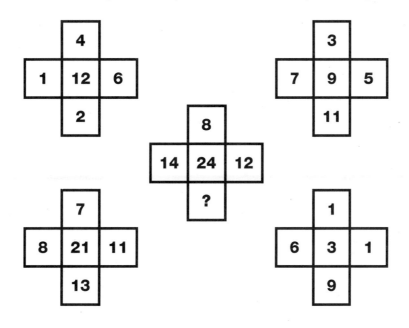

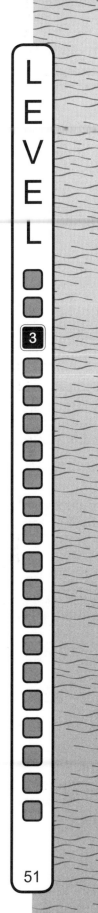

LEVEL 3

23 PUZZLE

Which number completes the last triangle?

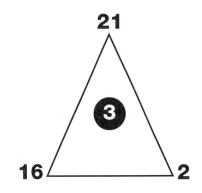

17

9

5   3

21

3

16   2

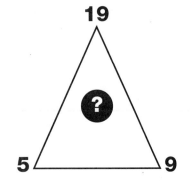

19

?

5   9

24 PUZZLE

Which number replaces the question mark and completes the puzzle?

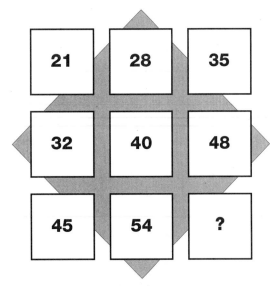

21	28	35
32	40	48
45	54	?

25 PUZZLE

Which number completes this sequence?

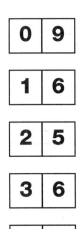

0	9
1	6
2	5
3	6
4	9
6	?

26 PUZZLE

Which letter replaces the question mark and completes the puzzle?

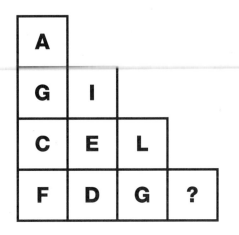

27 PUZZLE

Which number replaces the question mark and completes the puzzle?

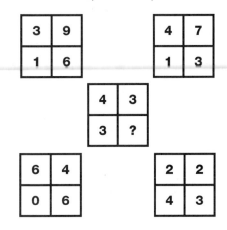

28 PUZZLE

Which playing card replaces the question mark and completes the puzzle?

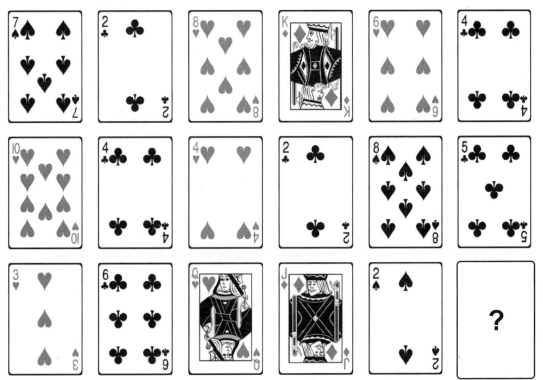

PUZZLE 29

What is missing from this circle?

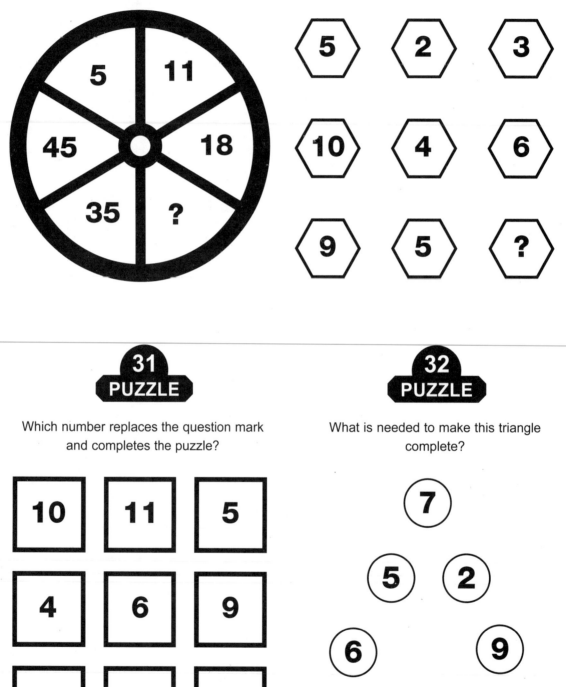

PUZZLE 30

What completes this pattern?

5   2   3

10   4   6

9   5   ?

PUZZLE 31

Which number replaces the question mark
and completes the puzzle?

10	11	5
4	6	9
3	0	?

PUZZLE 32

What is needed to make this triangle
complete?

7

5   2

6   9

3   3   4   ?

33 PUZZLE

Which letter replaces the question mark and completes the sequence?

P	U
K	P

Z	E
U	J

F	K
A	D

?	O
Y	T

34 PUZZLE

Which letter replaces the question mark and completes the puzzle?

D		F		I	
	X		R		M
E		M		O	
	A		V		R
G		N		V	
	E		A		?

35 PUZZLE

Where should the missing hour hand point?

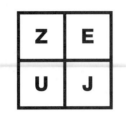
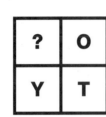

36 PUZZLE

Which letter replaces the question mark and completes the puzzle?

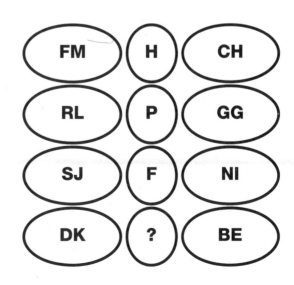

FM H CH

RL P GG

SJ F NI

DK ? BE

PUZZLE 37

Which number is missing?

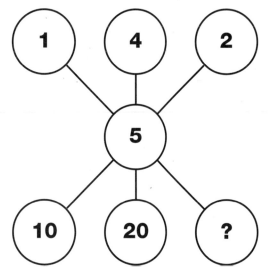

PUZZLE 38

Following a logical sequence, can you complete this puzzle?

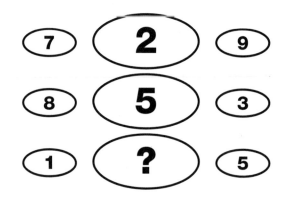

PUZZLE 39

What is needed to complete this pyramid?

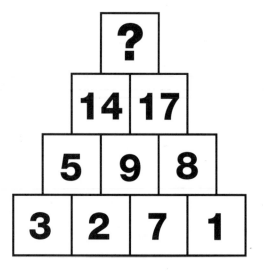

PUZZLE 40

Which number continues the sequence?

| 27 | 64 | 125 | 216 | ? |

	Bungalow	Flat	Terrace	Shangri-la Way	Honeysuckle Row	Meadow Rise	£40,000	£75,000	£100,000
Mavis									
Harold									
Bette									
£40,000									
£75,000									
£100,000									
Shangri-la Way									
Honeysuckle Row									
Meadow Rise									

Mavis, Harold and Bette all own properties in rather exclusive areas of the town, and have recently had them valued. Harold lives in Meadow Rise, but his property isn't worth £75,000. The property in Honeysuckle Row worked out as the cheapest, despite it being a lovely road. Bette lives in a terrace house, although there are no terraced houses along Shangri-La Way. Mavis' property isn't a bungalow. What type of property does each own, where, and at what price has it been valued?

Owner	Property	Road	Value

42 PUZZLE

Which letter replaces the question mark and completes the puzzle?

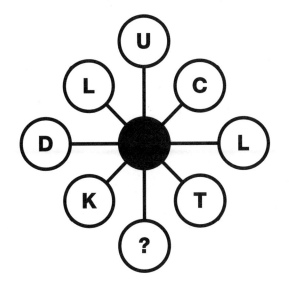

43 PUZZLE

Which number replaces the question mark and completes the puzzle?

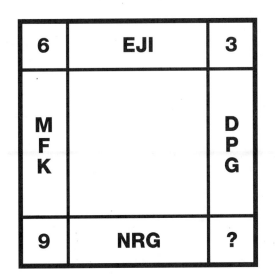

44 PUZZLE

Which of the bottom six grids fills the missing gap?

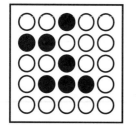 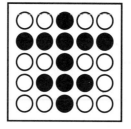 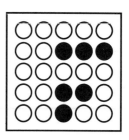

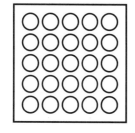 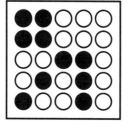 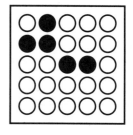

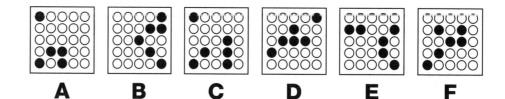

A   **B**   **C**   **D**   **E**   **F**

45 PUZZLE

Following a logical sequence, can you
complete this puzzle?

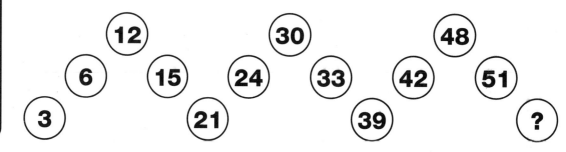

12   30   48
6   15   24   33   42   51
3   21   39   ?

Which picture cube does this shape make?

A

C

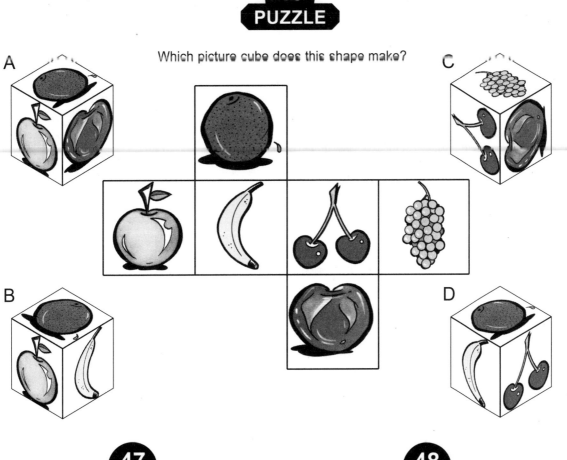

B

D

Which letter replaces the question mark and completes the puzzle?

Joe and John are playing marbles. If Joe loses one marble to John, they will both have the same number of marbles, but if John loses one marble to Joe, Joe will have twice the number of marbles as John. How many marbles do the two boys currently have?

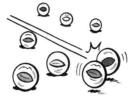

LEVEL

3

Which playing cards fill the blank spaces?

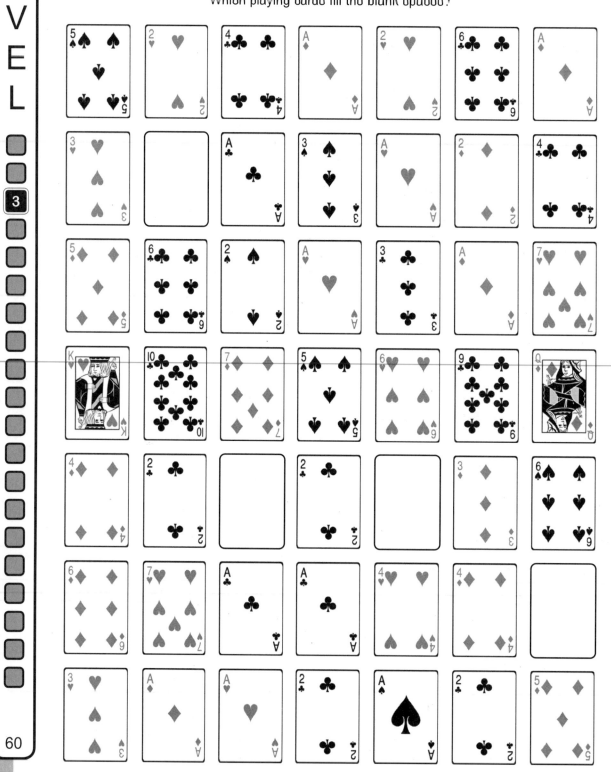

PUZZLE 50

Which number replaces the question mark and completes the puzzle?

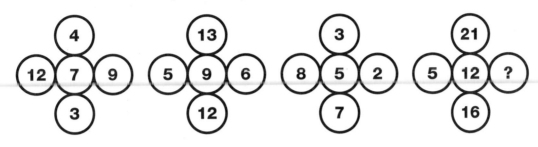

PUZZLE 51

Which number replaces the question mark and completes the puzzle?

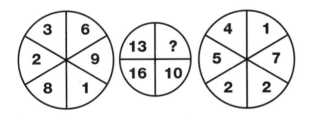

PUZZLE 52

Which number replaces the question mark and completes the puzzle?

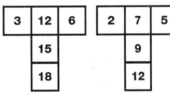

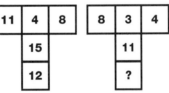

PUZZLE 53

Which domino replaces the question mark to complete the puzzle?

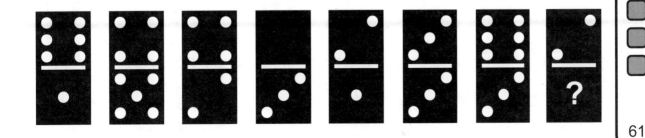

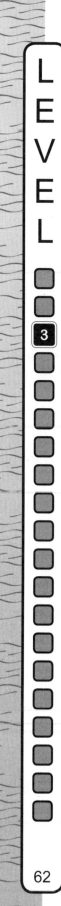

54 PUZZLE

Which number is missing?

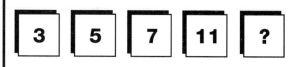

3   5   7   11   ?

55 PUZZLE

Here are 5 matches, which form 2 equilateral triangles. Can you add 1 match, and move two others, to form 8 equilateral triangles?

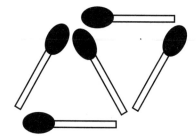

56 PUZZLE

Which letters are the odd ones out?

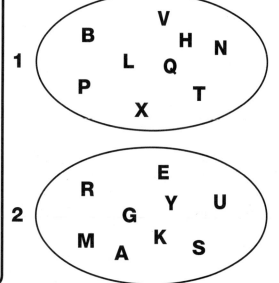

1

2

57 PUZZLE

Which number completes this circle?

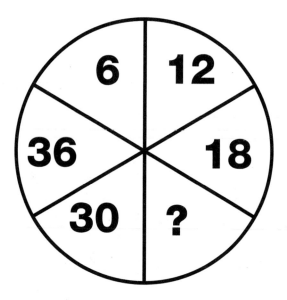

1 PUZZLE

Which number is missing?

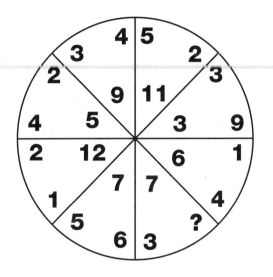

2 PUZZLE

Which letter completes the puzzle?

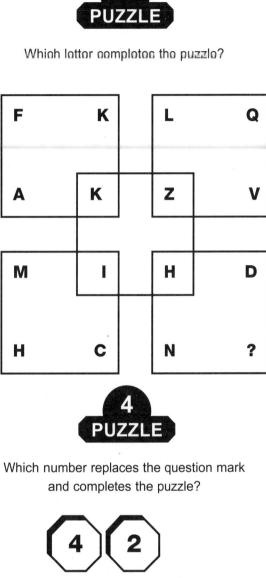

F		K
A	K	

L		Q
	Z	V

M	I	
H		C

	H	D
N		?

3 PUZZLE

Which symbol replaces the question mark and completes the puzzle?

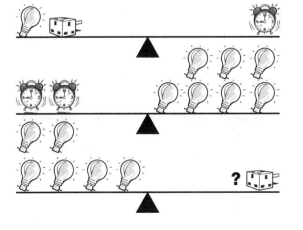

4 PUZZLE

Which number replaces the question mark and completes the puzzle?

4	2
9	8
15	15
22	?

5 PUZZLE

Which letter completes the puzzle?

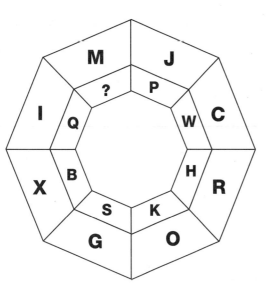

6 PUZZLE

Which number is missing?

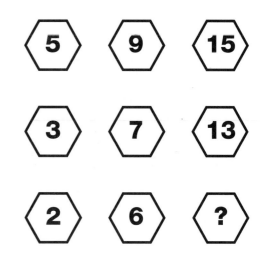

7 PUZZLE

Which letter is needed to complete this circle?

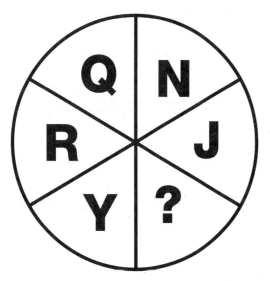

8 PUZZLE

Following a logical sequence, can you complete this puzzle?

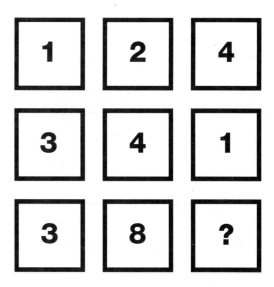

9 PUZZLE

What is missing from the last circle?

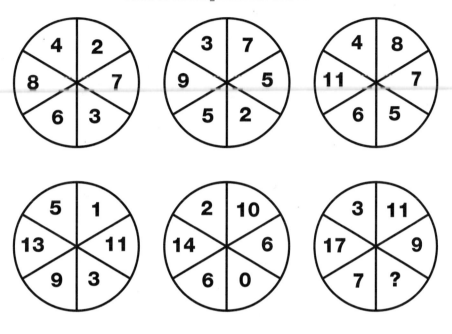

10 PUZZLE

Which letter replaces the question mark and completes the puzzle?

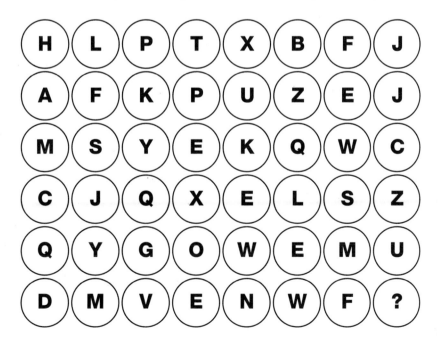

11 PUZZLE

Which of the bottom six grids completes the puzzle?

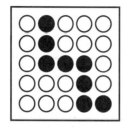
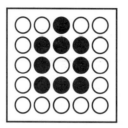
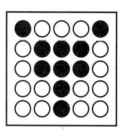

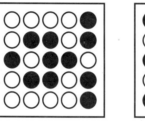
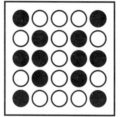

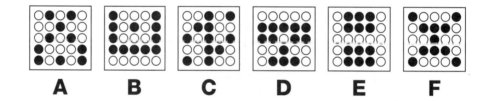

A **B** **C** **D** **E** **F**

12 PUZZLE

What time should the last watch show?

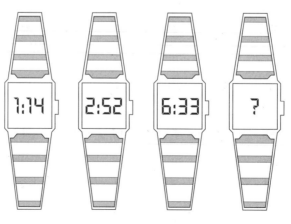

PUZZLE 13

What is missing from the bottom left circle?

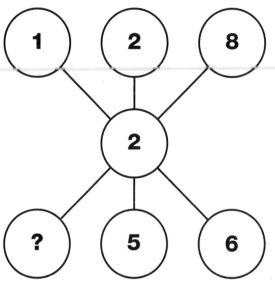

PUZZLE 14

Which letter completes the puzzle?

PUZZLE 15

Which number replaces the question mark and completes the puzzle?

| 32 | 45 | 60 | 77 | ? |

PUZZLE 16

Which number replaces the question mark and completes the puzzle?

3	5
4	1
4	7
5	3
5	?

17 PUZZLE

What is missing from the empty circle?

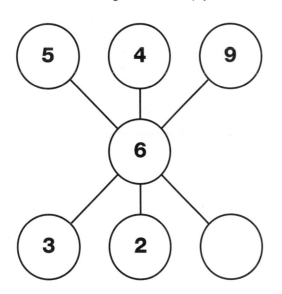

18 PUZZLE

What letter is missing?

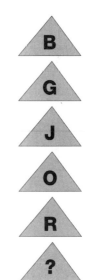

19 PUZZLE

What is missing from the empty segment?

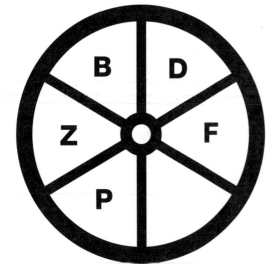

20 PUZZLE

Which letter completes the puzzle?

21 PUZZLE

What is missing from the last circle?

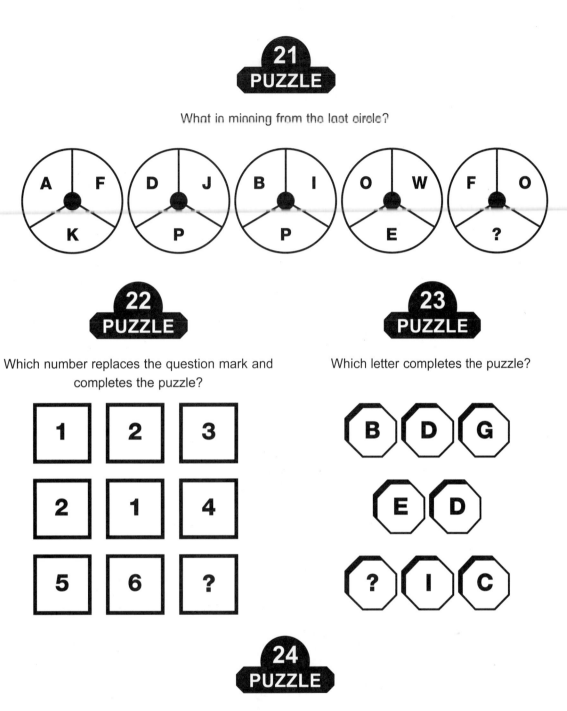

| A | F | D | J | B | I | O | W | F | O |
| K | | P | | P | | E | | ? | |

22 PUZZLE

Which number replaces the question mark and completes the puzzle?

1	2	3
2	1	4
5	6	?

23 PUZZLE

Which letter completes the puzzle?

B D G

E D

? I C

24 PUZZLE

Which number replaces the question mark and completes the puzzle?

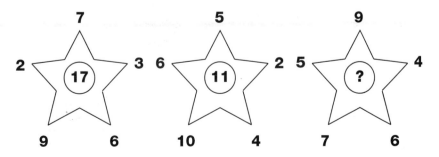

25 PUZZLE

Following a logical sequence, can you complete this puzzle?

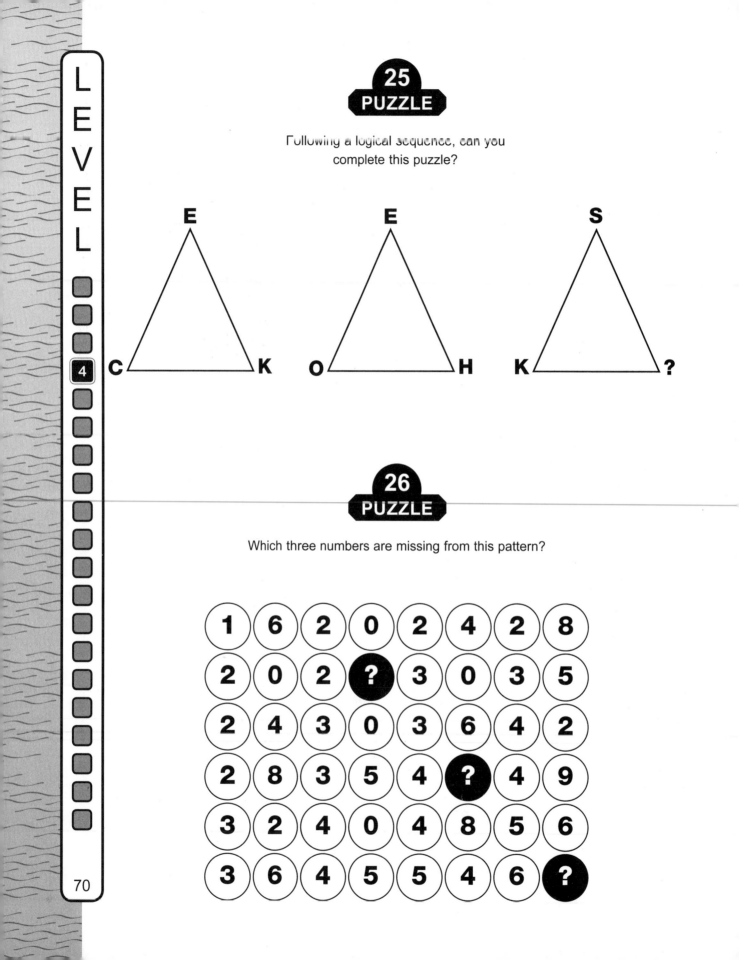

26 PUZZLE

Which three numbers are missing from this pattern?

PUZZLE 27

What is missing from the last circle?

(H) (C) (Z)

(K) (F) (W)

(N) (Q) (?)

PUZZLE 28

Which number completes the puzzle?

PUZZLE 29

Which of the bottom letters replace the question mark and completes the puzzle?

L	Z	E
T	A	M
V	N	?

H	D	X	W	B

PUZZLE 30

What number is missing?

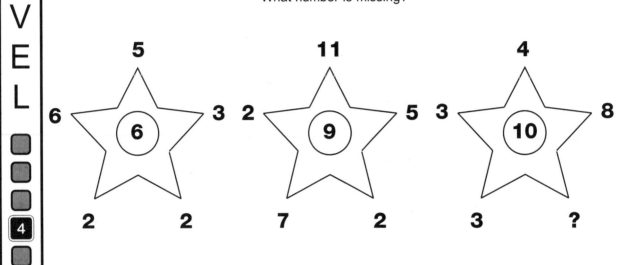

PUZZLE 31

Which letter is missing?

PUZZLE 32

Following a logical sequence, can you complete this puzzle?

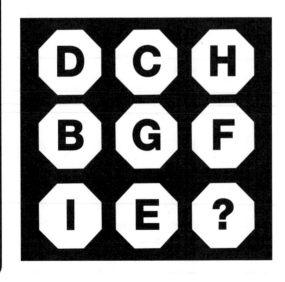

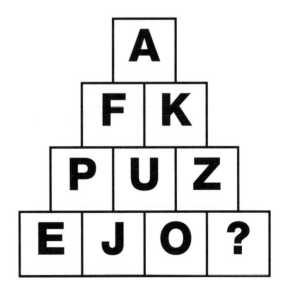

PUZZLE 33

What is missing from the last oval?

7122

6521

8332

4743

9911

387?

PUZZLE 34

Which number completes the puzzle?

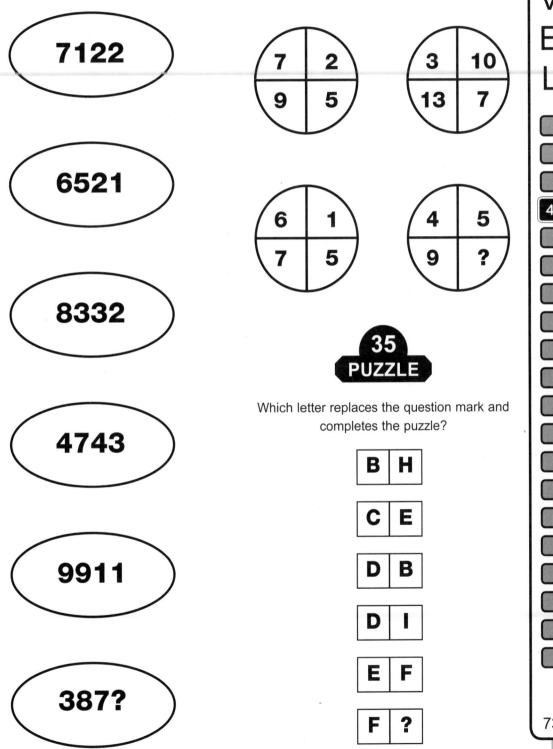

7	2
9	5

3	10
13	7

6	1
7	5

4	5
9	?

PUZZLE 35

Which letter replaces the question mark and completes the puzzle?

B	H

C	E

D	B

D	I

E	F

F	?

LEVEL

4

36 PUZZLE

What is missing from the last segment?

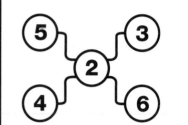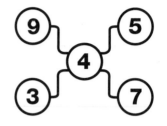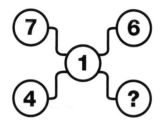

37 PUZZLE

Which number is missing?

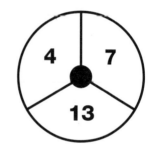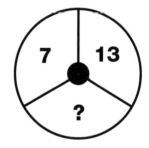

38 PUZZLE

Which letter completes the puzzle?

39
PUZZLE

What is missing from the control circle?

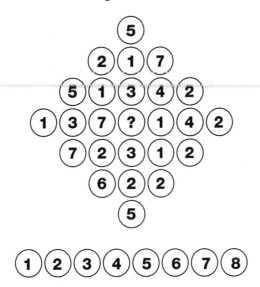

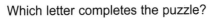

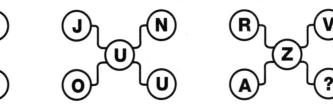

40
PUZZLE

Which single digit number replaces the question mark?

5
3 △ 2

6
4 △ 10

6
15 △ ?

41
PUZZLE

Which letter completes the puzzle?

B F
P
C I

J N
U
O U

R V
Z
A ?

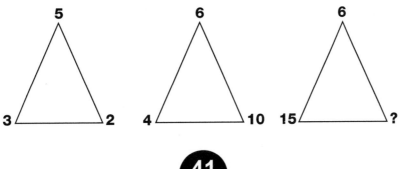

What completes this sequence?

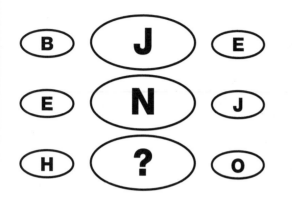

B   J   E

E   N   J

H   ?   O

Can you move just 3 coins to make the triangle point upwards?

Which number is missing?

3   5   7

11

13   17   ?

Which number is the odd one out in each shape?

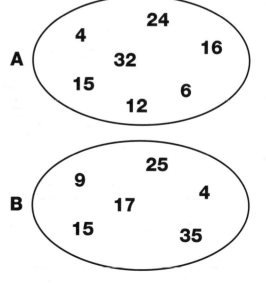

A
24
4
32   16
15
6
12

B
25
9
17   4
15
35

46 PUZZLE

What is missing from the last star?

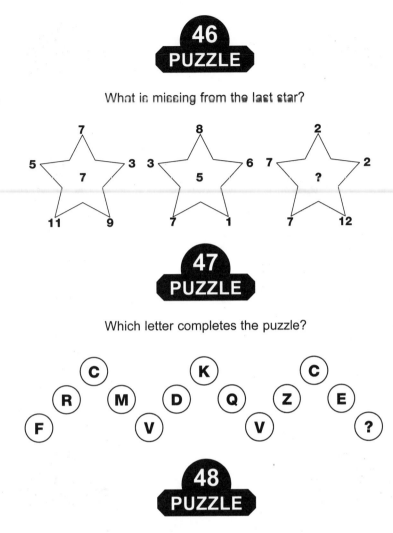

47 PUZZLE

Which letter completes the puzzle?

48 PUZZLE

Which number replaces the question mark and completes the puzzle?

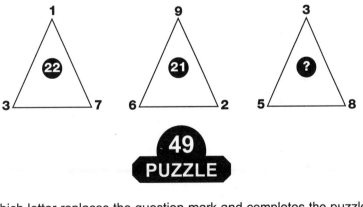

49 PUZZLE

Which letter replaces the question mark and completes the puzzle?

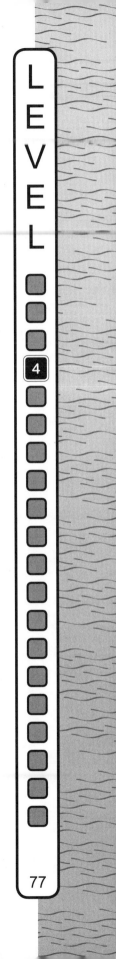

L
E
V
E
L

4

77

PUZZLE 50

What number is missing?

PUZZLE 51

Which letter completes the puzzle?

M   N   O

V   W   X

J   K   ?

PUZZLE 52

Following a logical sequence, can you complete this puzzle?

PUZZLE 53

What is missing from the bottom scale to make them balance?

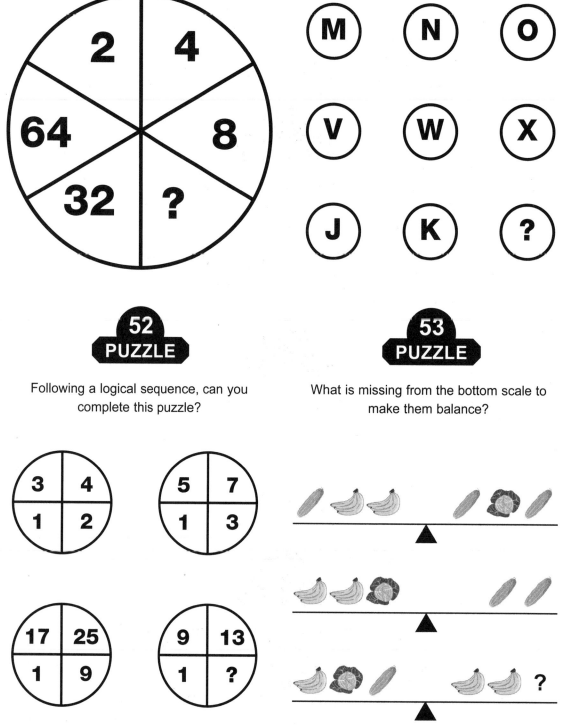

54 PUZZLE

Which shape completes the puzzle?

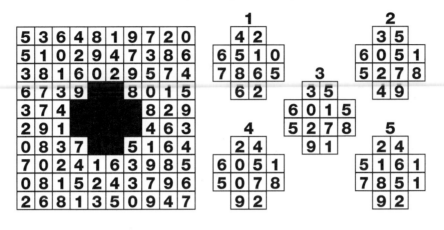

55 PUZZLE

Which number replaces the question mark and completes the puzzle?

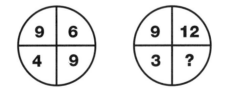

56 PUZZLE

Which letter replaces the question mark and completes the puzzle?

B   C   E   G   K   M   Q   ?

79

PUZZLE 57

Where does the missing hand go?

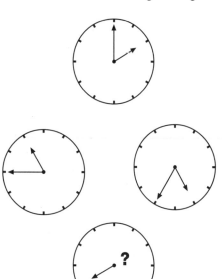

PUZZLE 58

What letter is missing?

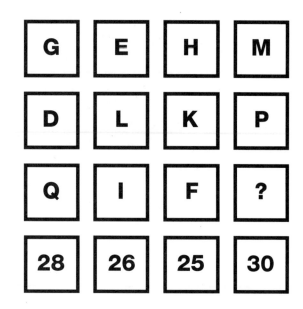

PUZZLE 59

Which piece fits back into the grid to
complete the pattern?

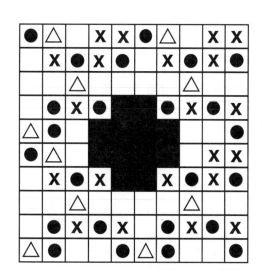

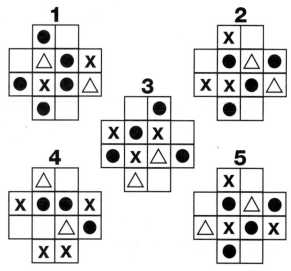

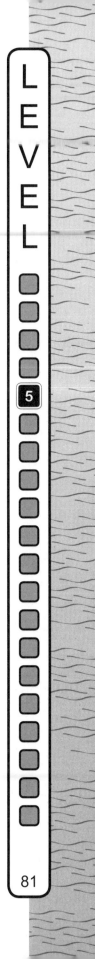

PUZZLE 1

Which grid replaces the question mark?

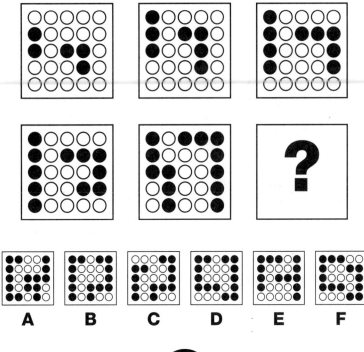

A   B   C   D   E   F

PUZZLE 2

Which time from the choices given follows the sequence?

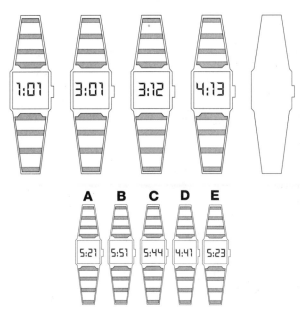

A   B   C   D   E

5:21   5:51   5:44   4:41   5:23

81

PUZZLE 3

Which number is missing?

PUZZLE 4

Which letter replaces the question mark?

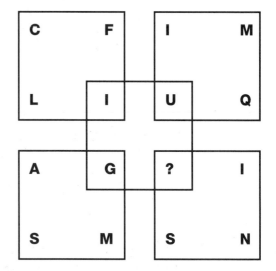

PUZZLE 5

Following a logical sequence, can you complete this puzzle?

PUZZLE 6

Which letter completes the puzzle?

7 PUZZLE

Which letter replaces the question mark from the choices given below?

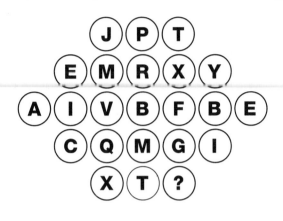

J P T
E M R X Y
A I V B F B E
C Q M G I
X T ?

B F H K L N Q S

8 PUZZLE

Which number replaces the question mark and completes the puzzle?

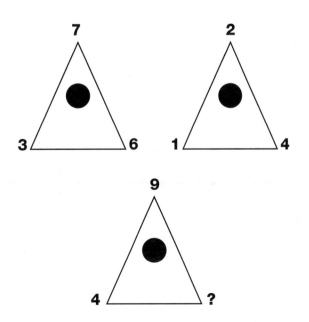

LEVEL

5

Which playing card will complete the puzzle?

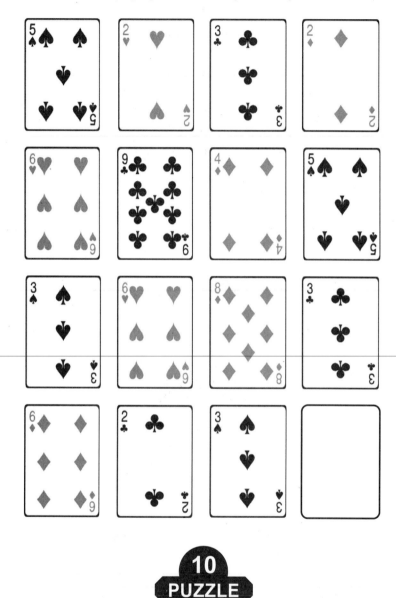

In this sequence of numbers what should go within the last shape to make it complete?

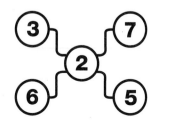
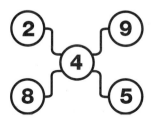
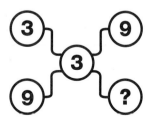

LEVEL

5

What is missing from this wheel?

Which letter completes the puzzle?

Which number replaces the question mark
and completes the puzzle?

Which number replaces the question mark
and completes the puzzle?

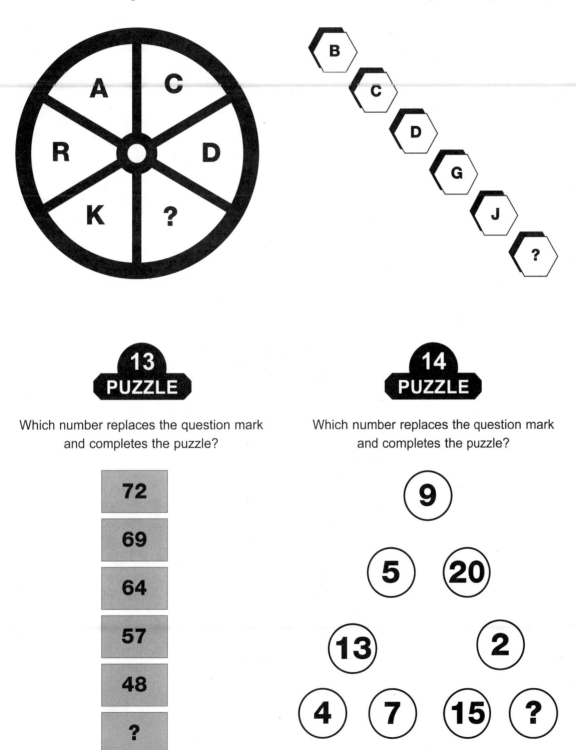

Puzzle 11 wheel letters: A, C, R, D, K, ?

Puzzle 12 hexagons: B, C, D, G, J, ?

Puzzle 13: 72, 69, 64, 57, 48, ?

Puzzle 14: 9; 5, 20; 13, 2; 4, 7, 15, ?

LEVEL

5

85

PUZZLE 15

What number is missing?

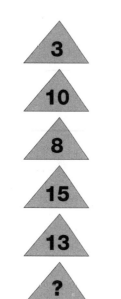

3
10
8
15
13
?

PUZZLE 16

Which letter completes the puzzle?

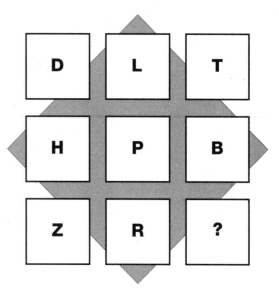

D	L	T
H	P	B
Z	R	?

PUZZLE 17

Which watch should go in the missing space to complete the sequence?

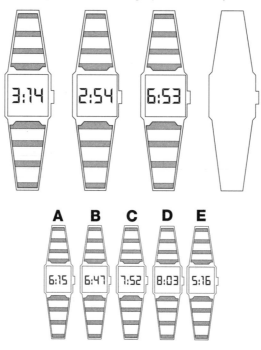

3:14 2:54 6:53

A B C D E

6:15 6:47 7:52 8:03 5:16

What is missing from the last hexagon?

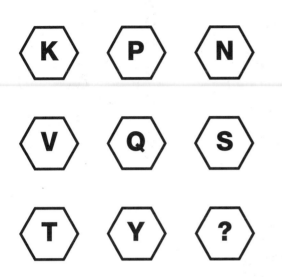

Which letter completes the puzzle?

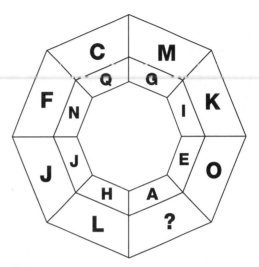

Which number replaces the question mark and completes the puzzle?

Which number replaces the question mark and completes the puzzle?

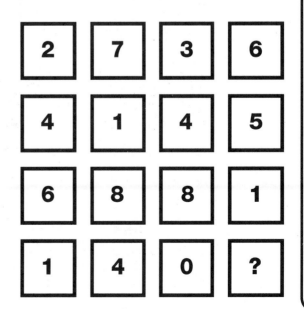

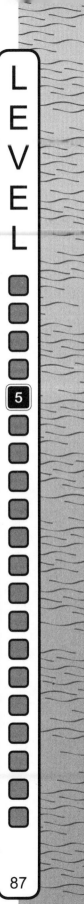

PUZZLE 22

Which number is missing?

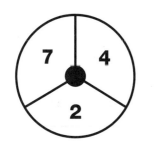  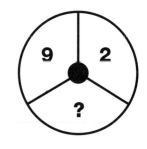

PUZZLE 23

Which of the bottom six grids completes the puzzle?

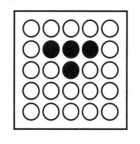 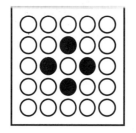 

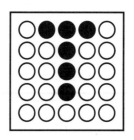  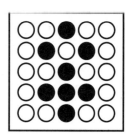

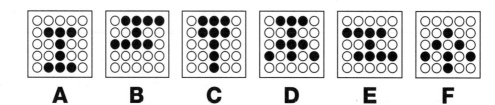

A   **B**   **C**   **D**   **E**   **F**

PUZZLE 24

What is missing from the last hexagon?

PUZZLE 25

Which letter completes the puzzle?

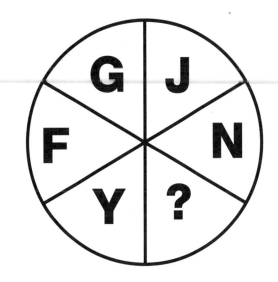

PUZZLE 26

Which number replaces the question mark and completes the puzzle?

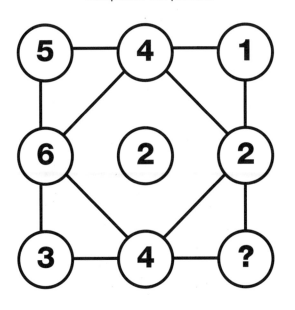

PUZZLE 27

Where should the hour hand be pointing on the bottom clock?

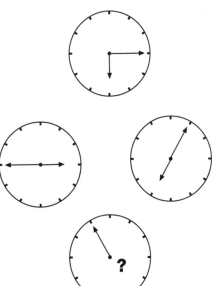

PUZZLE 28

What number is missing?

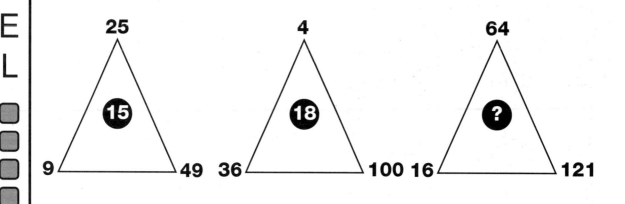

25

15

9 49

4

18

36 100

64

?

16 121

PUZZLE 29

Following a logical sequence, can you complete this puzzle?

| 24 | 35 | 48 | 63 | ? |

PUZZLE 30

Which numbers are the odd ones out in these selections?

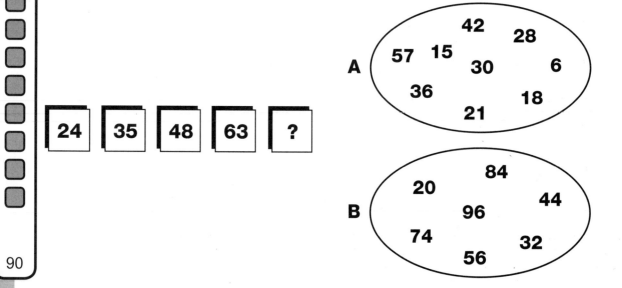

A

57 15 42 28
30 6
36 18
21

B

20 84
96 44
74 32
56

PUZZLE 31

What is missing from the last shape?

PUZZLE 32

Which letter completes the puzzle?

PUZZLE 33

Which letter replaces the question mark and completes the puzzle?

PUZZLE 34

Which number replaces the question mark and completes the chain?

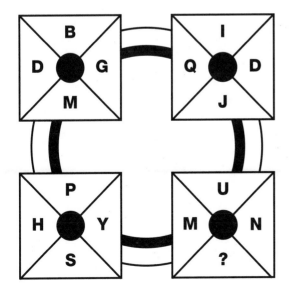

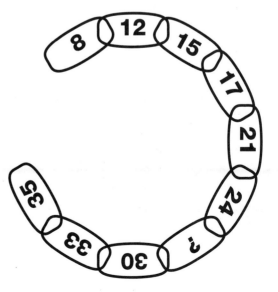

LEVEL

5

35 PUZZLE

What completes this triangle of numbers?

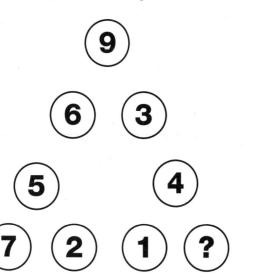

36 PUZZLE

What is missing from this puzzle?

37 PUZZLE

Following a logical sequence, can you complete this puzzle?

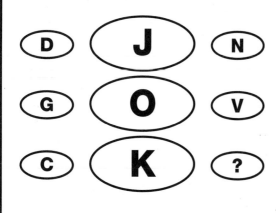

38 PUZZLE

Which letter completes the puzzle?

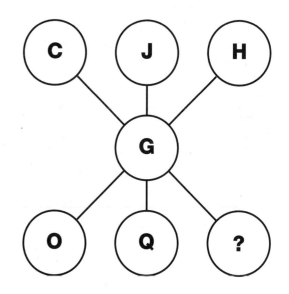

39 PUZZLE

What is missing from the last circle?

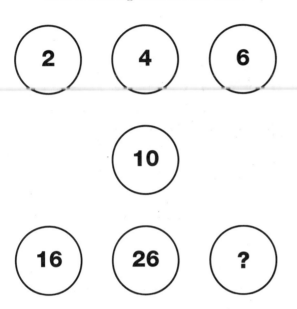

40 PUZZLE

Which letter completes the puzzle?

41 PUZZLE

Which number replaces the question mark and completes the puzzle?

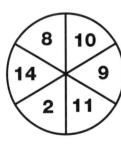
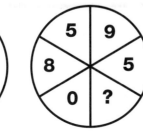

42 PUZZLE

Which number replaces the question mark and completes the puzzle?

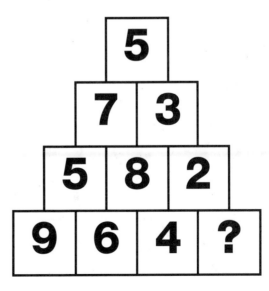

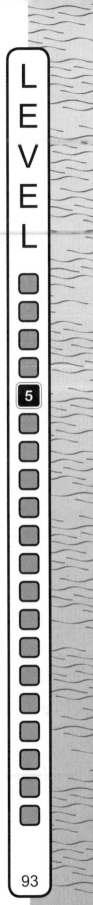

93

PUZZLE 43

Which number completes this puzzle?

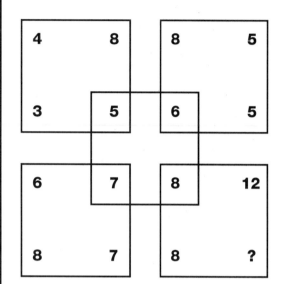

PUZZLE 44

In this logical sequence of letters, what is needed to make it complete?

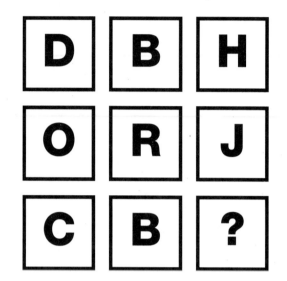

D	B	H
O	R	J
C	B	?

PUZZLE 45

What is missing?

1	7	7
6	5	4
8	3	?

PUZZLE 46

What number is missing?

15 22 29 36 ?

What is missing from the last circle?

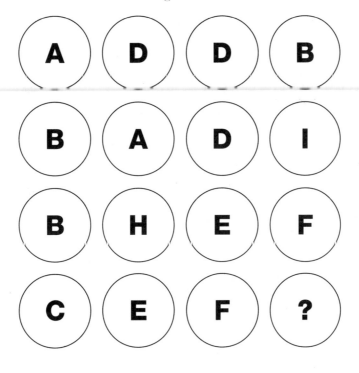

A	D	D	B
B	A	D	I
B	H	E	F
C	E	F	?

Which number replaces the question mark and completes the puzzle?

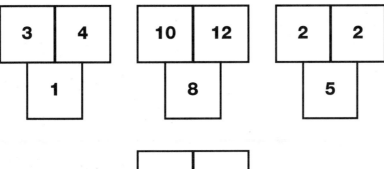

3	4
1	

10	12
8	

2	2
5	

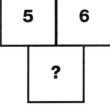

5	6
?	

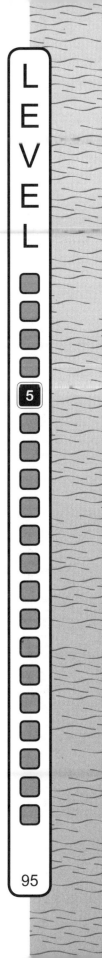

49 PUZZLE

Which number is missing?

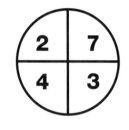

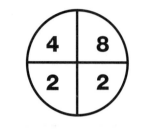

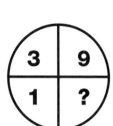

50 PUZZLE

Which value replaces the question mark and balances the scales?

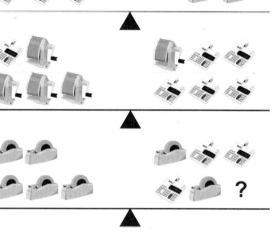

51 PUZZLE

Which playing card completes the puzzle?

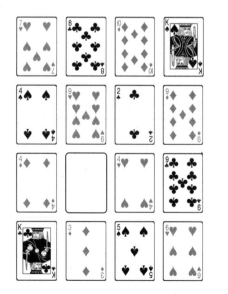

52 PUZZLE

What three numbers are missing from this grid?

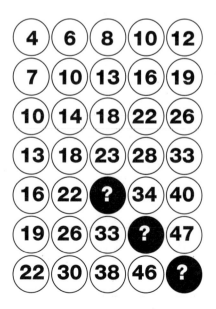

53 PUZZLE

What is missing from the last square?

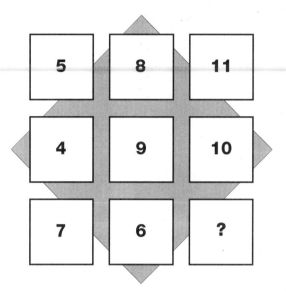

5	8	11
4	9	10
7	6	?

54 PUZZLE

Which letter completes the puzzle?

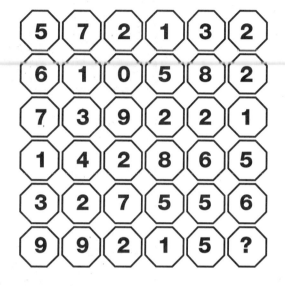

5	7	2	1	3	2
6	1	0	5	8	2
7	3	9	2	2	1
1	4	2	8	6	5
3	2	7	5	5	6
9	9	2	1	5	?

55 PUZZLE

Which number is the odd one out in each oval?

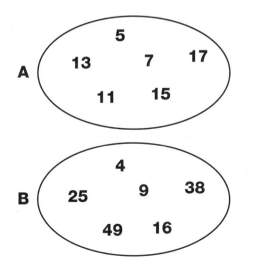

A   5   13   7   17   11   15

B   4   25   9   38   49   16

56 PUZZLE

Which number replaces the question mark and completes the puzzle?

5	4	7
12	6	6
7	?	2

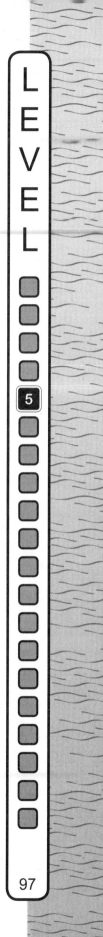

97

Which pattern completes this sequence?

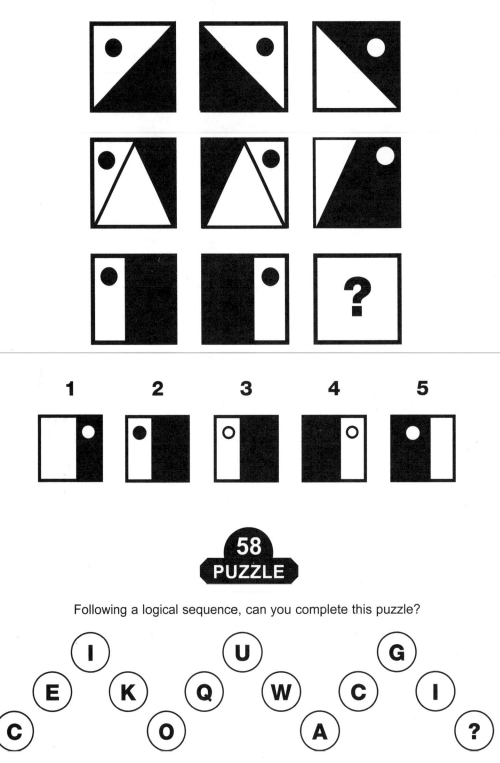

Following a logical sequence, can you complete this puzzle?

E   I   K   Q   U   W   C   G   I

C   O   A   ?

LEVEL

5

1 PUZZLE

Which letter replaces the question mark and completes the puzzle?

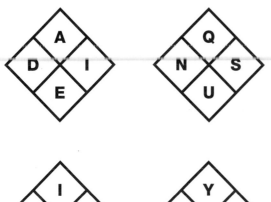

2 PUZZLE

Which letter replaces the question mark and completes the puzzle?

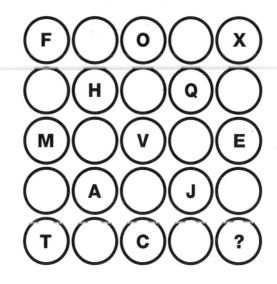

3 PUZZLE

Which number is missing?

4 PUZZLE

Which letter replaces the question mark and completes the puzzle?

E	LRCEX	C
I	IPHTL	D
M	XFTMH	B
N	RLXNF	C
?	OYJTQ	E

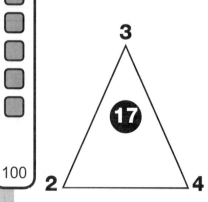

PUZZLE 5

Which of the lower six grids completes the sequence?

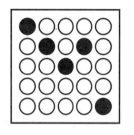
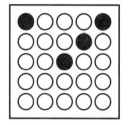
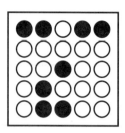

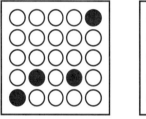
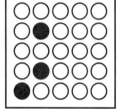

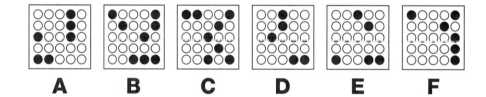

A **B** **C** **D** **E** **F**

PUZZLE 6

What is missing from the last triangle?

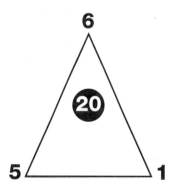
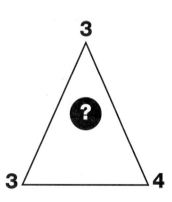

7 PUZZLE

Which letter completes this chain?

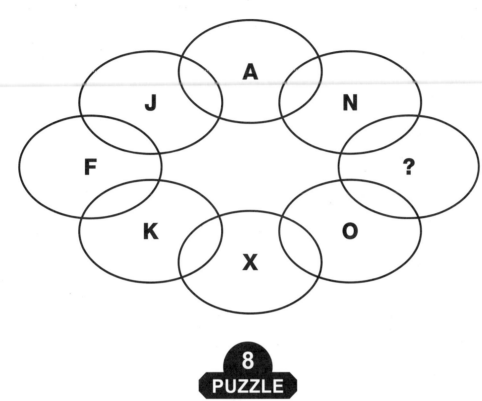

8 PUZZLE

Which number replaces the question mark and completes the puzzle?

3	6	2	6
2	7	5	15
11	5	10	1

9	1	17	3
2	3	6	1
9	2	4	0

12	7	19	9
4	10	11	16
20	7	14	1

6	5	15	3
0	4	1	14
2	3	6	?

PUZZLE 9

What number is missing?

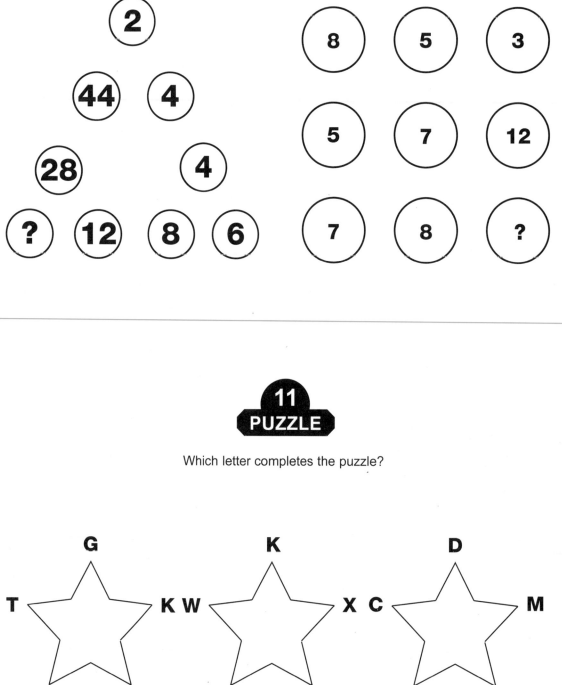

(2)

(44) (4)

(28)   (4)

(?) (12) (8) (6)

PUZZLE 10

Which number completes this sequence?

(8) (5) (3)

(5) (7) (12)

(7) (8) (?)

PUZZLE 11

Which letter completes the puzzle?

G   K   D

T   K W   X C   M

Q   N   S   V   B   ?

PUZZLE 12

Which letter replaces the question mark in the last star?

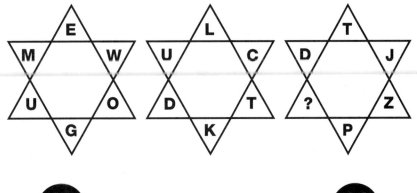

PUZZLE 13

Which number completes the puzzle?

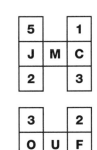

PUZZLE 14

Which number replaces the question mark and completes the puzzle?

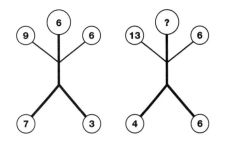

PUZZLE 15

Which letter replaces the question mark and completes the puzzle?

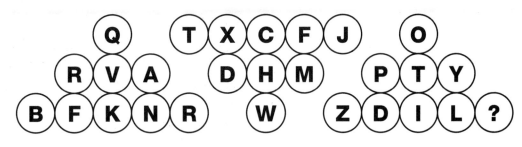

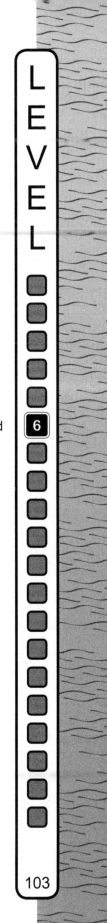

103

Following a logical sequence, can you complete this puzzle?

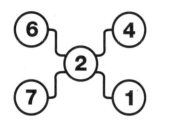
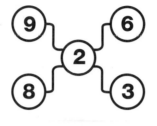

17 PUZZLE

What is missing from the last shape?

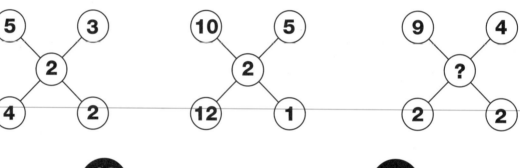

18 PUZZLE

Which number fits within the bottom right hand circle to complete the puzzle?

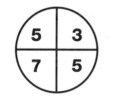

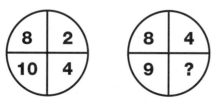

19 PUZZLE

Which letter completes the puzzle?

LEVEL

6

PUZZLE 20

Which letter replaces the question mark?

3	P	8
9	G	11
2	U	4
3	W	1
7	?	18

PUZZLE 21

Which number is missing from the puzzle?

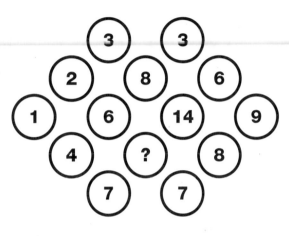

PUZZLE 22

Which number do you need to add to complete the puzzle?

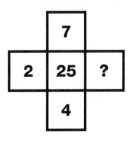

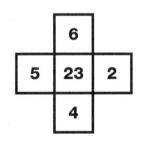

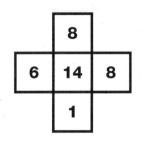

23 PUZZLE

Which number is missing from the last circle?

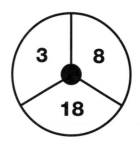

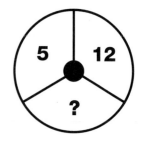

24 PUZZLE

What number is missing from the bottom pyramid?

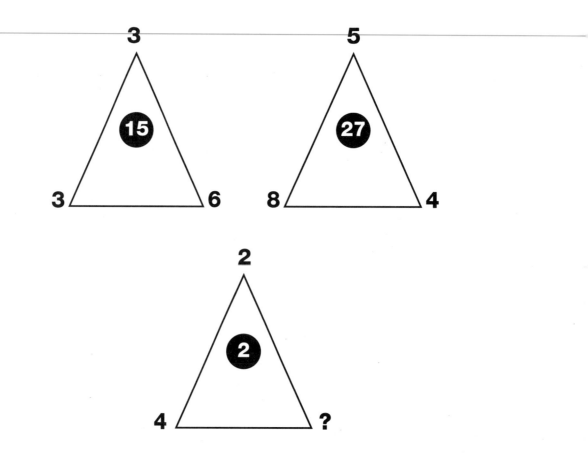

Which letter is missing?

G			
J	Y		
N	F	W	
S	?	G	R

Which letter replaces the question mark and completes the puzzle?

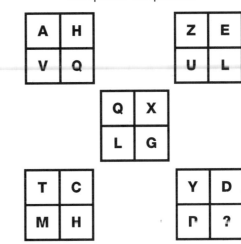

A	H
V	Q

Z	E
U	L

Q	X
L	G

T	C
M	H

Y	D
?	?

Which playing card replaces the question mark and completes the puzzle?

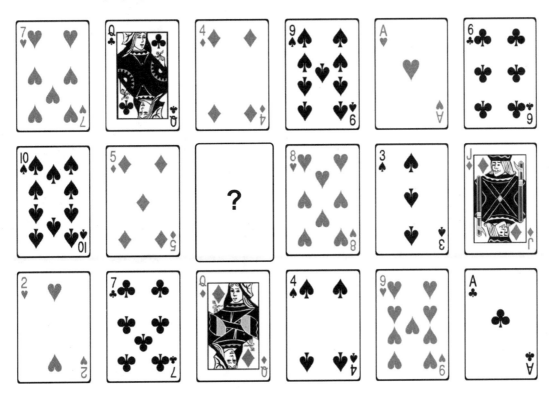

28 PUZZLE

Which number completes this puzzle?

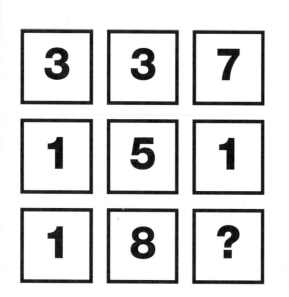

29 PUZZLE

In this sequence of letters, what is needed to complete the puzzle?

J	K
M	P
T	Y
E	L
T	C
M	?

30 PUZZLE

What is needed to complete this pyramid of numbers?

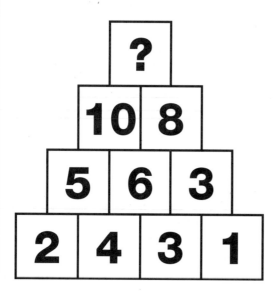

31 PUZZLE

Which letter completes the puzzle?

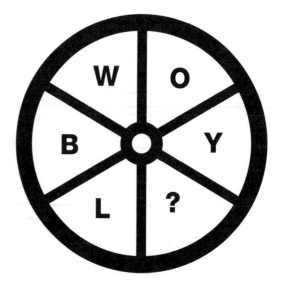

PUZZLE 32

Which letter completes this puzzle?

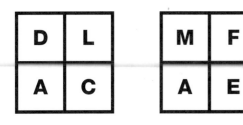

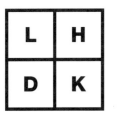 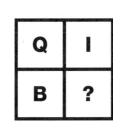

D	L
A	C

M	F
A	E

L	H
D	K

Q	I
B	?

PUZZLE 33

Which number will complete the grid?

1	0	0	2	5	6
1	2	1	2	8	9
1	4	4	3	2	4
1	6	9	3	6	1
1	9	6	4	0	0
2	2	5	4	4	?

PUZZLE 34

What time should the bottom clock show?

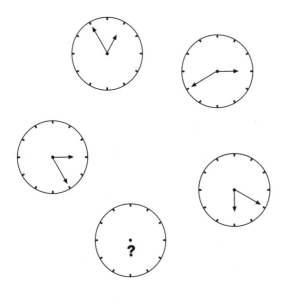

PUZZLE 35

Which letter replaces the question mark and completes the puzzle?

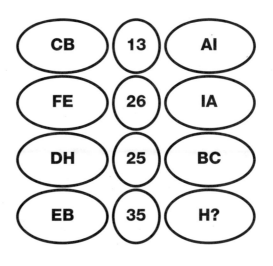

CB 13 AI
FE 26 IA
DH 25 BC
EB 35 H?

36 PUZZLE

Which letter goes within this triangle?

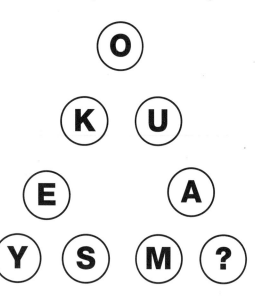

37 PUZZLE

What is missing from this sequence?

38 PUZZLE

Following a logical sequence, can you complete this puzzle?

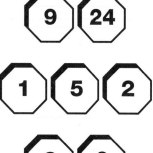

39 PUZZLE

What letter is missing?

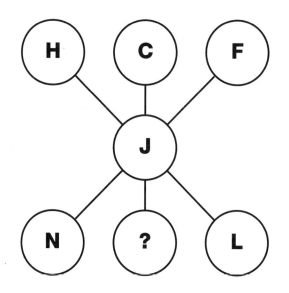

PUZZLE 40

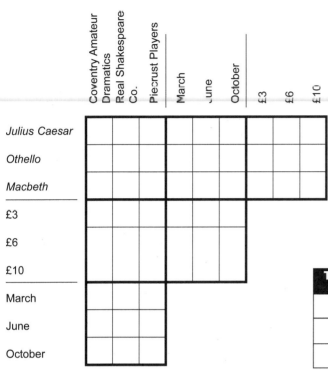

	Coventry Amateur Dramatics	Real Shakespeare Co.	Piecrust Players	March	June	October	£3	£6	£10
Julius Caesar									
Othello									
Macbeth									
£3									
£6									
£10									
March									
June									
October									

Newtown has a thriving amateur dramatics scene. This year, the Piecrust Players put on a production of *Macbeth*. *Othello*, not performed by the Coventry Amateur Dramatics, had the cheapest tickets. *Julius Caesar* was on in March and, although it had the best set yet seen in Newtown, wasn't the most expensive to see. The Real Shakespeare Company's production was put on later than that of the Piecrust Players. Which group put on each play, what was the ticket price and in which month could each play be seen?

Theatre group	Play	Opening month	Ticket price

PUZZLE 41

Which number is missing from this puzzle?

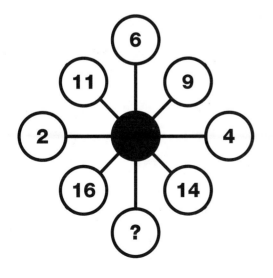

6
11   9
2   4
16   14
?

PUZZLE 42

Which letter replaces the question mark and completes the sequence?

J	O?J	V
L O S		I W L
X	DKS	B

43 PUZZLE

What is needed to complete this puzzle?

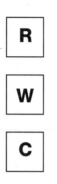

R

W

C

J

?

44 PUZZLE

Which letters complete the puzzle?

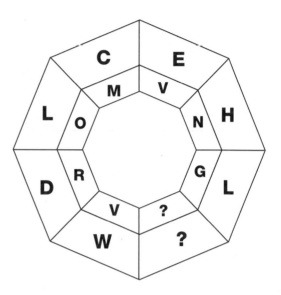

45 PUZZLE

What letter completes this pyramid?

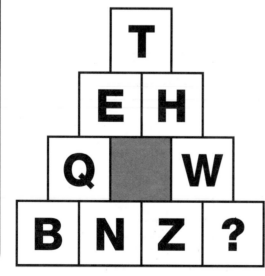

46 PUZZLE

Can you move just 4 matches to make 3 equilateral triangles?

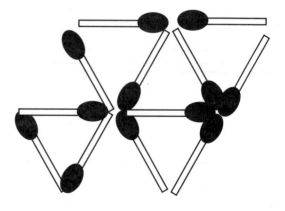

Which picture cube does this shape make?

A

C

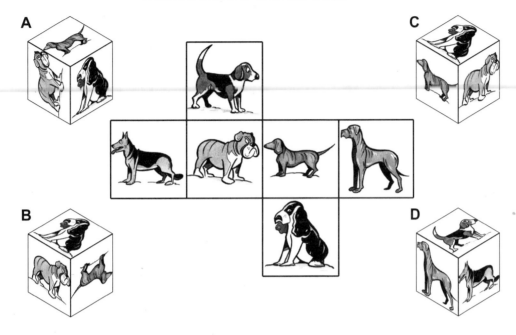

B

D

Which number replaces the question mark and completes the puzzle?

6	7	2

13	9

22

17	5

13	4	?

Penelope buys a small bottle of her favourite perfume for £10. If the perfume is worth £9 more than the cost of the ornate bottle it comes in, how much is the bottle worth?

PUZZLE 50

Which letter is the odd one out in each oval?

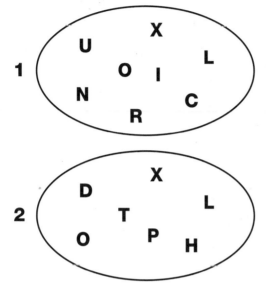

PUZZLE 51

Where does the missing hand go?

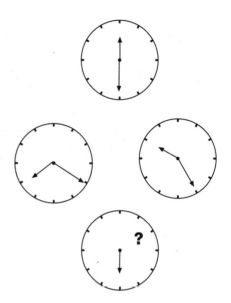

PUZZLE 52

Following a logical sequence, can you complete this puzzle?

PUZZLE 53

What goes in the empty segment?

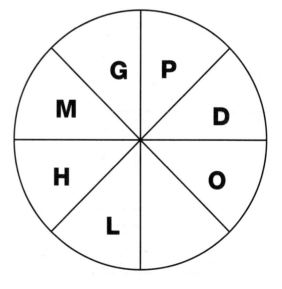

PUZZLE 54

Which letter is missing from the last grid?

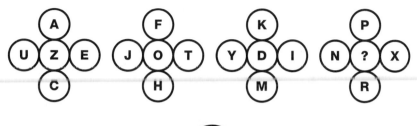

PUZZLE 55

Which letter is missing from the puzzle?

PUZZLE 56

Which letter replaces the question mark and completes the puzzle?

J	O	T		D	J	P		M	T	A		V	D	L
	U				Q				B				M	
	A				X				J				?	

PUZZLE 57

What is required to complete the puzzle?

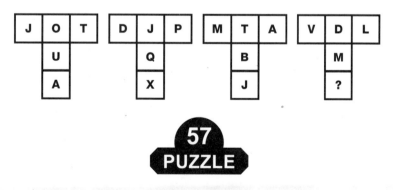

What number is missing?

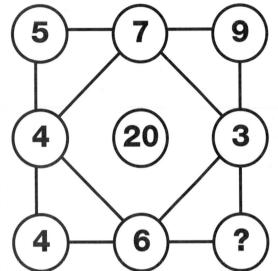

Following a logical sequence, can you complete this puzzle?

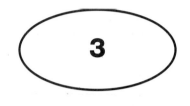

3

11

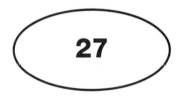

27

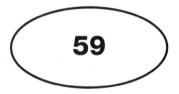

59

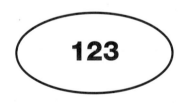

123

?

What is needs to be added to the third set of scales to make it balance perfectly?

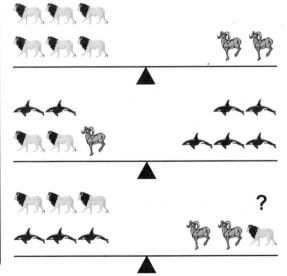

PUZZLE 1

What is missing from the last grid?

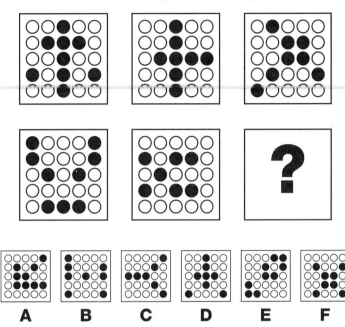

A B C D E F

PUZZLE 2

Which watch shown below fills the missing space?

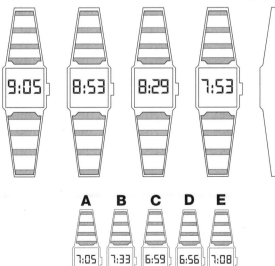

A B C D E

3 PUZZLE

What completes this puzzle?

G N Q

C

D K ?

4 PUZZLE

Which letter completes the puzzle?

N

V Z

D R

L T B ?

5 PUZZLE

Which of the lower patterns replaces the question mark to continue the sequence?

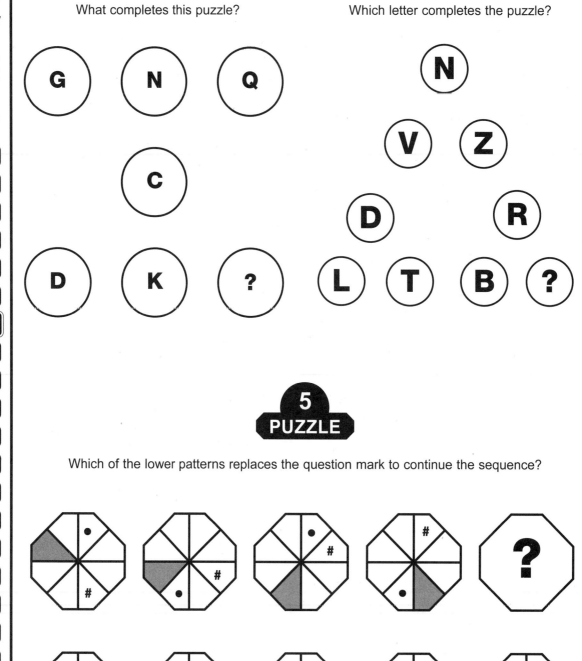

A B C D E

What is missing from the last circle?

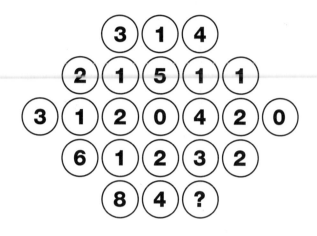

Which number replaces the question mark and completes the puzzle?

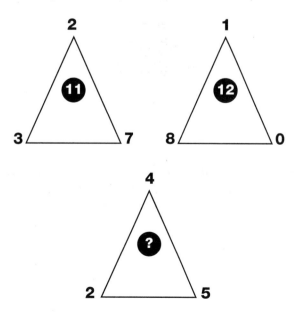

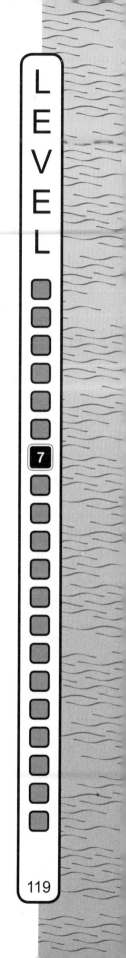

L
E
V
E
L

7

8
PUZZLE

What number is missing from the bottom triangle?

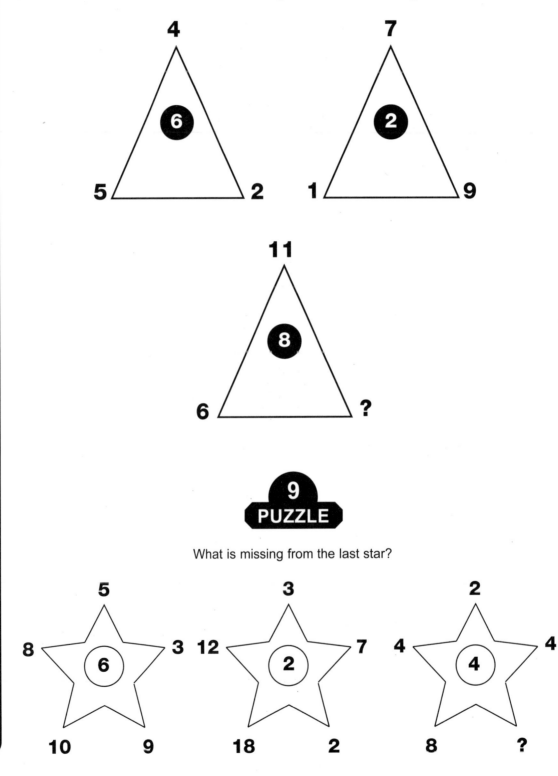

9
PUZZLE

What is missing from the last star?

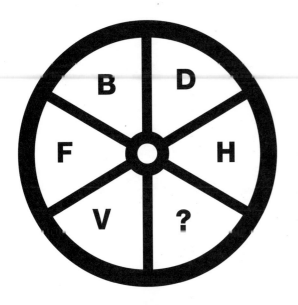

PUZZLE 12

Which number replaces the question mark and completes the puzzle?

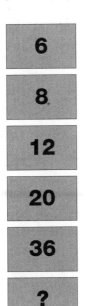

PUZZLE 13

Which number replaces the question mark and completes the puzzle?

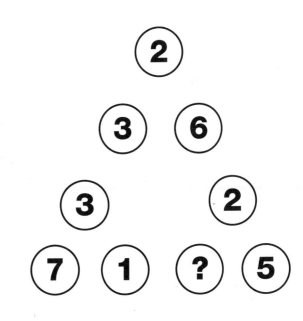

PUZZLE 14

Which letter from the bottom row completes the puzzle?

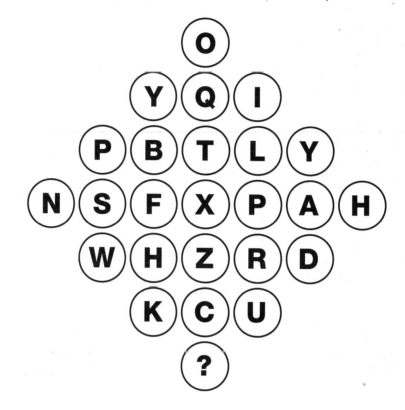

O

Y Q I

P B T L Y

N S F X P A H

W H Z R D

K C U

?

P G R I T K V M

PUZZLE 15

Following a logical sequence, can you complete this puzzle?

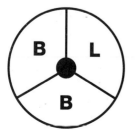

B L
B

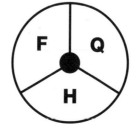

F Q
H

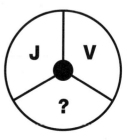

J V
?

PUZZLE 16

What is missing from the last hexagon?

B	B	E
B	E	F
B	H	?

PUZZLE 17

Which letter completes the puzzle?

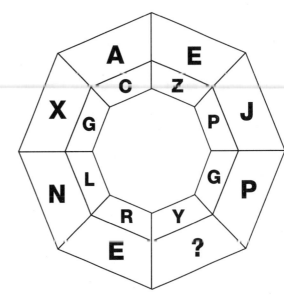

A E C Z X G P J N L G P R Y E ?

PUZZLE 18

Which number replaces the question mark and completes the puzzle?

5
8
10
11
14
?

PUZZLE 19

Which number replaces the question mark and completes the puzzle?

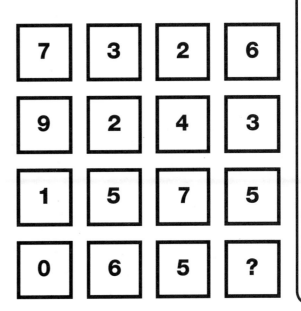

7	3	2	6
9	2	4	3
1	5	7	5
0	6	5	?

20 PUZZLE

Which number complete this puzzle?

21 PUZZLE

Where does the missing hand go?

22 PUZZLE

Which letter follows? (Clue: this is the first time you have needed to think like this)

B   C   D   G   ?

23 PUZZLE

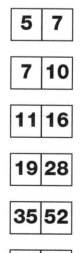

In this sequence of numbers, what completes the puzzle?

5	7

7	10

11	16

19	28

35	52

67	?

PUZZLE 24

What is missing from the last hexagon?

Which letter completes the puzzle?

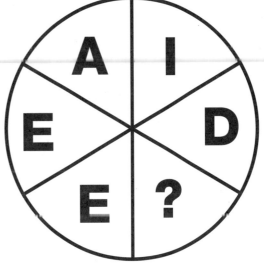

PUZZLE 26

Which number replaces the question mark and completes the puzzle?

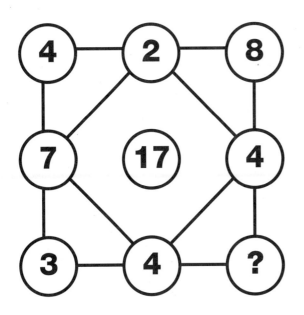

PUZZLE 27

Where should the hour hand point to on the bottom clock?

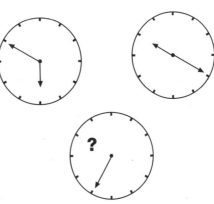

LEVEL

7

125

PUZZLE

What number is missing?

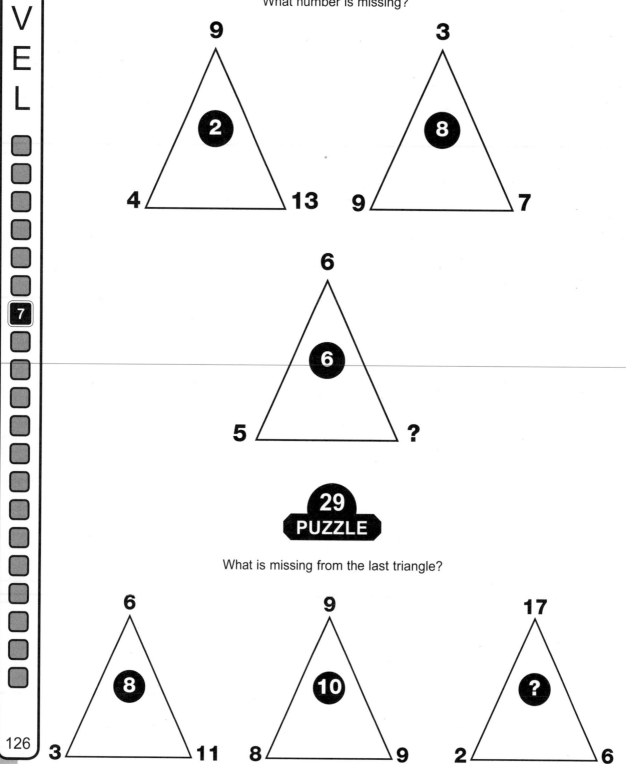

9

2

4   13

3

8

9   7

6

6

5   ?

29 PUZZLE

What is missing from the last triangle?

6

8

3   11

9

10

8   9

17

?

2   6

126

What is missing from the last hexagon?

Which letter completes the puzzle?

Which number replaces the question mark and completes the puzzle?

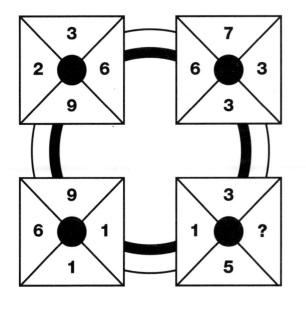

Which number replaces the question mark and completes the chain?

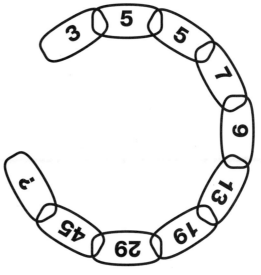

LEVEL

7

PUZZLE 34

What is needed in this triangle to complete the puzzle?

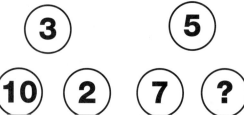

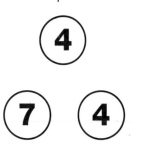

(4)

(7) (4)

(3)   (5)

(10) (2) (7) (?)

PUZZLE 35

Which letter completes the puzzle?

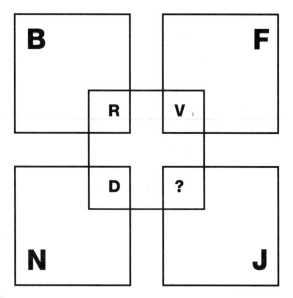

B   F
R V
D ?
N   J

PUZZLE 36

Following a logical sequence, can you complete this puzzle?

92

74

46

22

?

PUZZLE 37

What letter is missing?

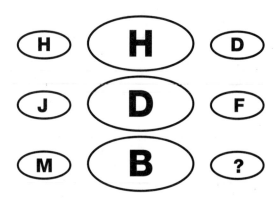

H   H   D

J   D   F

M   B   ?

What is missing from the last circle?

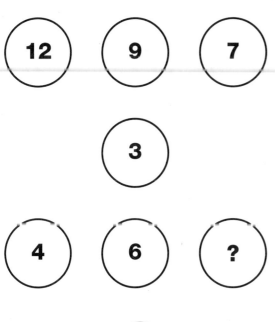

Which number completes the puzzle?

Which number replaces the question mark and completes the puzzle?

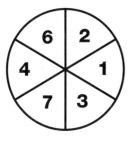
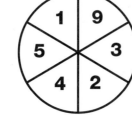
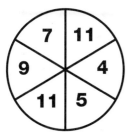

Which letter replaces the question mark and completes the puzzle?

42 PUZZLE

Which number goes in the lower right hand segment?

43 PUZZLE

What replaces the question mark?

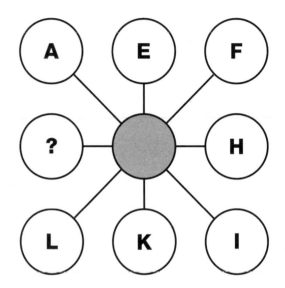

44 PUZZLE

Following a logical sequence, can you complete this puzzle?

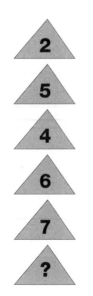

45 PUZZLE

Can you remove three matches to leave three squares?

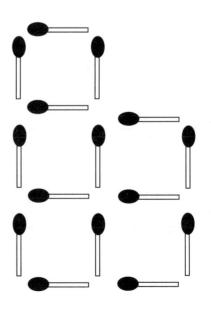

46 PUZZLE

What is missing from the last circle?

E	L	B	I
G	D	F	M
J	A	F	B
C	H	K	?

47 PUZZLE

Which letter replaces the question mark and completes the puzzle?

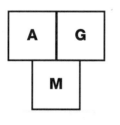

A | G
M

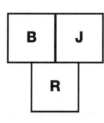

P | W
D

B | J
R

E | N
?

What completes this sequence?

Which letter completes the puzzle?

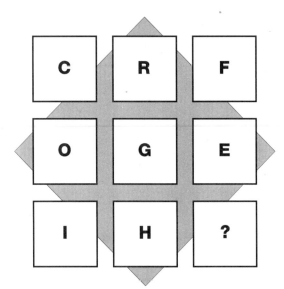

PUZZLE 50

What number is missing?

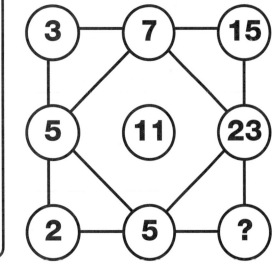

PUZZLE 51

Can you trace around this figure using only 10 straight lines, without lifting your pen off the paper, or drawing over any line twice?

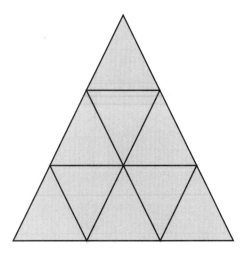

132

PUZZLE 52

What is missing from the last square?

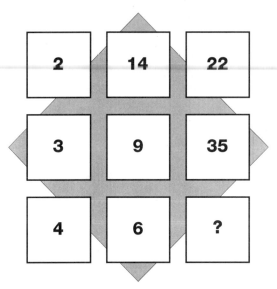

2	14	22
3	9	35
4	6	?

PUZZLE 53

Which number completes the puzzle?

4	1	2	5	2	3
6	3	5	7	4	6
1	5	4	2	6	5
7	4	5	6	3	4
9	6	8	8	5	7
4	8	7	3	7	?

PUZZLE 54

Which two numbers are the odd ones out in each of these ovals?

1

5
1   21   11
15   9

2

1
16
8   5   6
12   20

PUZZLE 55

Which number replaces the question mark and completes the puzzle?

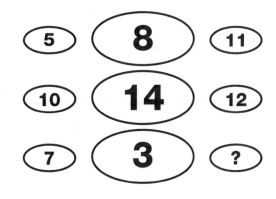

5   **8**   11

10   **14**   12

7   **3**   ?

Complete this puzzle.

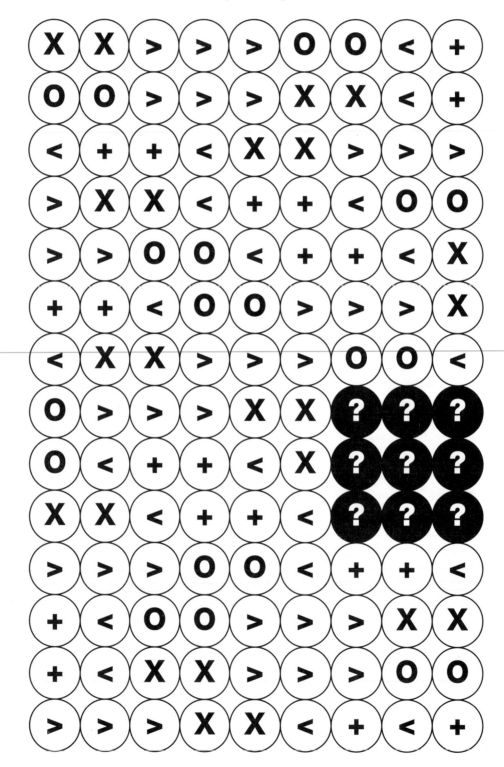

LEVEL 7

PUZZLE 1

What is missing from the last segment?

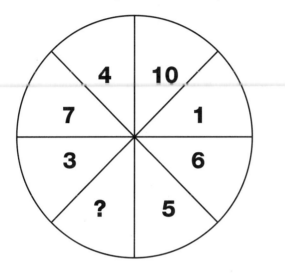

PUZZLE 2

Which letter completes the puzzle?

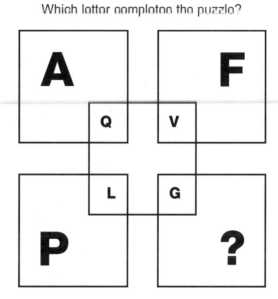

PUZZLE 3

What object is needed to make the scales balance?

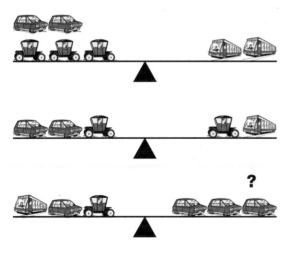

PUZZLE 4

Which letter replaces the question mark and completes the puzzle?

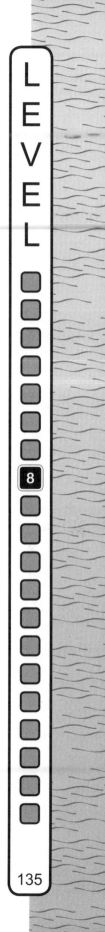

LEVEL
8

135

5 PUZZLE

Which letter completes the puzzle?

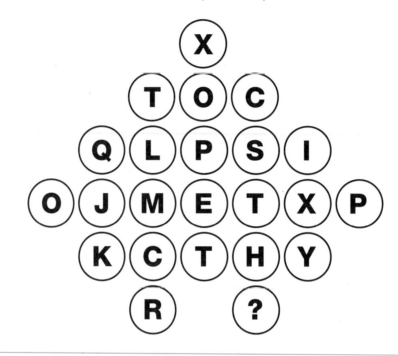

6 PUZZLE

Which number is missing?

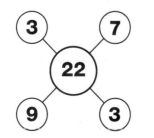

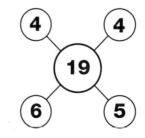

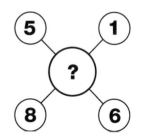

PUZZLE 7

What is missing from the last circle?

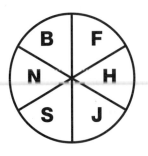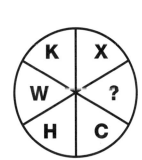

PUZZLE 8

Which letter replaces the question mark and completes the puzzle?

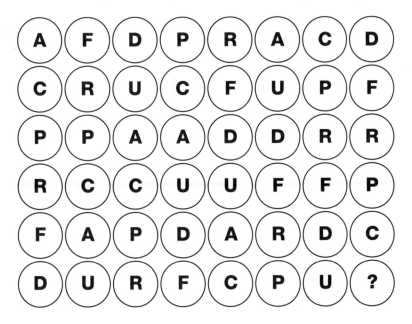

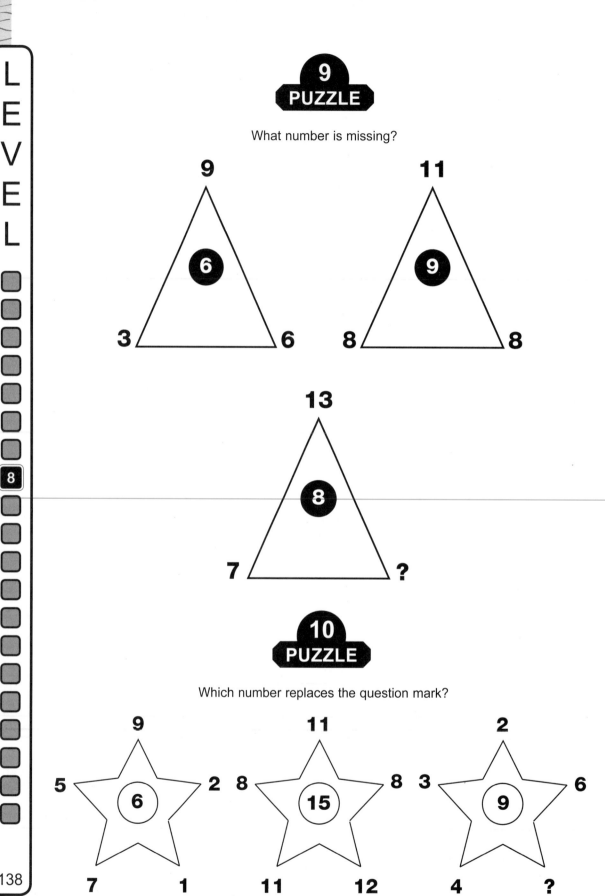

9
PUZZLE

What number is missing?

9

6

3   6

11

9

8   8

13

8

7   ?

10
PUZZLE

Which number replaces the question mark?

9

5   6   2

7   1

11

8   15   8

11   12

2

3   9   6

4   ?

PUZZLE 11

What is missing from the last circle?

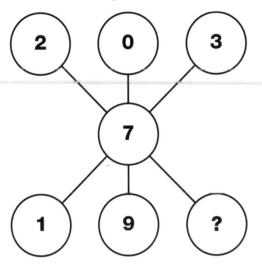

PUZZLE 12

Which letter completes the puzzle?

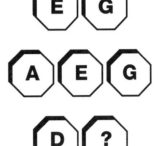

PUZZLE 13

Which number replaces the question mark and completes the puzzle?

PUZZLE 14

Which number replaces the question mark and completes the puzzle?

2	3
6	4
8	12
24	?

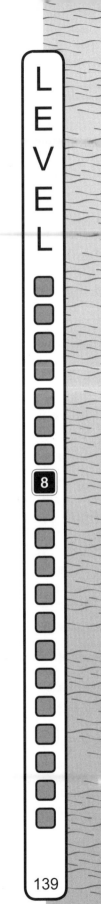

15 PUZZLE

What is missing from the bottom square?

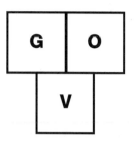
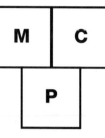
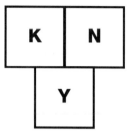

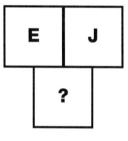

16 PUZZLE

Which of the bottom watches fills the empty space?

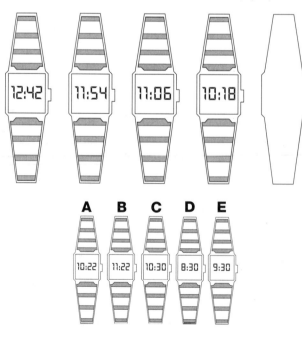

What is missing from the middle circle?

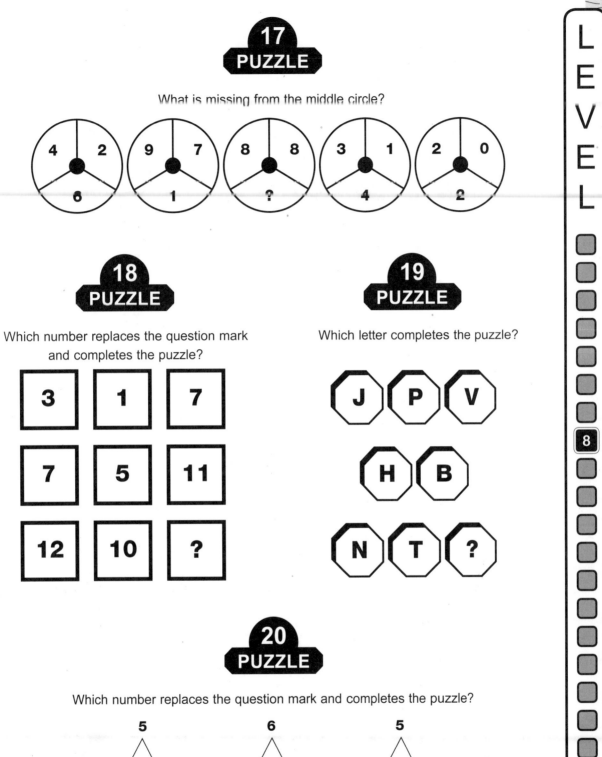

Which number replaces the question mark and completes the puzzle?

3	1	7
7	5	11
12	10	?

Which letter completes the puzzle?

J P V

H B

N T ?

Which number replaces the question mark and completes the puzzle?

LEVEL

8

21 PUZZLE

Following a logical sequence, can you complete this puzzle?

22 PUZZLE

What letter is missing?

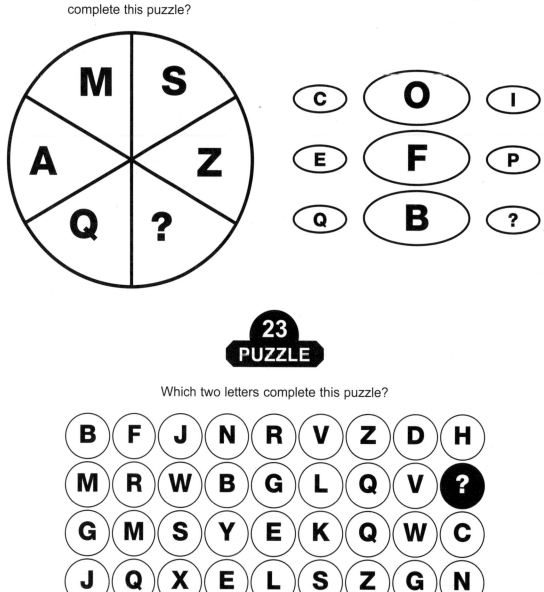

23 PUZZLE

Which two letters complete this puzzle?

PUZZLE 24

What is missing from the last circle?

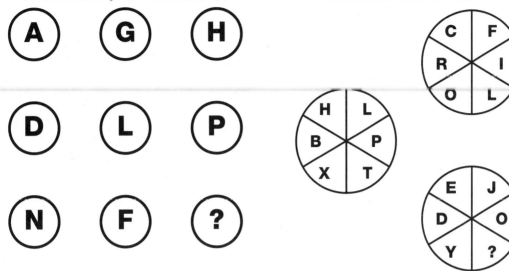

PUZZLE 25

Which letter completes the puzzle?

PUZZLE 26

Which number replaces the question mark and completes the puzzle?

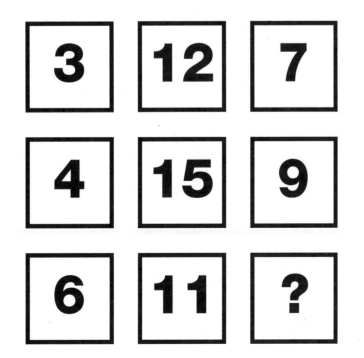

PUZZLE 27

What completes this puzzle?

5	6	3
9	11	5
17	21	?

PUZZLE 28

Which letter is needed to complete the puzzle?

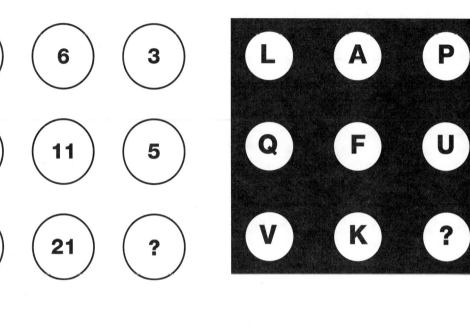

L	A	P
Q	F	U
V	K	?

PUZZLE 29

Which of the lower patterns finishes the sequence?

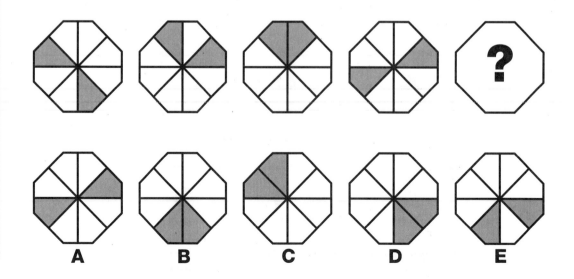

A B C D E

PUZZLE 30

What is missing from the last oval?

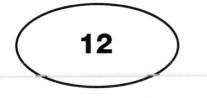
12

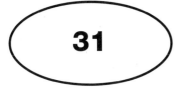
31

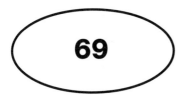
69

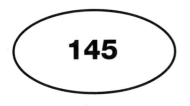
145

297

?

PUZZLE 31

Which letter completes the puzzle?

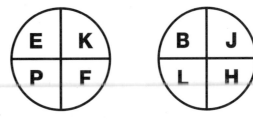

PUZZLE 32

Which number replaces the question mark
and completes the puzzle?

3	4

4	5

6	8

11	16

24	37

58	?

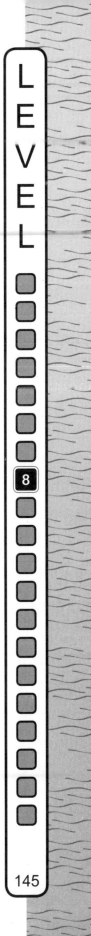

L
E
V
E
L

8

PUZZLE 33

What number is missing?

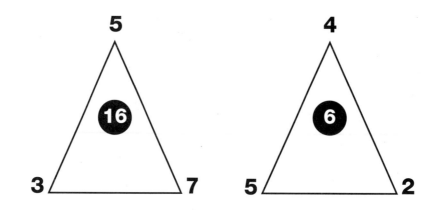

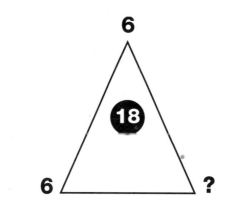

PUZZLE 34

Following a logical sequence, can you complete this puzzle?

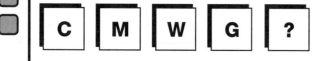

PUZZLE 35

What is needed to complete this sequence?

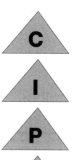

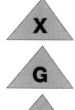

36 PUZZLE

Which of the letters below is missing from the bottom circle?

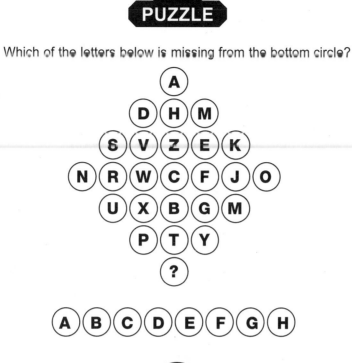

A B C D E F G H

37 PUZZLE

Which number replaces the question mark and completes the puzzle?

3 12 17

5 23 30

8 38 ?

38 PUZZLE

Which letter completes the puzzle?

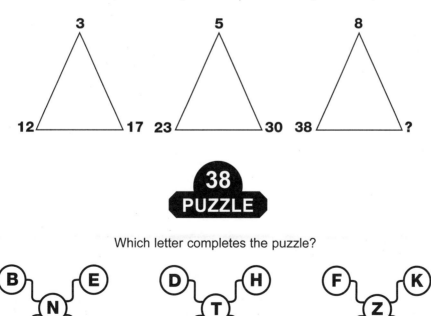

LEVEL

8

39 PUZZLE

Which number from the bottom row is missing from the centre?

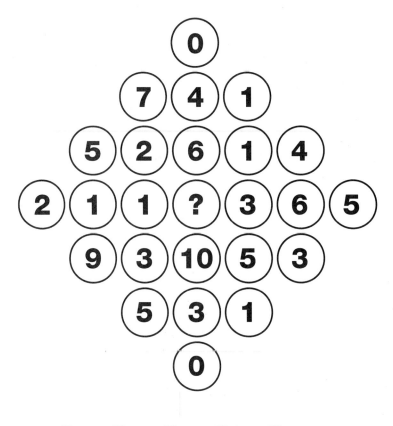

```
            0
         7  4  1
       5  2  6  1  4
    2  1  1  ?  3  6  5
       9  3  10 5  3
         5  3  1
            0
```

(1) (3) (5) (7) (9)

40 PUZZLE

Move two matches only to make this sum correct.

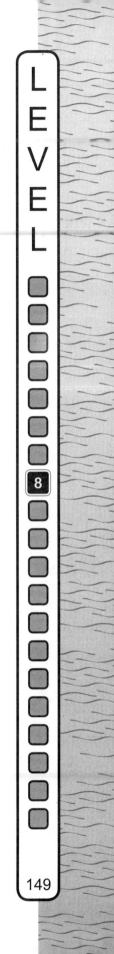

PUZZLE 41

What is missing from the last star?

Star 1: 3, 4, 4, 5
Star 2: 7, 7, 8, 6
Star 3: 9, ?, 7, 11

PUZZLE 42

Which letter completes the puzzle?

D, T, B, Z, J, F, H, L, P, R, N, X, ?

PUZZLE 43

Which number replaces the question mark and completes the puzzle?

Triangle 1: 4 (top), 3 (bottom left), 1 (bottom right), 16 (center)
Triangle 2: 6 (top), 7 (bottom left), 2 (bottom right), 54 (center)
Triangle 3: 3 (top), 4 (bottom left), 3 (bottom right), ? (center)

PUZZLE 44

Which number replaces the question mark and completes the puzzle?

Circle 1: 7, 9, 14
Circle 2: 3, 2, 3
Circle 3: 6, ?, 5

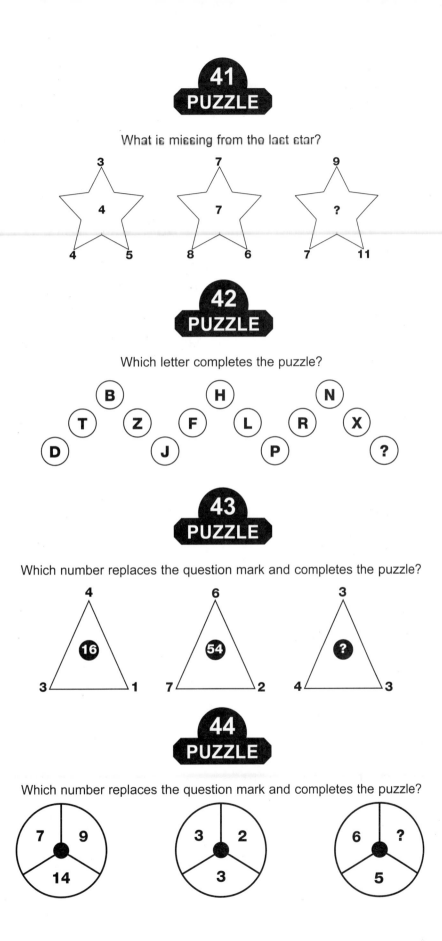

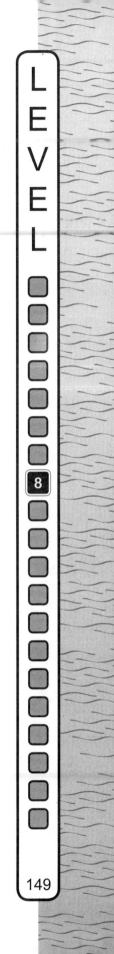

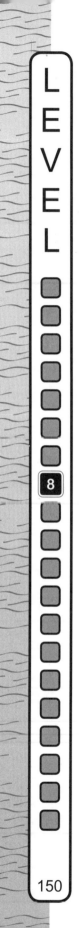

Which letter is missing?

A

D

I

P

?

Which number completes this wheel?

Which number completes the puzzle?

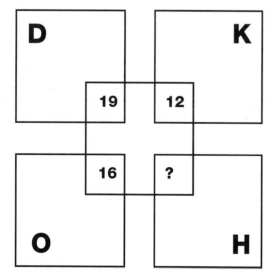

What is needed to complete this sequence?

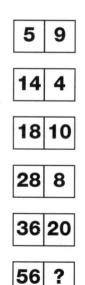

5	9
14	4
18	10
28	8
36	20
56	?

49 PUZZLE

Which segment fills the gap?

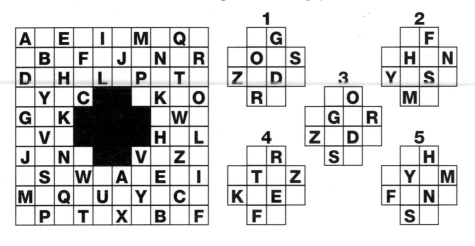

50 PUZZLE

Which number replaces the question mark and completes the puzzle?

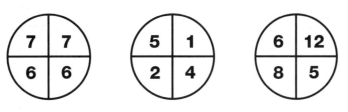

51 PUZZLE

Which number replaces the question mark and completes the sequence?

52 PUZZLE

Following a logical sequence, can you complete this puzzle?

53 PUZZLE

What number is missing?

54 PUZZLE

What number is missing from the bottom right hand circle?

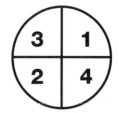 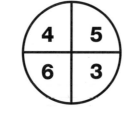

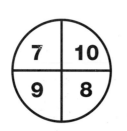 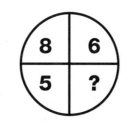

55 PUZZLE

Where should the missing hand go?

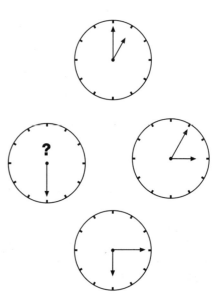

1 PUZZLE

Which letter replaces the question mark and completes the sequence?

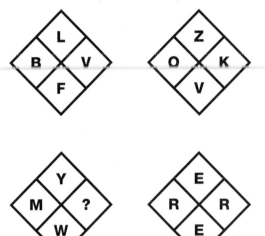

2 PUZZLE

Which single digit number replaces the question mark and completes the puzzle?

3 PUZZLE

Which number replaces the question mark and completes the puzzle?

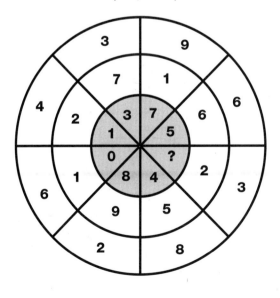

4 PUZZLE

Which letter is missing?

A	DH	M
F	KN	R
L	PU	X
S	VZ	E
X	CF	?

5 PUZZLE

Which number is missing from this wheel?

3 14

6 ?

5 10

6 PUZZLE

Which letter completes the puzzle?

B   F   J   P   ?

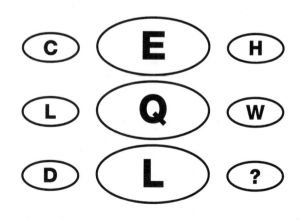

7 PUZZLE

What number is missing?

4   19   6

5   30   7

4   3   ?

8 PUZZLE

What is needed to complete this puzzle?

C   **E**   H

L   **Q**   W

D   **L**   ?

Which number replaces the question mark and completes the sequence?

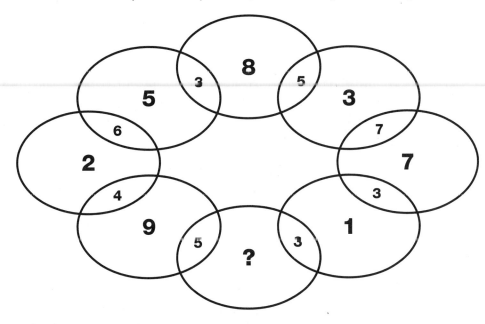

PUZZLE 10

Which number completes the bottom grid?

3	5	4	8
1	11	7	3
2	6	1	12

4	7	8	13
5	14	9	11
9	7	4	13

1	2	4	5
4	3	2	8
7	1	3	1

2	3	0	3
3	8	5	5
5	5	2	?

PUZZLE 11

What number is missing from the bottom triangle?

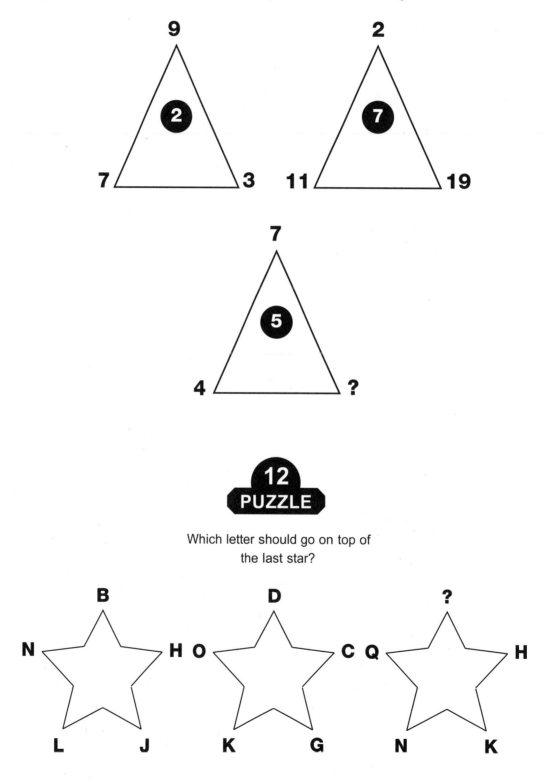

PUZZLE 12

Which letter should go on top of
the last star?

PUZZLE 13

Which letter replaces the question mark and completes the puzzle?

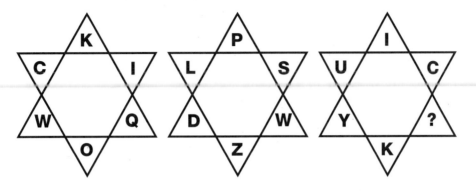

PUZZLE 14

Which number replaces the question mark and completes the puzzle?

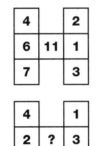

PUZZLE 15

Which number completes the puzzle?

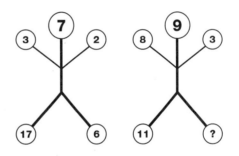

PUZZLE 16

Which number replaces the question mark on the third triangle?

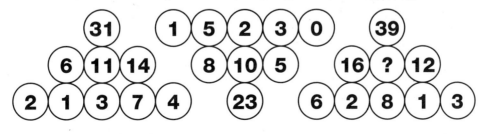

PUZZLE 17

What number completes this grid?

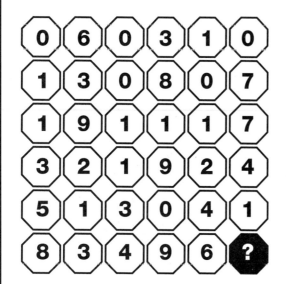

PUZZLE 18

Following a logical sequence, can you complete this puzzle?

6

9

15

27

?

PUZZLE 19

Which piece fits back into the grid?

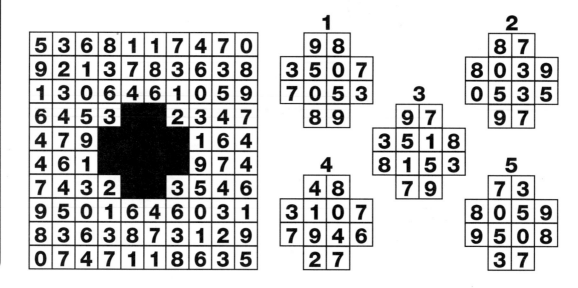

PUZZLE 20

Which number replaces the question mark to complete the puzzle?

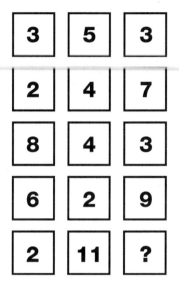

3	5	3
2	4	7
8	4	3
6	2	9
2	11	?

PUZZLE 21

Which number replaces the question mark and completes the sequence?

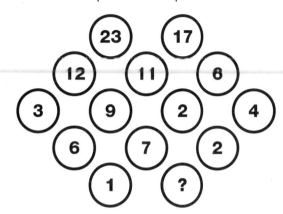

Circles: 23, 17, 12, 11, 6, 3, 9, 2, 4, 6, 7, 2, 1, ?

PUZZLE 22

Which letter replaces the question mark and completes the puzzle?

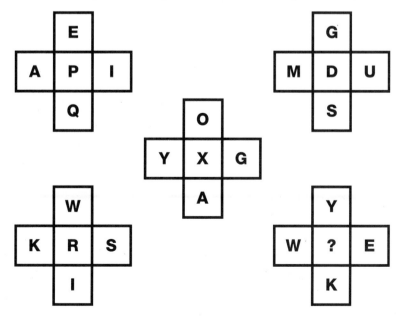

First cross:
- E
- A P I
- Q

Second cross:
- G
- M D U
- S

Middle cross:
- O
- Y X G
- A

Third cross:
- W
- K R S
- I

Fourth cross:
- Y
- W ? E
- K

Which of the bottom watches fills the gap?

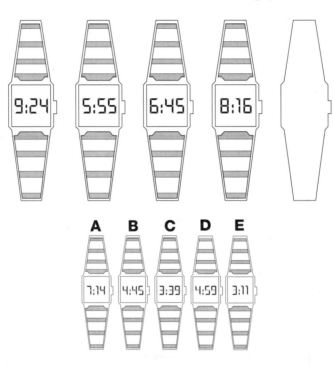

Which of the bottom patterns replaces the question mark?

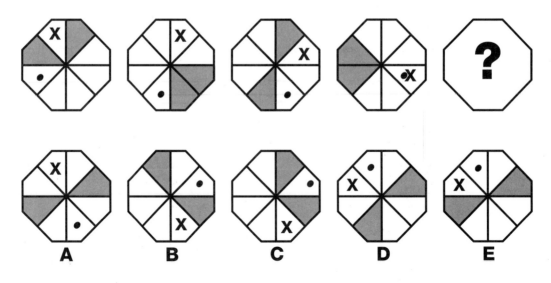

L E V E L

9

Which number replaces the question mark and completes the puzzle?

4			
6	2		
9	3	1	
19	10	7	?

Which number replaces the question mark to finish this puzzle?

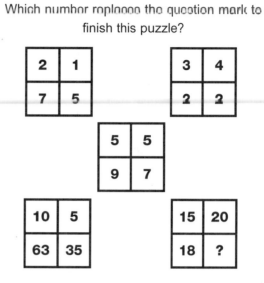

2	1
7	5

3	4
2	2

5	5
9	7

10	5
63	35

15	20
18	?

Which playing card replaces the question mark and completes the puzzle?

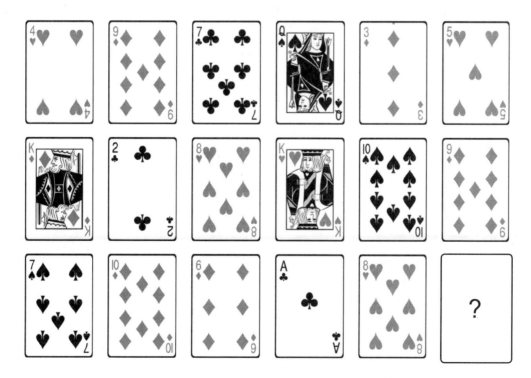

PUZZLE 28

Following a logical sequence, can you complete this puzzle?

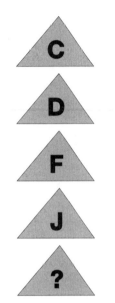

C
D
F
J
?

PUZZLE 29

What number is missing?

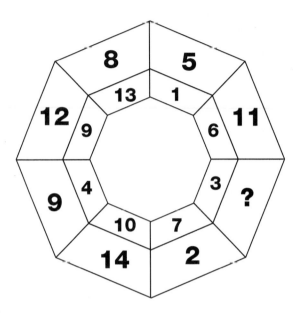

PUZZLE 30

Which number complete the puzzle?

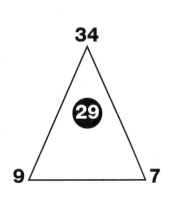

34
29
9   7

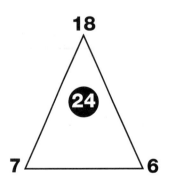

18
24
7   6

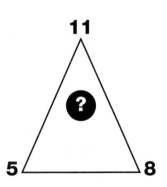

11
?
5   8

31 PUZZLE

Which letter replaces the question mark and completes the sequence?

A	M
J	U

R	F
B	S

E	P
P	H

I	Z
Y	?

32 PUZZLE

Which letter replaces the question mark and completes the grid?

B		N		Z	
	H		T		F
Q		E		S	
	X		L		Z
E		U		K	
	M		C		?

33 PUZZLE

Where should the missing hour hand point to?

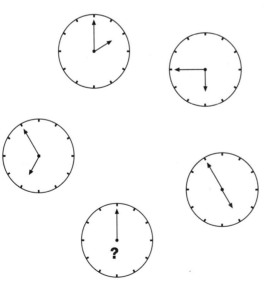

34 PUZZLE

Which letter completes this puzzle?

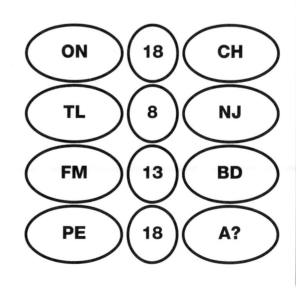

ON	18	CH
TL	8	NJ
FM	13	BD
PE	18	A?

What is needed to complete this grid?

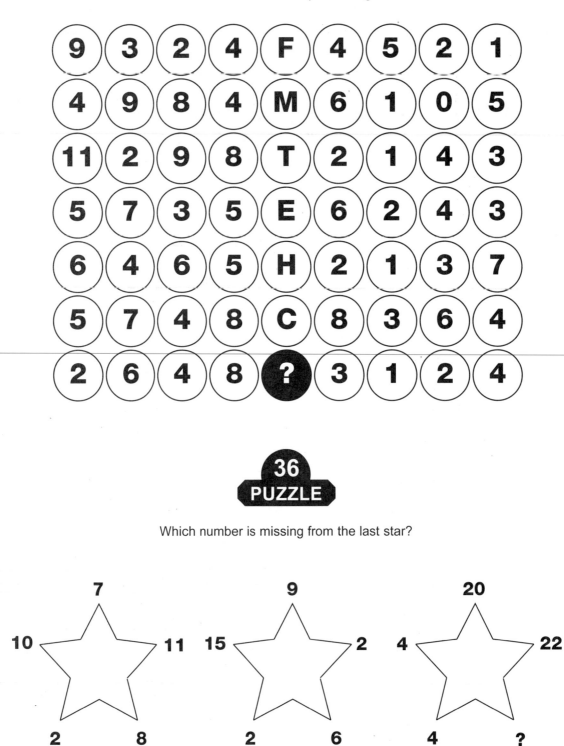

9	3	2	4	F	4	5	2	1
4	9	8	4	M	6	1	0	5
11	2	9	8	T	2	1	4	3
5	7	3	5	E	6	2	4	3
6	4	6	5	H	2	1	3	7
5	7	4	8	C	8	3	6	4
2	6	4	8	**?**	3	1	2	4

36
PUZZLE

Which number is missing from the last star?

7
10   11
2   8

9
15   2
2   6

20
4   22
4   ?

PUZZLE 37

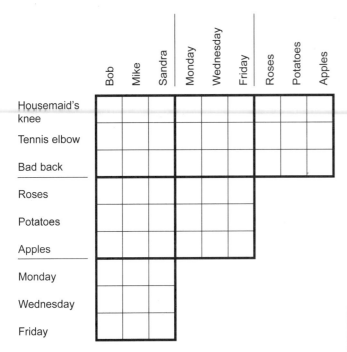

	Bob	Mike	Sandra	Monday	Wednesday	Friday	Roses	Potatoes	Apples
Housemaid's knee									
Tennis elbow									
Bad back									
Roses									
Potatoes									
Apples									
Monday									
Wednesday									
Friday									

Bob, Mike and Sandra are all keen gardeners, and are proud of their allotments. Bob never works on his patch on a Friday, and without the knee problems which affect some of his friends, produces the best roses in the village. Sandra, who suffers from tennis elbow, only gets chance to work on Mondays, and is not known for her apples. The person who grows apples always works on the allotments on a Friday. There is enough information here to work out which gardener produces which crop, which day of the week they can usually be found at the allotments, and what kind of injury each one tended to suffer from.

Gardener	Injury	Crop	Day

PUZZLE 38

Which letter replaces the question mark and completes the sequence?

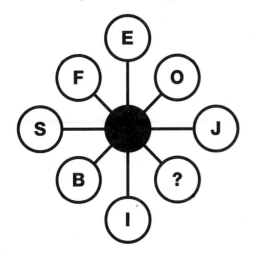

PUZZLE 39

Which letter replaces the question mark and completes the sequence?

U	K		B
	O	S	
E			F
	C	C	
M	R		?

PUZZLE

Which letter is missing?

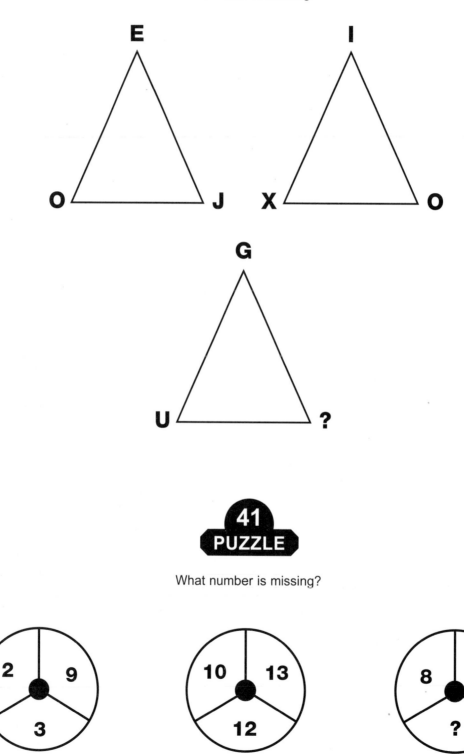

41
PUZZLE

What number is missing?

Which picture cube does this shape make?

A

C

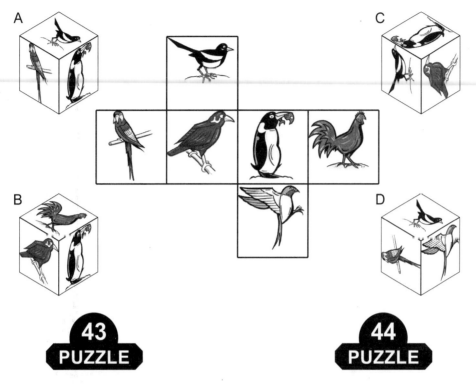

B

D

Which letter replaces the question mark and completes the puzzle?

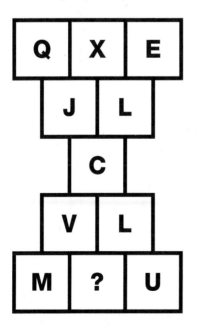

For Christmas this year, the Taylor family had a get together. The following people were present: one grandmother, one grandfather, two mothers, two fathers, one father-in-law, one mother-in-law, one daughter-in-law, four children, three grandchildren, one brother, two sisters, two sons and two daughters. What is the fewest number of individuals that could have been there?

45 PUZZLE

Which number is missing from the last shape?

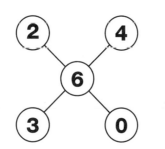 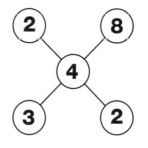 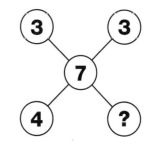

46 PUZZLE

Following a logical sequence, can you complete this puzzle?

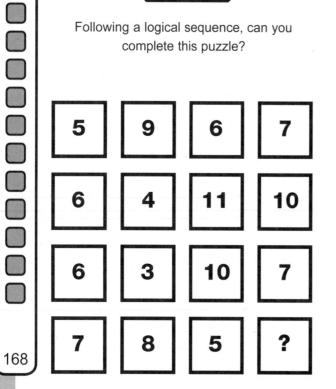

47 PUZZLE

Move just four matches to reduce the area of this triangle by exactly half.

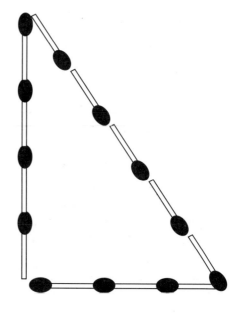

PUZZLE 48

Which letter replaces the question mark and completes the puzzle?

```
     D              G              P              J
  F  H  J       I  N  S       R  U  X       M  Q  U
     L              U              Z              ?
```

PUZZLE 49

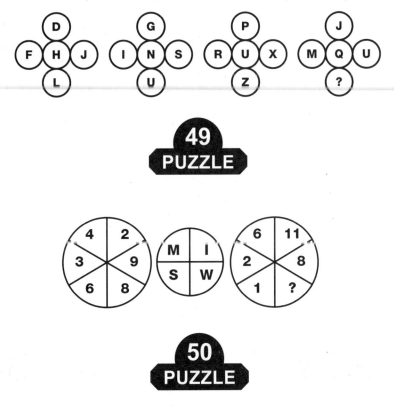

```
   4   2              6   11
 3       9      M  I   2       8
   6   8        S  W     1   ?
```

PUZZLE 50

Which letter replaces the question mark and completes the puzzle?

```
J O T      N T Z      H O V      C K S
  Y          F          C          A
  D          L          J          ?
```

PUZZLE 51

What number should the last domino show on the top to complete this puzzle?

PUZZLE 52

Which number is missing from the bottom shape?

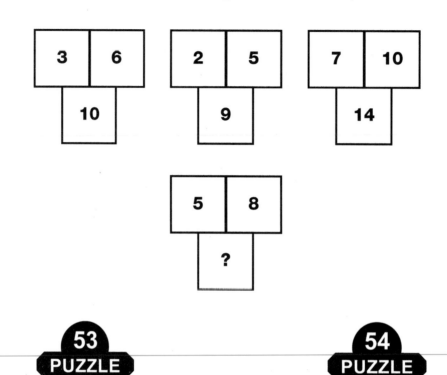

3	6
10	

2	5
9	

7	10
14	

5	8
?	

PUZZLE 53

Which letter completes the wheel?

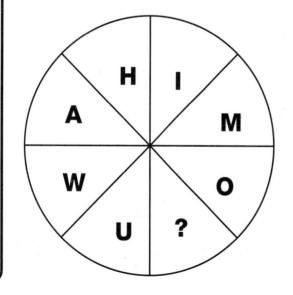

PUZZLE 54

Place every digit from 1 to 9 in this puzzle, so that all horizontal, vertical and diagonal lines add up to the same number.

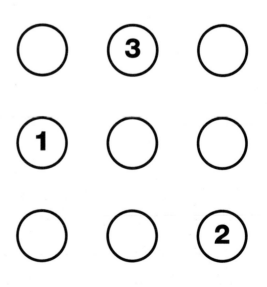

PUZZLE 1

Which letter completes the wheel?

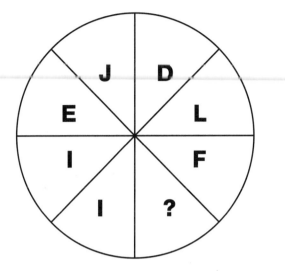

PUZZLE 2

Which number completes the puzzle?

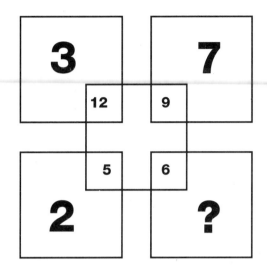

PUZZLE 3

Which symbol is needed to balance the bottom scale?

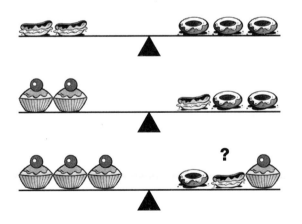

PUZZLE 4

Which letter replaces the question mark and completes the puzzle?

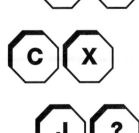

L E V E L

10

171

PUZZLE 5

Which letter completes the puzzle?

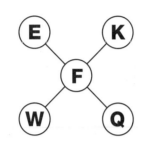

E   K
F
W   Q

L   P
D
X   T

G   L
?
V   Q

PUZZLE 6

Fill in the empty segment

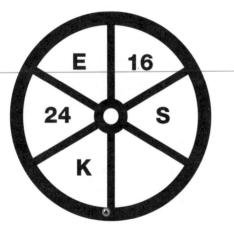

E   16
24   S
K

PUZZLE 7

What letter is missing?

F   J   P
B   M   O
D   H   ?

PUZZLE 8

What number is missing?

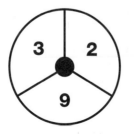

3   2
9

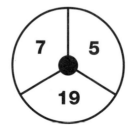

7   5
19

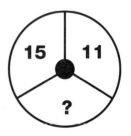

15   11
?

PUZZLE 9

What is missing from the bottom middle circle?

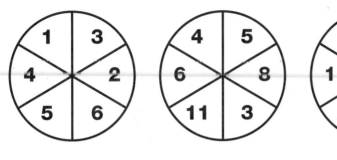

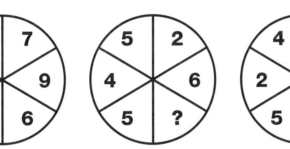

PUZZLE 10

Which letter replaces the question mark and completes the puzzle?

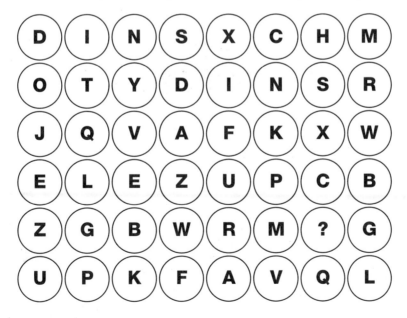

11 PUZZLE

What number goes in the centre of the bottom triangle?

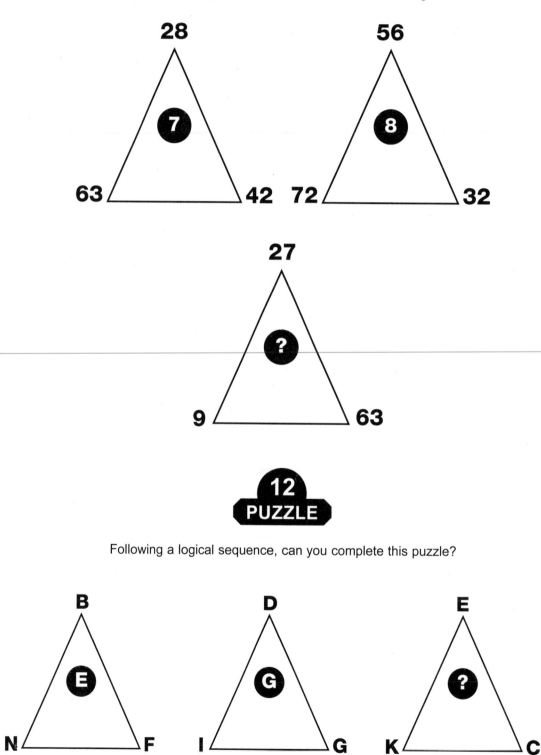

12 PUZZLE

Following a logical sequence, can you complete this puzzle?

PUZZLE 13

What is missing from the bottom right hand circle?

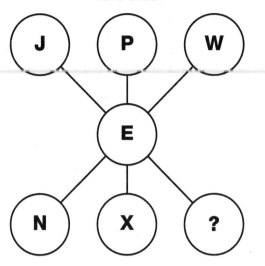

PUZZLE 14

Which number completes the puzzle?

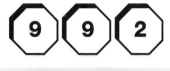

PUZZLE 15

Which number replaces the question mark and completes the puzzle?

PUZZLE 16

Which number replaces the question mark and completes the puzzle?

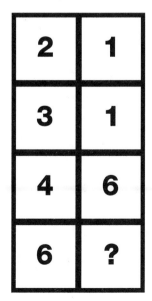

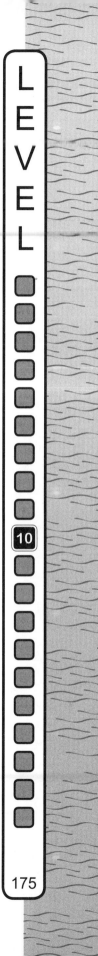

LEVEL

10

17 PUZZLE

Where does the missing hand go?

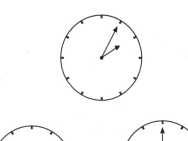

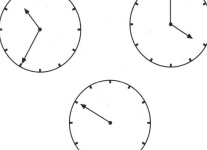

18 PUZZLE

Which letter completes the puzzle?

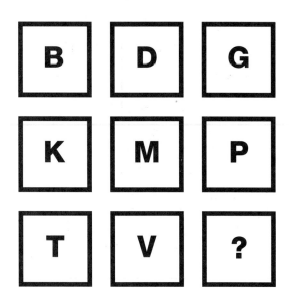

19 PUZZLE

What number is missing?

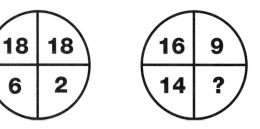

PUZZLE 20

What is missing from the last circle?

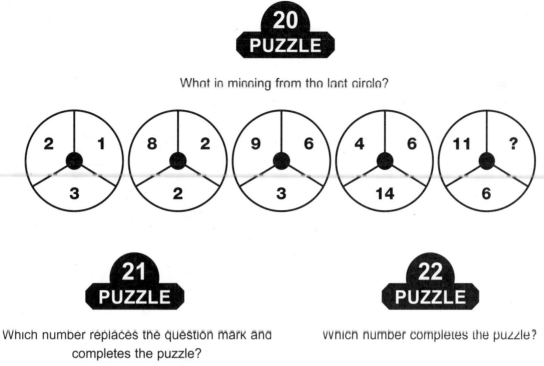

PUZZLE 21

Which number replaces the question mark and completes the puzzle?

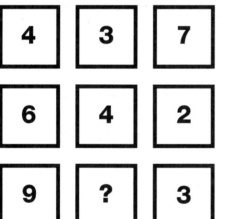

PUZZLE 22

Which number completes the puzzle?

PUZZLE 23

Which number replaces the question mark and completes the puzzle?

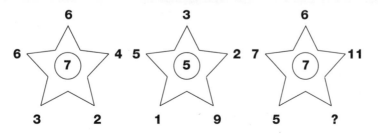

LEVEL

10

LEVEL 10

178

24 PUZZLE

Which letter completes the puzzle?

H

X   Q

M   Y

A   Q   L   ?

25 PUZZLE

What number is missing?

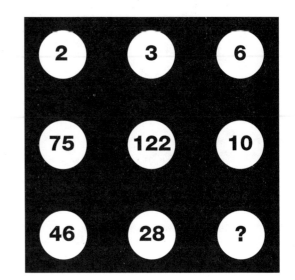

2	3	6
75	122	10
46	28	?

26 PUZZLE

Which letter completes this puzzle?

G   L   E

C   R   O

K   T   ?

27 PUZZLE

Following a logical sequence, can you complete this puzzle?

13

17

19

23

?

PUZZLE 28

What is missing from the last circle?

(A) (Z) (E)

(F) (U) (J)

(K) (P) (?)

PUZZLE 29

Which letter completes the puzzle?

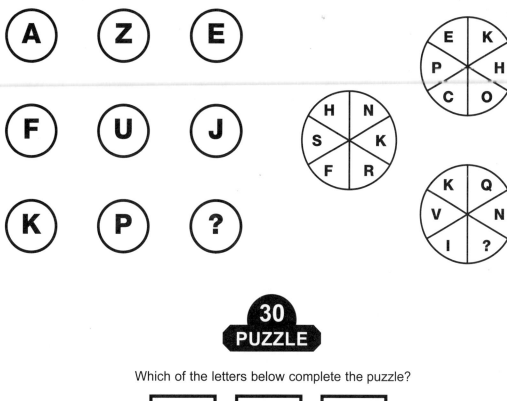

PUZZLE 30

Which of the letters below complete the puzzle?

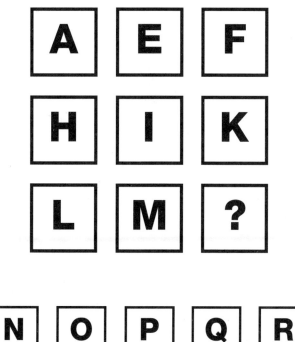

A	E	F
H	I	K
L	M	?

| N | O | P | Q | R |

Which of the bottom watches completes the sequence?

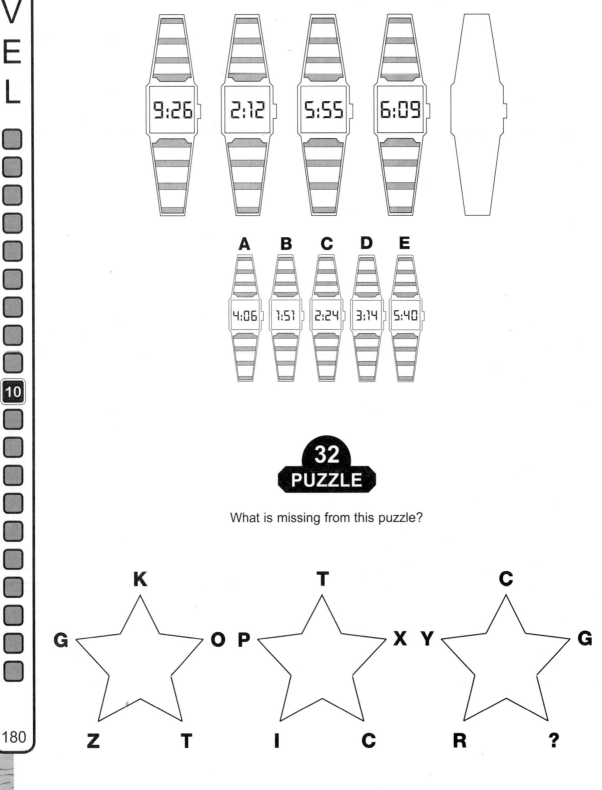

9:26   2:12   5:55   6:09

A   **B**   **C**   **D**   **E**

4:06   1:51   2:24   3:14   5:40

32
PUZZLE

What is missing from this puzzle?

K   T   C

G   O   P   X   Y   G

Z   T   I   C   R   ?

33 PUZZLE

What is missing from the bottom oval?

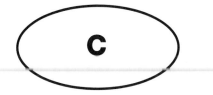
C

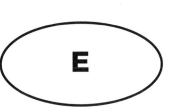
E

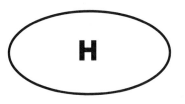
H

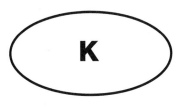
K

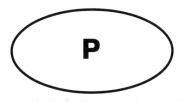
P

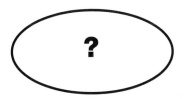
?

34 PUZZLE

Which number completes the puzzle?

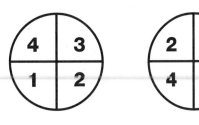

 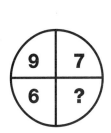

35 PUZZLE

Which number replaces the question mark and completes the puzzle?

1	2

1	5

2	1

2	4

3	0

3	?

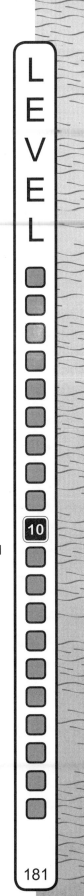

LEVEL

10

181

PUZZLE 36

Which letter completes this puzzle?

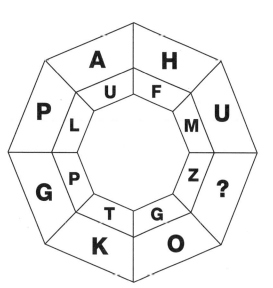

PUZZLE 37

What is missing from this sequence of numbers?

4
5
7
11
19
?

PUZZLE 38

What number is missing?

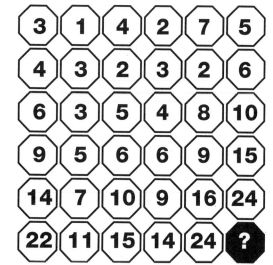

3	1	4	2	7	5
4	3	2	3	2	6
6	3	5	4	8	10
9	5	6	6	9	15
14	7	10	9	16	24
22	11	15	14	24	?

PUZZLE 39

What completes this puzzle?

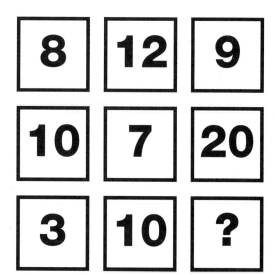

8	12	9
10	7	20
3	10	?

Which of the lower letters replace the question mark to complete the puzzle?

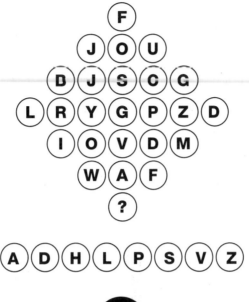

(F)
(J)(O)(U)
(D)(J)(S)(C)(G)
(L)(R)(Y)(G)(P)(Z)(D)
(I)(O)(V)(D)(M)
(W)(A)(F)
(?)

(A)(D)(H)(L)(P)(S)(V)(Z)

Which number replaces the question mark and completes the puzzle?

11   10   11

7   6   5   8   9   ?

Which number completes the puzzle?

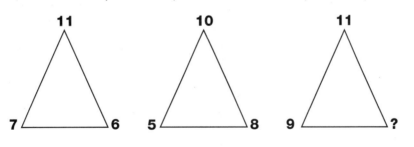

(6)   (3)
(10)
(2)   (9)

(8)   (4)
(8)
(2)   (2)

(1)   (8)
(?)
(3)   (6)

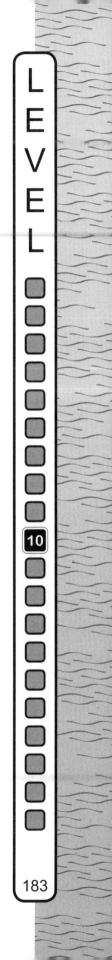

LEVEL

10

PUZZLE 43

What completes this pyramid?

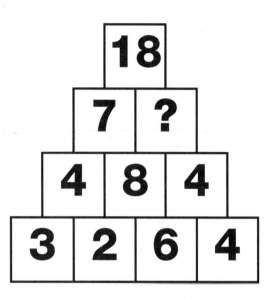

PUZZLE 44

What is missing from the wheel?

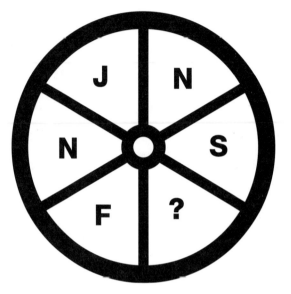

PUZZLE 45

What is missing from the empty segment?

PUZZLE 46

What completes this puzzle?

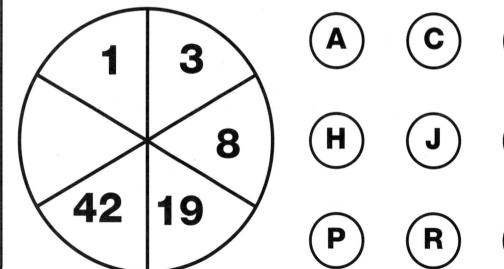

47 PUZZLE

What is missing from the last star?

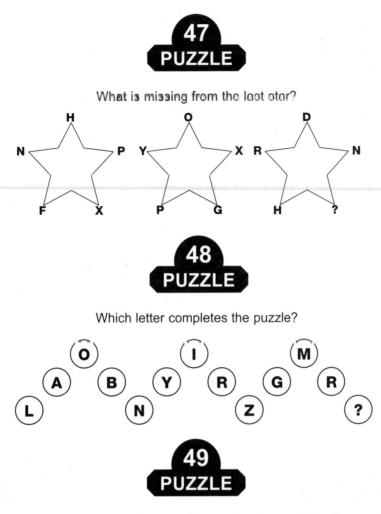

48 PUZZLE

Which letter completes the puzzle?

O
A   B   Y   R   G   R
L   N   Z   ?

I   M

49 PUZZLE

Which number replaces the question mark and completes the puzzle?

2   9   4
5   9   ?
12   1   11   7   15   17

50 PUZZLE

Which number replaces the question mark and completes the puzzle?

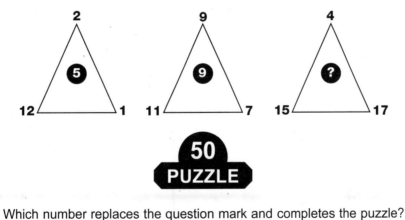

PUZZLE 51

Following a logical sequence, can you complete this puzzle?

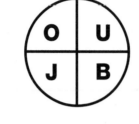

PUZZLE 52

Which three letters complete this puzzle?

PUZZLE 53

Can you draw 4 straight lines, without lifting your pencil, which will pass through the middle of each of these dots?

PUZZLE 54

Can you fill in the blank boxes in the diagram, so that all horizontal, vertical and diagonal lines add up to 33?

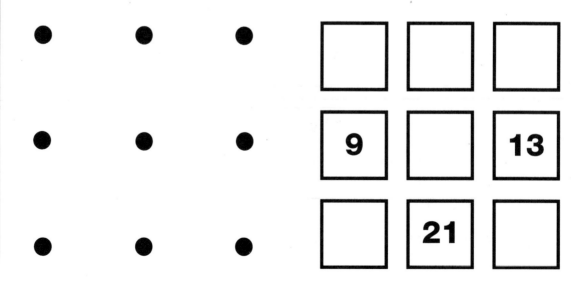

55 PUZZLE

Which segment completes the puzzle?

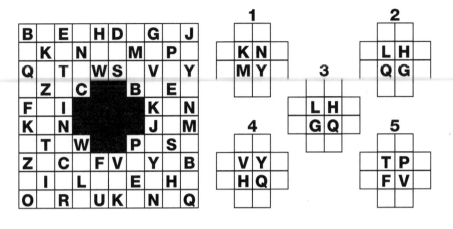

56 PUZZLE

Which number replaces the question mark and completes the puzzle?

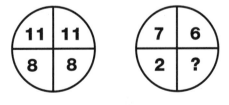

57 PUZZLE

Which number replaces the question mark and completes the puzzle?

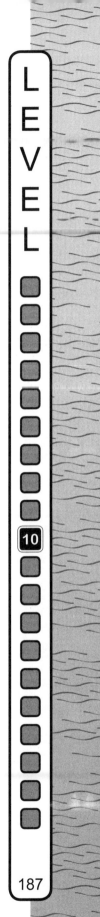

Which playing cards fill in the gaps?

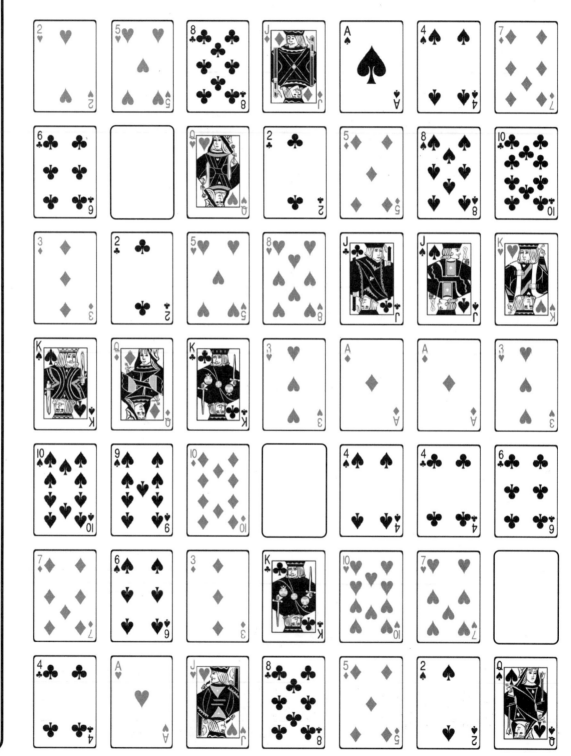

LEVEL 10

PUZZLE 1

What is missing from the last grid?

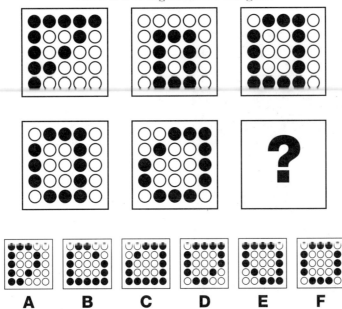

A B C D E F

PUZZLE 2

Which watch shown below fills in the missing shape?

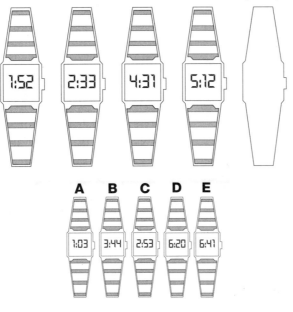

A B C D E

PUZZLE 3

What is missing from this arrangement of circles?

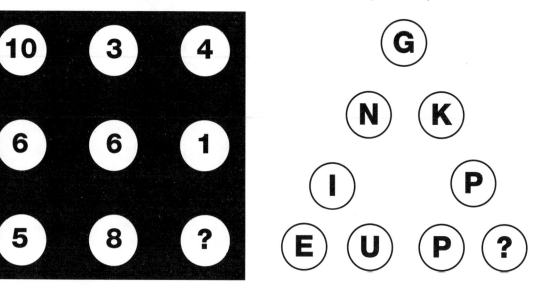

PUZZLE 4

Following a logical sequence, can you complete this puzzle?

G

N   K

I   P

E   U   P   ?

PUZZLE 5

Which number completes the puzzle?

4   1   11

3   5   21

2   4   ?

PUZZLE 6

Which letter completes the puzzle?

Which of the lower circles replace the question mark to complete the puzzle?

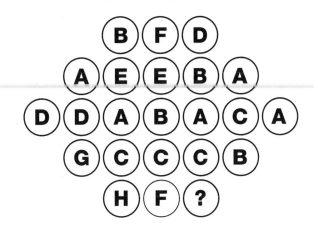

Which number replaces the question mark and completes the puzzle?

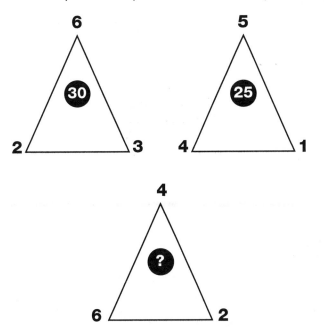

PUZZLE 9

Which number is missing from the bottom triangle?

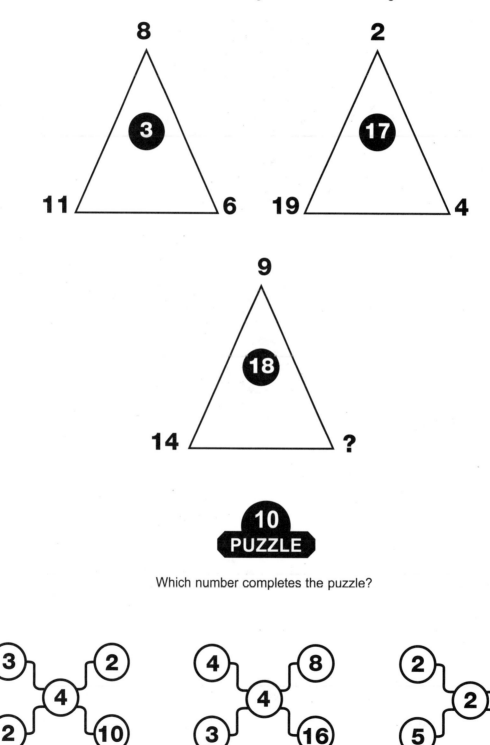

PUZZLE 10

Which number completes the puzzle?

Which letter is missing from the right hand segment?

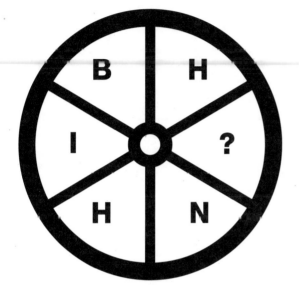

Which letter completes the puzzle?

Which number replaces the question mark and completes the puzzle?

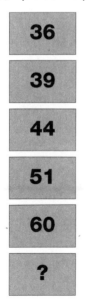

36

39

44

51

60

?

Which letter replaces the question mark and completes the puzzle?

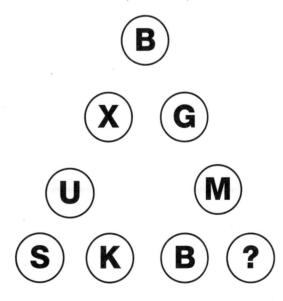

B

X   G

U   M

S   K   B   ?

LEVEL

11

193

15 PUZZLE

Which two letters are needed to complete this puzzle?

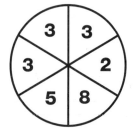

16 PUZZLE

Following a logical sequence, can you complete this puzzle?

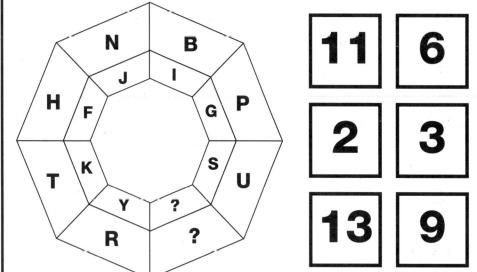

17 PUZZLE

Which number is missing from this arrangement of circles?

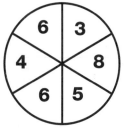

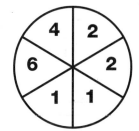

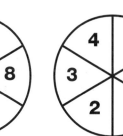
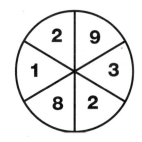

What is missing from the last hexagon?

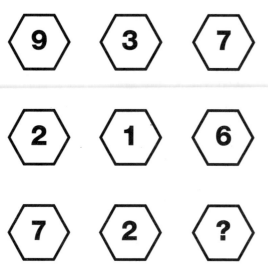

9 3 7

2 1 6

7 2 ?

Which letter completes the puzzle?

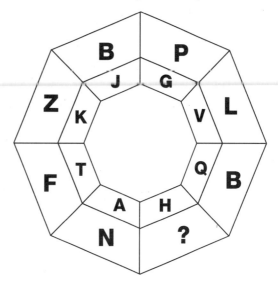

B P
J G
Z K V L
T Q
F A H B
N ?

Which number replaces the question mark and completes the puzzle?

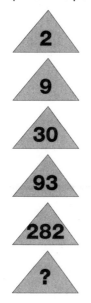

2
9
30
93
282
?

Which number replaces the question mark and completes the puzzle?

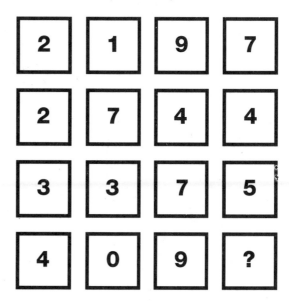

2	1	9	7
2	7	4	4
3	3	7	5
4	0	9	?

22 PUZZLE

Which letter from the bottom row completes the puzzle?

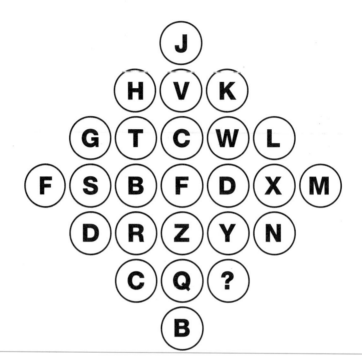

J

H V K

G T C W L

F S B F D X M

D R Z Y N

C Q ?

B

L P T Y D I N S

23 PUZZLE

Which number completes the puzzle?

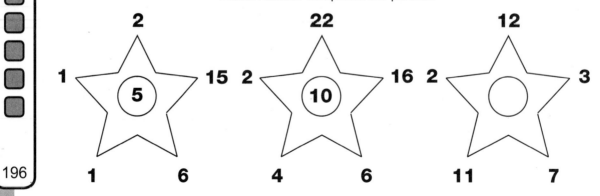

What is missing from the last octagon?

Which letter completes the puzzle?

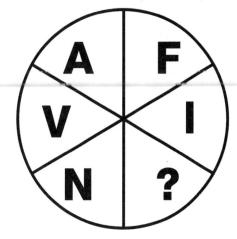

Which number replaces the question mark and completes the puzzle?

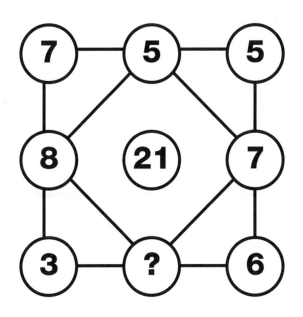

Where should the hour hand point to on the bottom clock?

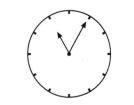

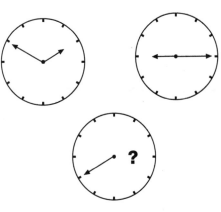

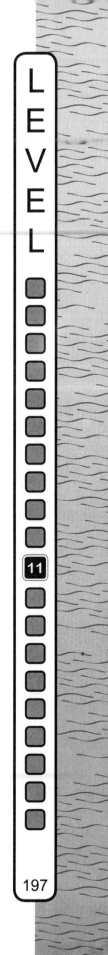

Following a logical sequence, can you
complete this puzzle?

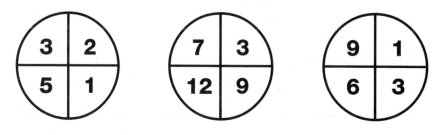

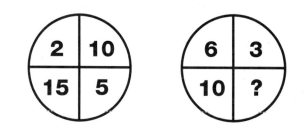

Which of the lower patterns continue the sequence?

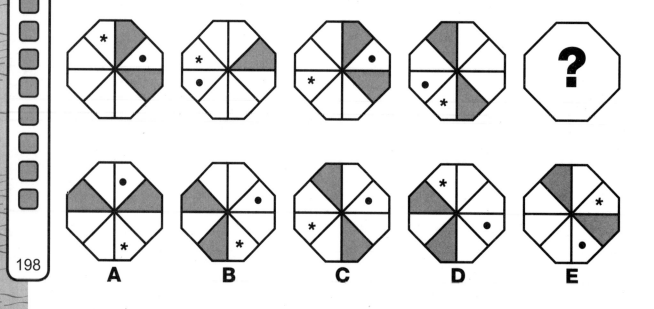

A   B   C   D   E

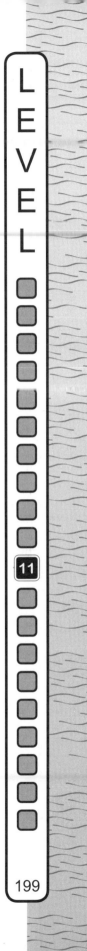

PUZZLE 30

What is missing from the last hexagon?

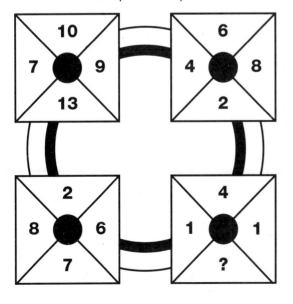

PUZZLE 31

Which letter completes the puzzle?

B

C

E

H

?

PUZZLE 32

Which number replaces the question mark
and completes the puzzle?

PUZZLE 33

Which number replaces the question mark
and completes the chain?

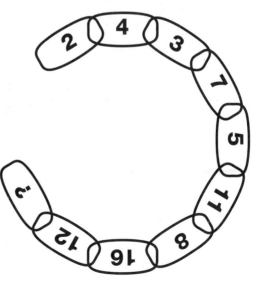

199

34 PUZZLE

Which letter completes the puzzle?

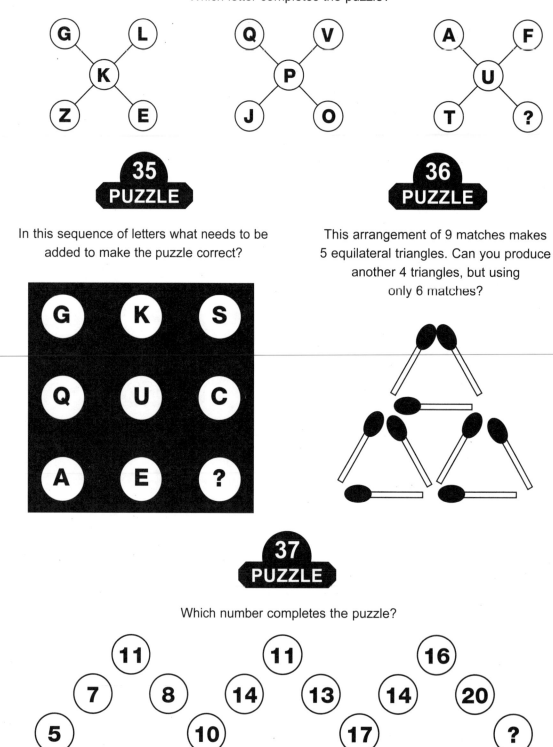

G L
K
Z E

Q V
P
J O

A F
U
T ?

35 PUZZLE

In this sequence of letters what needs to be added to make the puzzle correct?

G K S
Q U C
A E ?

36 PUZZLE

This arrangement of 9 matches makes 5 equilateral triangles. Can you produce another 4 triangles, but using only 6 matches?

37 PUZZLE

Which number completes the puzzle?

11   11   16
7   8   14   13   14   20
5   10   17   ?

What is missing from the last circle?

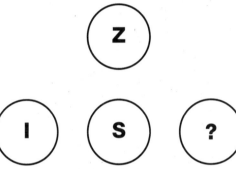

E   K   R

Z

I   S   ?

Which number completes the puzzle?

1   2

2   5   ?

2   1

Which number replaces the question mark and completes the puzzle?

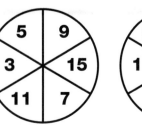

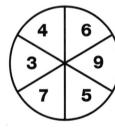

4   6
3   9
7   5

12   2
7   6
4   8

5   9
3   15
11   7

21   1
11   9
5   ?

Which number replaces the question mark and completes the puzzle?

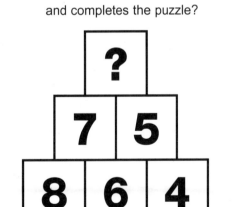

?
7   5
8   6   4
9   7   5   3

42 PUZZLE

Can you place the given dominos in this grid, so that each horizontal, vertical and diagonal line has a spot total of 10?

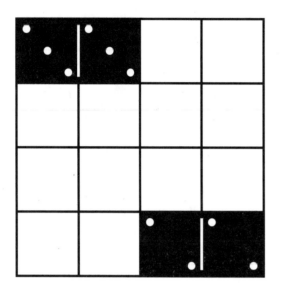

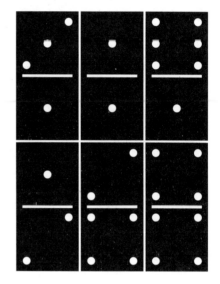

43 PUZZLE

Which number is the odd one out in each shape?

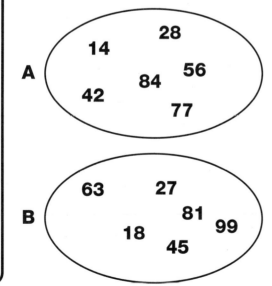

A

28
14
56
84
42
77

B

63   27
81
18   99
45

44 PUZZLE

Following a logical sequence, can you complete this puzzle?

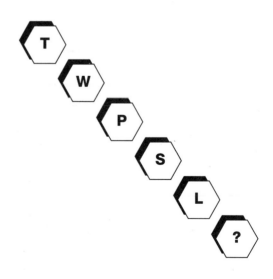

T
W
P
S
L
?

45 PUZZLE

What is missing from the last circle?

C F J O

G L R Y

B I Q Z

K T D ?

46 PUZZLE

Which letter replaces the question mark and completes the puzzle?

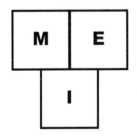

M	E
	I

O	Q
	P

L	D
	H

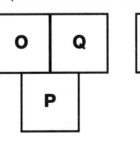

J	T
	?

Which three numbers are needed to complete this puzzle?

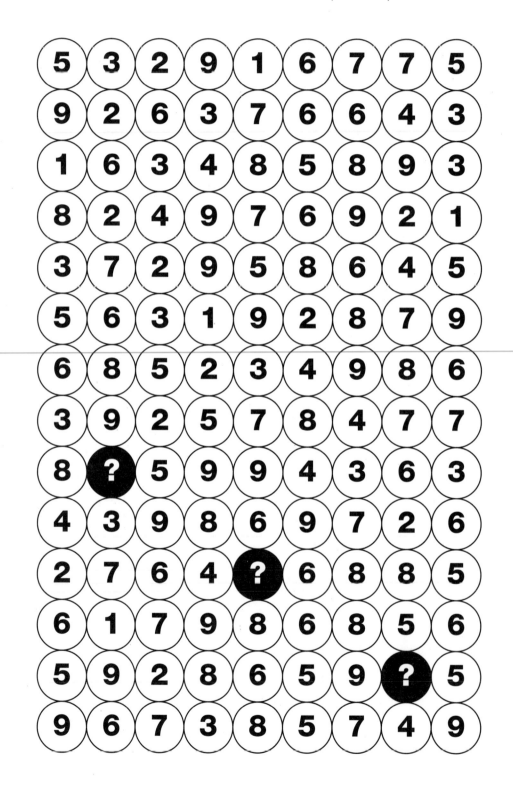

PUZZLE 48

What is missing from the last square?

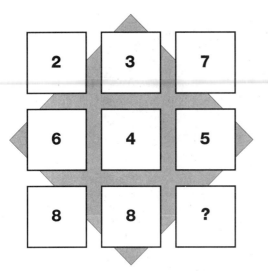

2	3	7
6	4	5
8	8	?

PUZZLE 49

Which letter completes the puzzle?

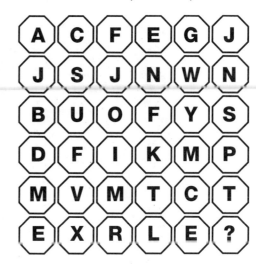

A	C	F	E	G	J
J	S	J	N	W	N
B	U	O	F	Y	S
D	F	I	K	M	P
M	V	M	T	C	T
E	X	R	L	E	?

PUZZLE 50

Which letter is the odd one out in each oval?

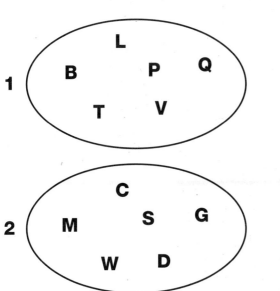

1.

L
B P Q
T V

2.

C
M S G
W D

PUZZLE 51

Which number replaces the question mark and completes the puzzle?

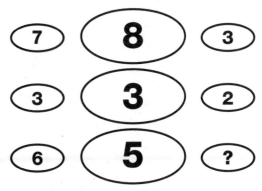

7	8	3
3	3	2
6	5	?

LEVEL 11

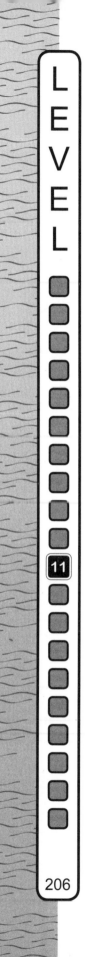

Which two dominos are missing from this puzzle?

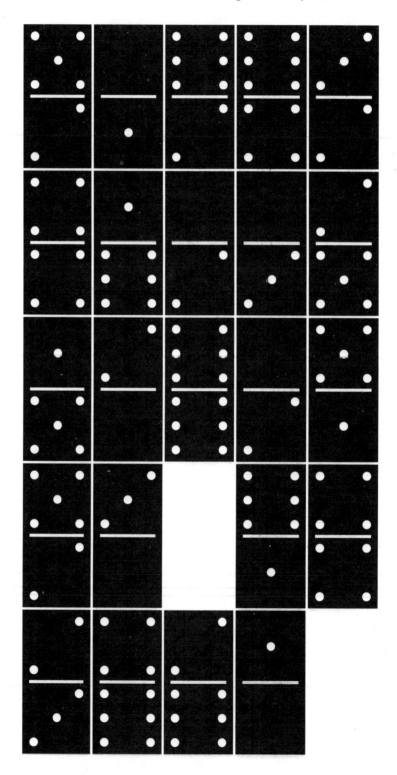

PUZZLE 1

Which letter replaces the question mark and completes the puzzle?

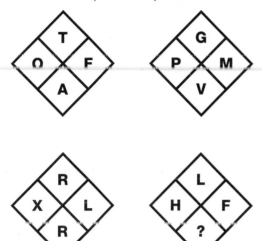

PUZZLE 2

Which number completes this puzzle?

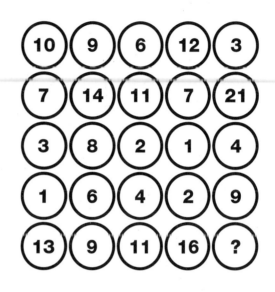

PUZZLE 3

Which letter will make this puzzle correct?

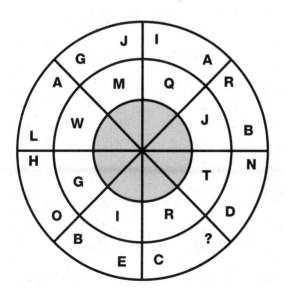

PUZZLE 4

Which letter replaces the question mark and completes the puzzle?

N	252	R
T	500	Y
Y	400	P
K	132	L
G	182	?

PUZZLE 5

Which of the bottom patterns continues the sequence?

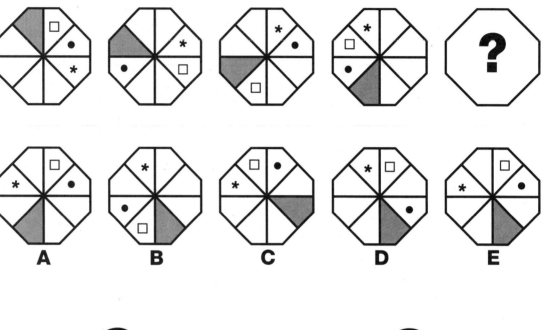

A   **B**   **C**   **D**   **E**

PUZZLE 6

Where does the missing hand go?

PUZZLE 7

What is missing from this arrangement of circles?

5	5	6
10	7	8
20	8	

Which letter replaces the question mark and completes the sequence?

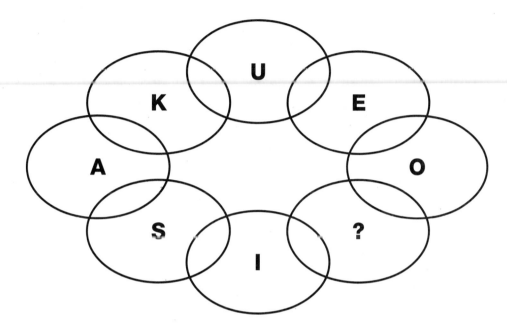

Which number needs to be added to the final grid?

4	1	6	2
16	10	20	6
3	9	11	4

3	8	1	7
13	14	6	13
6	6	3	1

12	8	3	0
7	10	17	6
4	2	17	6

9	11	2	5
9	14	4	8
4	3	4	?

10 PUZZLE

Which number completes the puzzle?

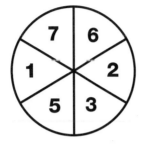

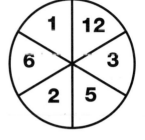
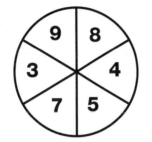
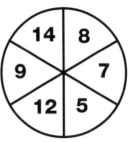
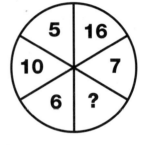

11 PUZZLE

Following a logical sequence, can you complete this puzzle?

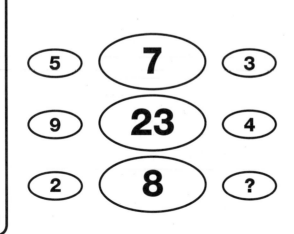

12 PUZZLE

What is missing from the bottom right square in this pyramid?

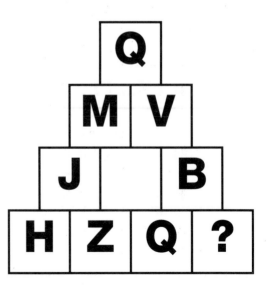

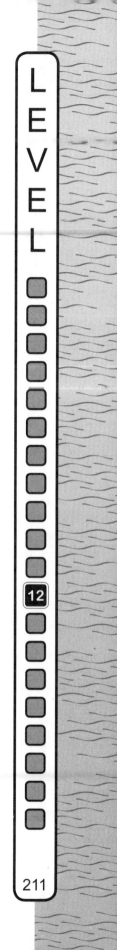

13 PUZZLE

Which number fills the centre of the last star to complete the puzzle?

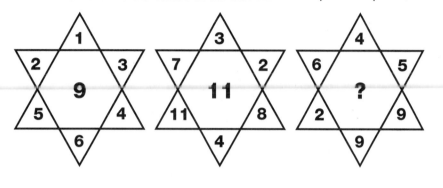

14 PUZZLE

Which letter replaces the question mark and completes the puzzle?

E		B
9	3	6
A		H

D		A
9	4	3
B		C

B		E
9	7	5
C		I

A		G
6	1	2
C		?

15 PUZZLE

Which number needs to be added to complete the puzzle?

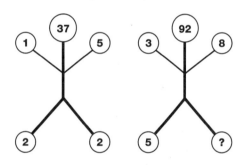

16 PUZZLE

Which letter replaces the question mark and completes the sequence?

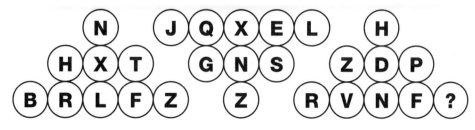

211

17
PUZZLE

17 PUZZLE

Which letter from the bottom row completes the puzzle?

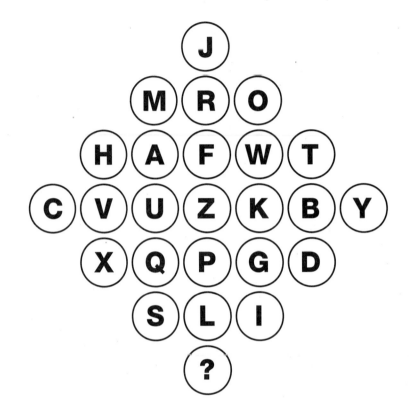

18 PUZZLE

What is missing from the last shape?

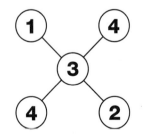 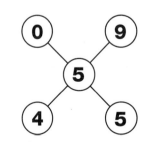 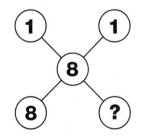

19 PUZZLE

Which number replaces the question mark and completes the puzzle?

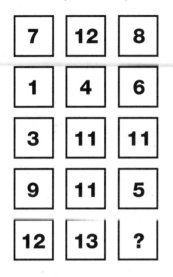

7	12	8
1	4	6
3	11	11
9	11	5
12	13	?

20 PUZZLE

Which letter is missing from the bottom of the grid?

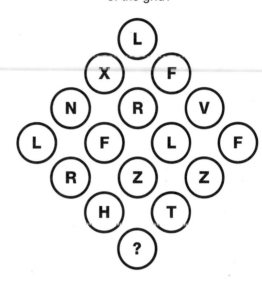

```
          L
       X     F
     N     R     V
   L     F     L     F
       R     Z     Z
          H     T
             ?
```

21 PUZZLE

Which number is missing from the bottom shape?

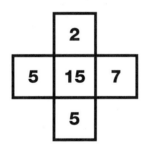

```
      2
  5  15  7
      5
```

```
      6
  4  19  11
      2
```

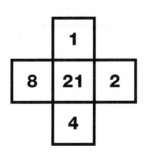

```
      1
  8  21  2
      4
```

```
      3
  8  23  6
      ?
```

22 PUZZLE

Following a logical sequence, can you complete this puzzle?

125

216

343

512

729

?

23 PUZZLE

Which number completes the puzzle?

24 PUZZLE

What is missing from this arrangement of circles?

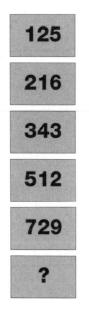

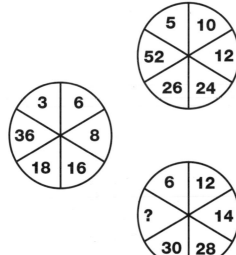

25 PUZZLE

What is missing from this sequence?

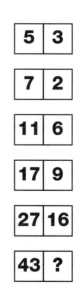

26 PUZZLE

Which number replaces the question mark and completes the sequence?

9			
3	4		
1	5	16	
?	14	7	23

27 PUZZLE

Which number replaces the question mark and completes the sequence?

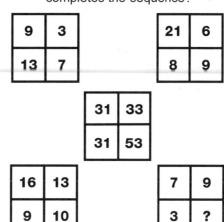

9	3
13	7

21	6
8	9

31	33
31	53

16	13
9	10

7	9
3	?

28 PUZZLE

Which playing card replaces the question mark and completes the puzzle?

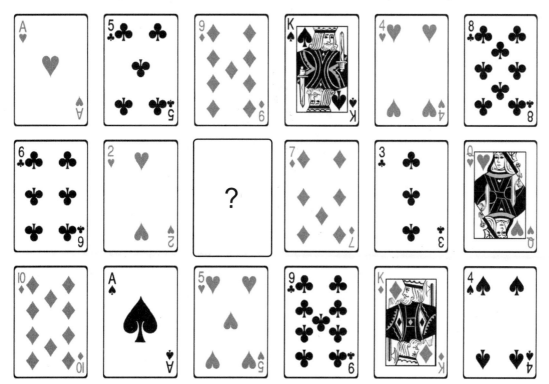

LEVEL

12

29 PUZZLE

Which letter completes the puzzle?

X	D
A	

L	Q
O	

T	Y
U	

G	M
?	

30 PUZZLE

Following a logical sequence, can you complete this puzzle?

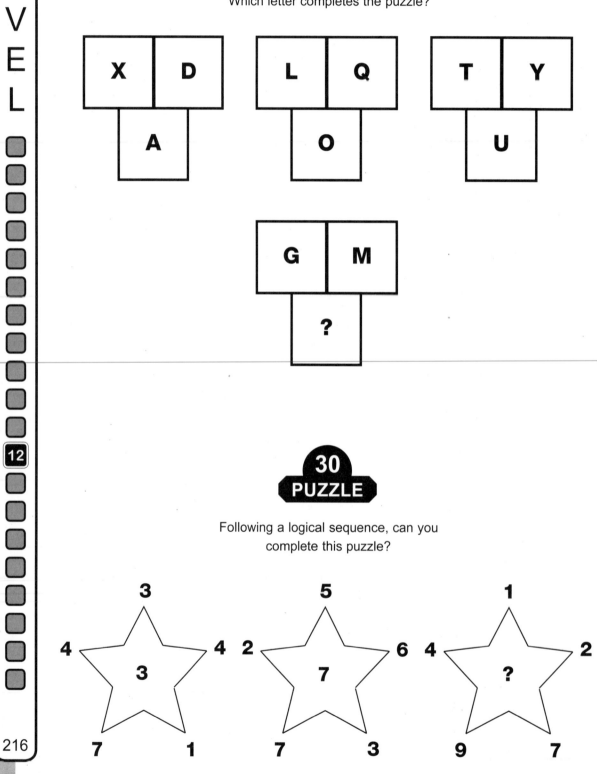

3
4   4
  3
7   1

5
2   6
  7
7   3

1
4   2
  ?
9   7

31 PUZZLE

Which letter replaces the question mark and completes the sequence?

B	G
K	F

L	Q
A	V

P	U
?	T

Z	E
O	J

32 PUZZLE

Which number replaces the question mark and completes the sequence?

0	6	4	1	2	1
1	2	5	1	4	4
2	1	6	1	6	9
3	4	3	1	9	6
5	1	2	2	2	5
7	2	9	2	5	?

33 PUZZLE

Where should the missing hour hand point to?

34 PUZZLE

Which letter replaces the question mark and completes the puzzle?

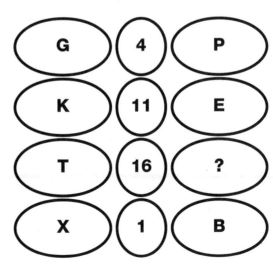

G	4	P
K	11	E
T	16	?
X	1	B

PUZZLE 35

In this sequence of letters what needs to be added to make the puzzle correct?

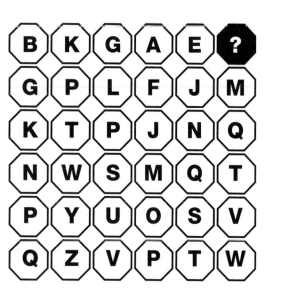

B	K	G	A	E	?
G	P	L	F	J	M
K	T	P	J	N	Q
N	W	S	M	Q	T
P	Y	U	O	S	V
Q	Z	V	P	T	W

PUZZLE 36

What is the minimum number of matches you can remove from this diagram to leave just 2 squares?

PUZZLE 37

Which letter is the odd one out in each ellipse?

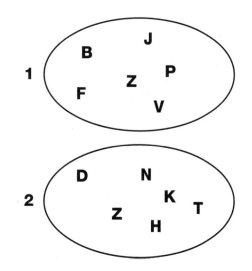

1 B, J, F, Z, P, V

2 D, N, Z, K, H, T

PUZZLE 38

Which two numbers complete the puzzle?

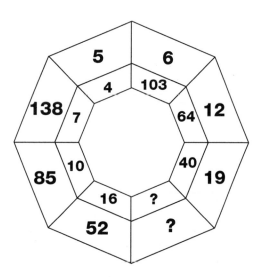

5   6
4   103
138   7   64   12
85   10   40   19
16   ?
52   ?

PUZZLE 39

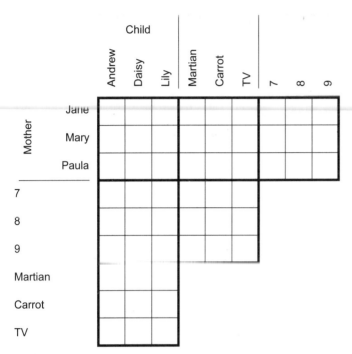

	Andrew	Daisy	Lily	Martian	Carrot	TV	7	8	9
Jane									
Mary									
Paula									
7						
8						
9						
Martian			
Carrot			
TV			

(Mother / Child)

Andrew, Daisy and Lily were all excited about their school's fancy dress competition, and their mothers had spent a good deal of time getting their costumes ready. Jane's child is the youngest of the group, and had gone dressed up as a TV set. Mary was so proud of her child, who is 9 years old. Andrew, whose mum is Paula, didn't go as a Martian. Daisy loved Andrew's costume but, being younger than him, thought she looked sweeter in hers.

From all this information, can you link each mother to her child, what costume he or she wore and his or her age?

Child	Mother	Costume	Age

PUZZLE 40

Which letter replaces the question mark and completes the puzzle?

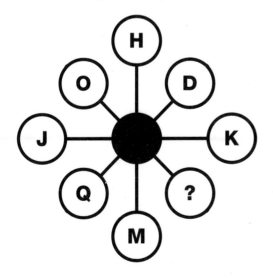

PUZZLE 41

Which letter replaces the question mark and completes the sequence?

A	EJP	W
Y U K		E N X
B	?MG	B

42 PUZZLE

Which patterns replace the question marks?

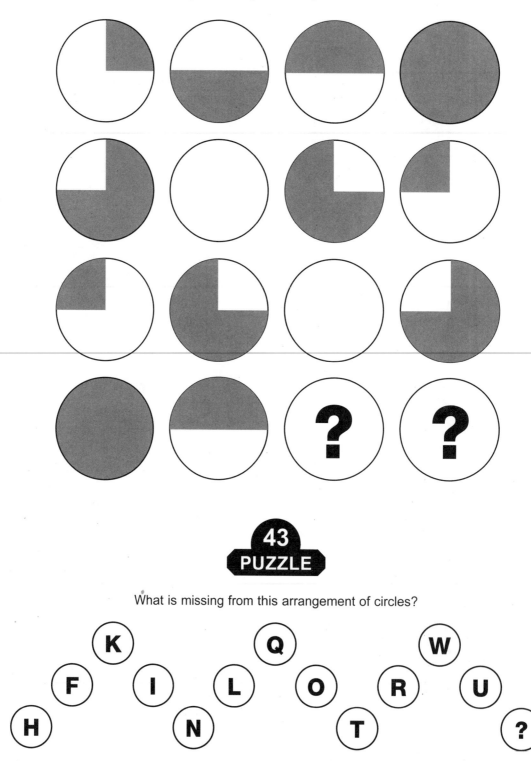

43 PUZZLE

What is missing from this arrangement of circles?

K   Q   W

F   I   L   O   R   U

H   N   T   ?

Which picture cube does this shape make?

A

C

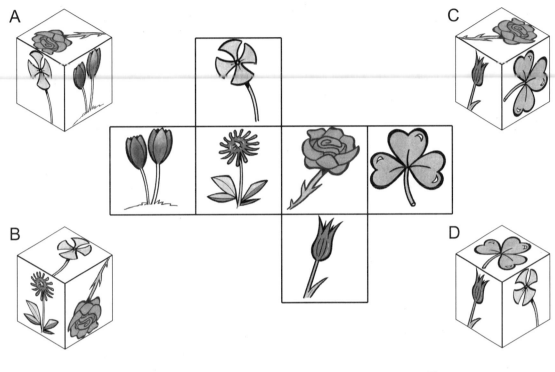

B

D

Which letter replaces the question mark and completes the puzzle?

S	B	K
	J	T
	A	
	J	H
C	V	?

If five men can dig 100 holes over four days, how many men would be needed to dig 150 holes in one day?

L E V E L

12

LEVEL 12

222

PUZZLE 47

Following a logical sequence, can you complete this puzzle?

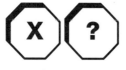

PUZZLE 49

In this sequence of letters what needs to be added to make the puzzle correct?

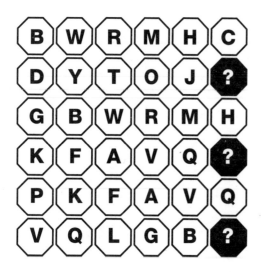

PUZZLE 48

Which letter completes the puzzle?

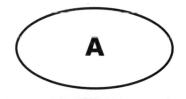

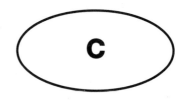

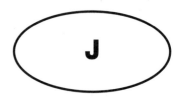

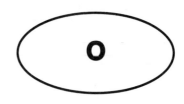

50 PUZZLE

Which number replaces the question mark and completes the puzzle?

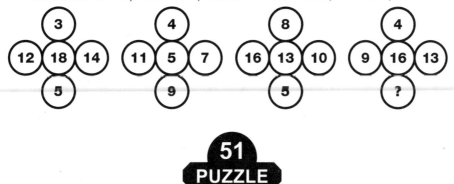

	3				4				8				4	
12	18	14		11	5	7		16	13	10		9	16	13
	5				9				5				?	

51 PUZZLE

Which letter replaces the question mark and completes the puzzle?

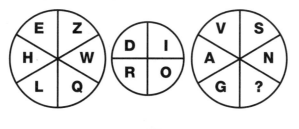

Circle 1: E, Z, H, W, L, Q
Circle 2: D, I, R, O
Circle 3: V, S, A, N, G, ?

52 PUZZLE

Which number replaces the question mark and completes the puzzle?

5	6	1		8	11	3		2	8	6		7	11	?
	5				24				12				28	
	4				5				4				3	

53 PUZZLE

What spot total should be shown where the question mark is?

54 PUZZLE

Following a logical sequence, can you complete this puzzle?

55 PUZZLE

Which letter completes the puzzle?

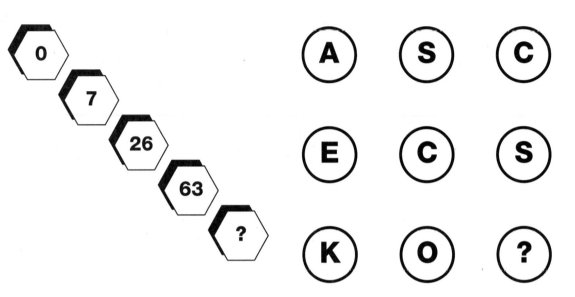

| 0 | 7 | 26 | 63 | ? |

A   S   C
E   C   S
K   O   ?

56 PUZZLE

Which grid fills the gap in the middle?

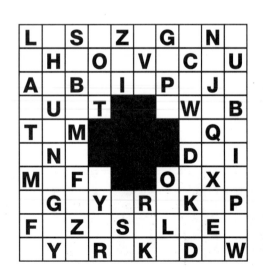

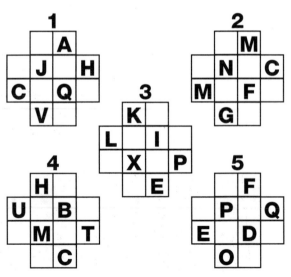

PUZZLE 1

What is missing from the last grid?

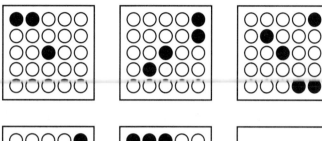

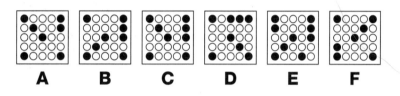

A **B** **C** **D** **E** **F**

PUZZLE 2

Which watch completes the puzzle?

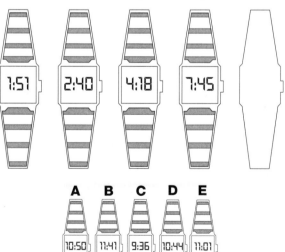

A **B** **C** **D** **E**

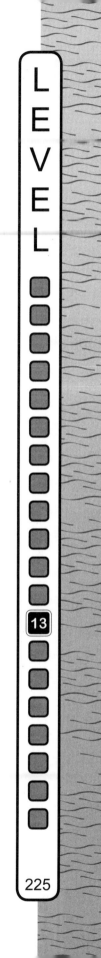

PUZZLE 3

What sequence of letters will complete this puzzle?

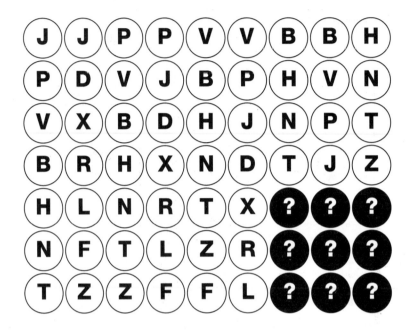

PUZZLE 4

Which number completes the puzzle?

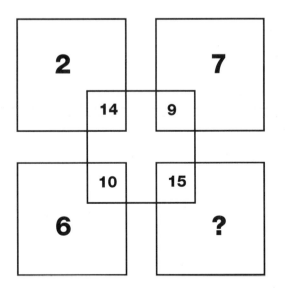

PUZZLE 5

Following a logical sequence, can you complete this puzzle?

A

E

F

H

?

PUZZLE 6

Which of the lower circles is the missing one from the puzzle?

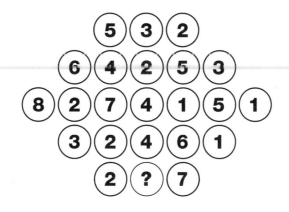

PUZZLE 7

Which letter replaces the question mark and completes the puzzle?

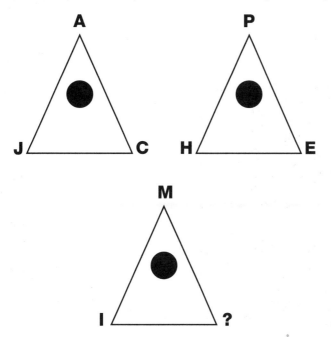

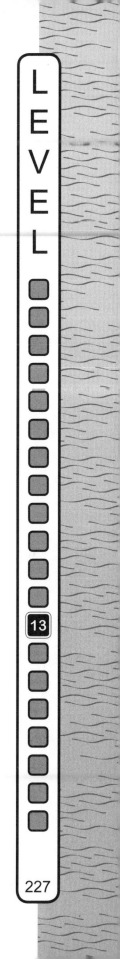

8 PUZZLE

What is missing from this arrangement of circles?

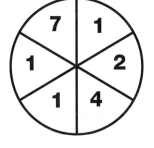
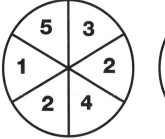

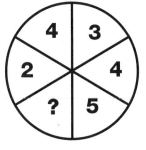

9 PUZZLE

Which number completes the puzzle?

10 PUZZLE

Following a logical sequence, can you complete this puzzle?

What is missing from the last segment?

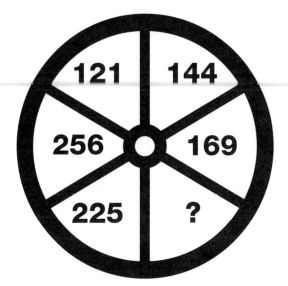

Which letter completes the puzzle?

13 PUZZLE

Which number replaces the question mark and completes the puzzle?

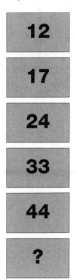

| 12 |
| 17 |
| 24 |
| 33 |
| 44 |
| ? |

14 PUZZLE

Which number replaces the question mark and completes the puzzle?

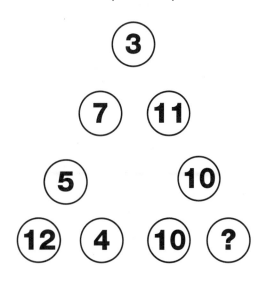

What is missing from this pyramid?

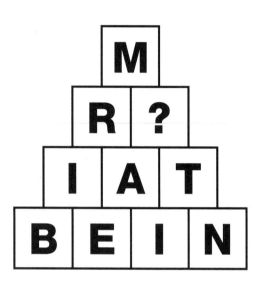

Which letter completes the puzzle?

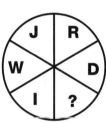

17 PUZZLE

In this sequence of letters what needs to be added to make the puzzle correct?

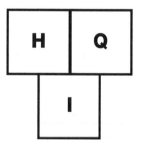

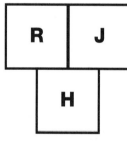

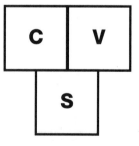

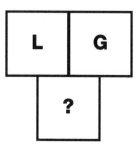

What is missing from the last hexagon?

B G I

U P N

W B ?

Which letter completes the puzzle?

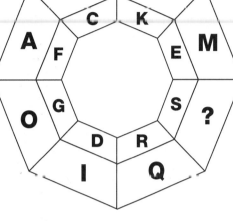

B P
C K
A
F E M
O G S ?
D R
I Q

Which number replaces the question mark and completes the puzzle?

7

9

13

21

37

?

Which number replaces the question mark and completes the puzzle?

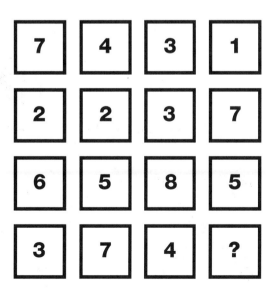

7	4	3	1
2	2	3	7
6	5	8	5
3	7	4	?

L
E
V
E
L

13

LEVEL

13

22 PUZZLE

Which numbers complete the puzzle?

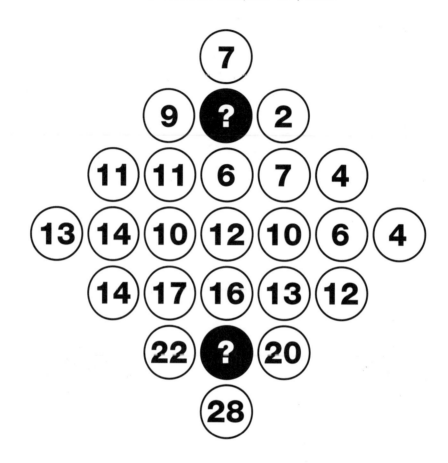

23 PUZZLE

In this sequence of letters what needs to be added to make the puzzle correct?

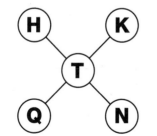

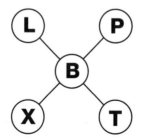

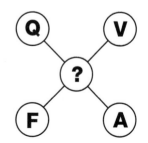

What is missing from the last circle?

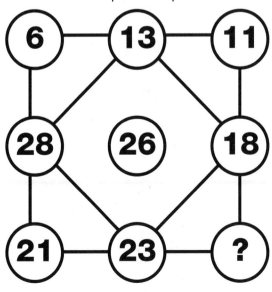

Which letter completes the puzzle?

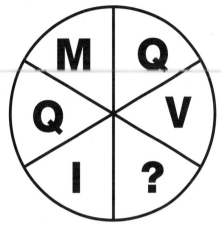

Which number replaces the question mark and completes the puzzle?

Where should the minute hand point to on the bottom clock?

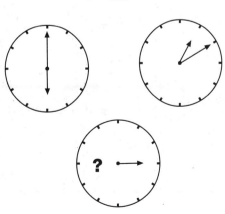

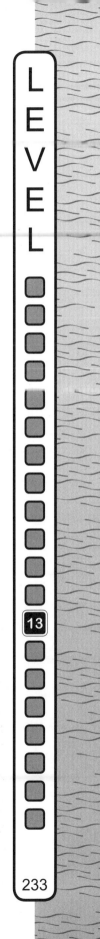

LEVEL

13

PUZZLE 28

What is missing from the last star?

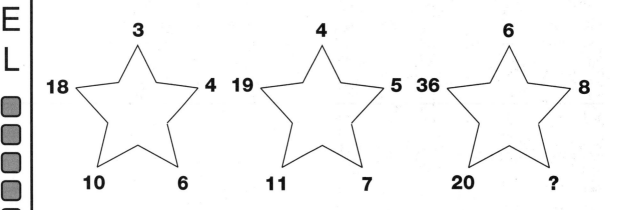

3
18   4
10   6

4
19   5
11   7

6
36   8
20   ?

PUZZLE 29

Which letter completes the puzzle?

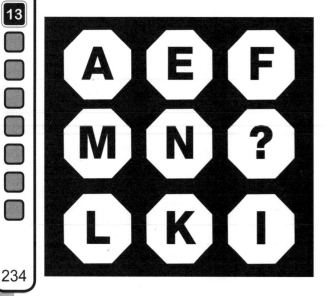

PUZZLE 30

Following a logical sequence, can you complete this puzzle?

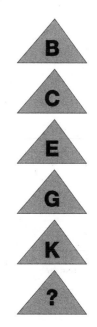

PUZZLE 31

What is missing from the last hexagon?

PUZZLE 32

Which letter completes the puzzle?

PUZZLE 33

Which letter replaces the question mark
and completes the puzzle?

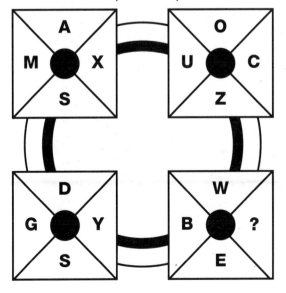

PUZZLE 34

Which number replaces the question mark
and completes the chain?

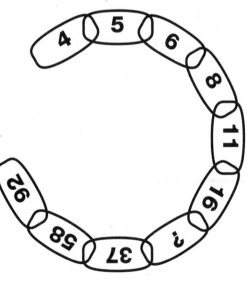

35 PUZZLE

What number is missing?

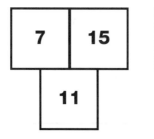
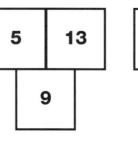
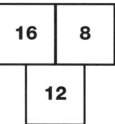

| 7 | 15 |
| 11 | |

| 5 | 13 |
| 9 | |

| 16 | 8 |
| 12 | |

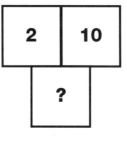

| 2 | 10 |
| ? | |

36 PUZZLE

Which dominos are missing from this group?

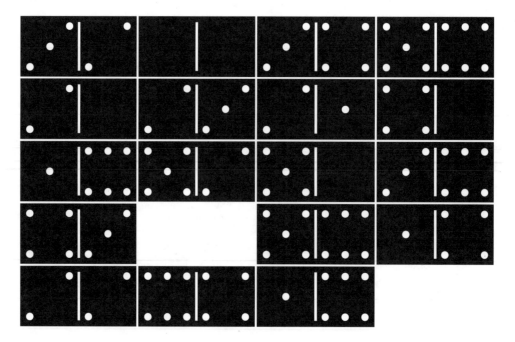

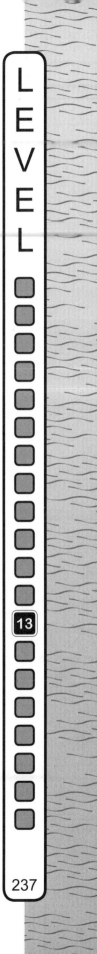

PUZZLE 37

What is missing from the last circle?

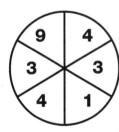

PUZZLE 38

Which letter completes the puzzle?

PUZZLE 39

Which number replaces the question mark
and completes the puzzle?

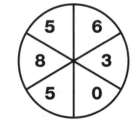

PUZZLE 40

Which letter replaces the question mark
and completes the puzzle?

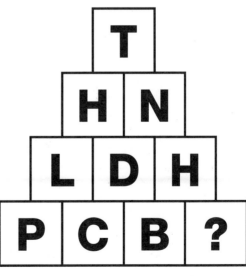

237

41 PUZZLE

Remove two matches from this arrangement, to leave just four squares. If you can do that, can you remove 4 matches from the original arrangement to leave only 3 squares?

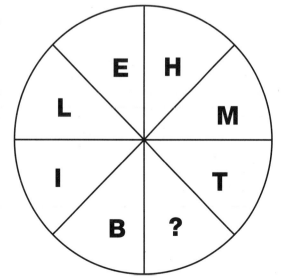

42 PUZZLE

Following a logical sequence, can you complete this puzzle?

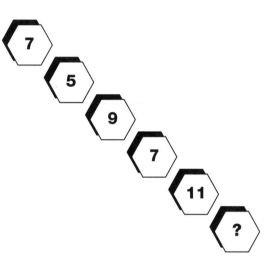

43 PUZZLE

Which letter completes the puzzle?

44 PUZZLE

Which number completes the puzzle?

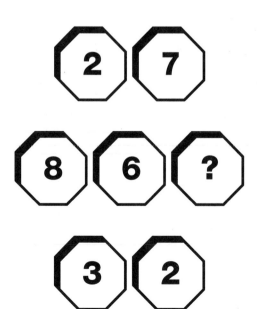

Which letter replaces the question mark?

E	J	O	T
Z	S	?	Y
U	N	I	D
P	K	F	A

46
PUZZLE

Which number replaces the question mark and completes the puzzle?

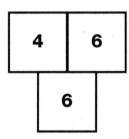

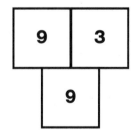

```
+---+---+       +---+---+       +---+---+
| 4 | 6 |       | 3 | 3 |       | 9 | 3 |
+---+---+       +---+---+       +---+---+
    | 6 |           | 5 |           | 9 |
    +---+           +---+           +---+
```

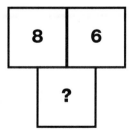

```
+---+---+
| 8 | 6 |
+---+---+
    | ? |
    +---+
```

47 PUZZLE

Which number completes the puzzle?

9 5 1

4 3 8

2 7 ?

49 PUZZLE

John bought a bag of apples from the supermarket, but when he got them home, he found that two-thirds of them were bruised, half had mildew, a quarter were both bruised and had mildew, and only one was fit to eat.

How many apples were in the bag John bought?

48 PUZZLE

Following a logical sequence, can you complete this puzzle?

146

255

366

479

684

?

PUZZLE 50

What is missing from the last square?

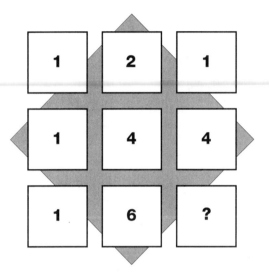

1	2	1
1	4	4
1	6	?

PUZZLE 51

Which letter completes the puzzle?

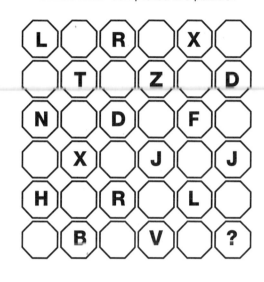

L		R		X	
	T		Z		D
N		D		F	
	X		J		J
H		R		L	
	B		V		?

PUZZLE 52

Which number is the odd one out in each oval?

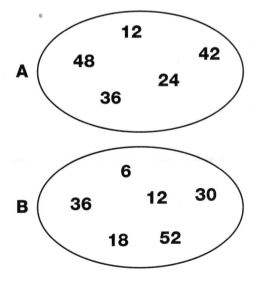

A: 12, 48, 42, 24, 36

B: 6, 36, 12, 30, 18, 52

PUZZLE 53

Which number replaces the question mark and completes the puzzle?

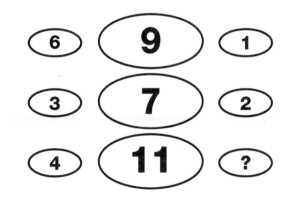

6 9 1

3 7 2

4 11 ?

Which playing cards fill in the missing gaps to complete the puzzle?

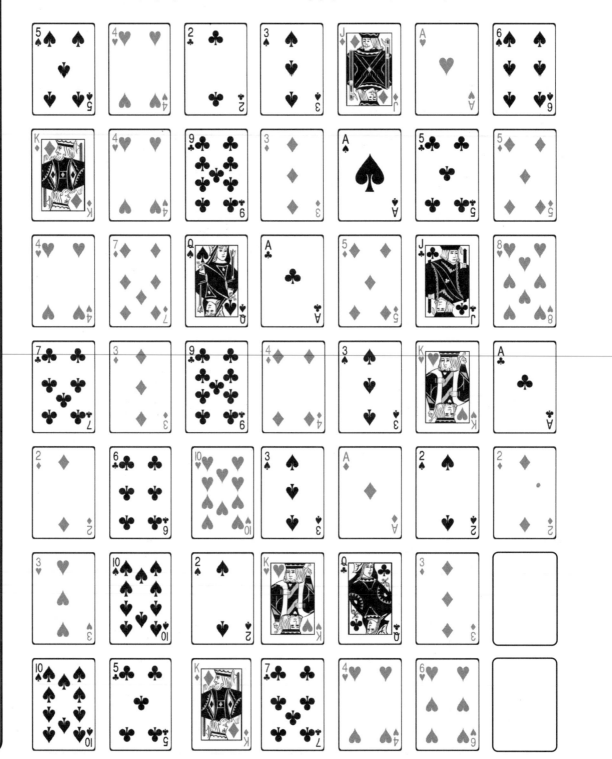

1 PUZZLE

Which number completes this wheel?

2 PUZZLE

Which number completes the puzzle?

3 PUZZLE

Where should the missing hour hand point to on the bottom clock face?

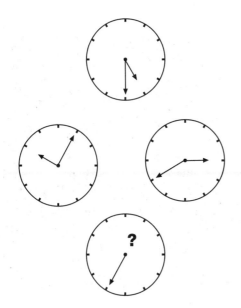

4 PUZZLE

Which letter replaces the question mark and completes the puzzle?

14

243

5 PUZZLE

What is missing from this puzzle?

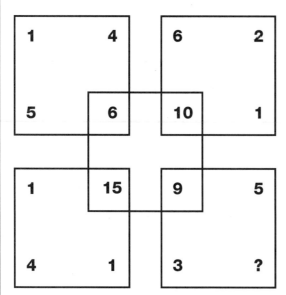

1		4
5	6	10	1
1	15	9	5
4	1	3	?

6 PUZZLE

Following a logical sequence, can you complete this puzzle?

C	X
H	S
L	O
R	I
G	T
P	?

7 PUZZLE

Which number completes this wheel?

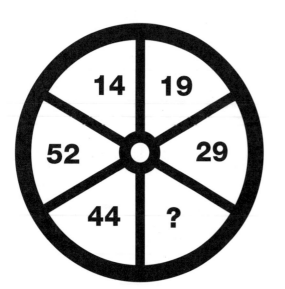

14 | 19
52 | 29
44 | ?

8 PUZZLE

Which letter completes the puzzle?

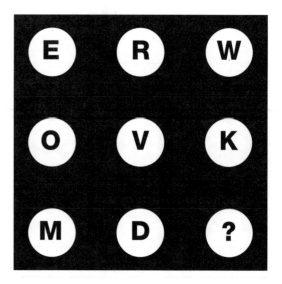

E R W
O V K
M D ?

What is missing from the lower middle circle?

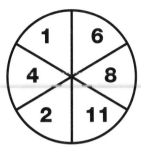

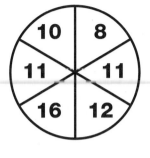

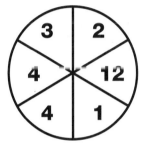

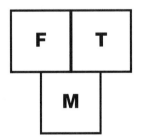

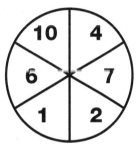

10
PUZZLE

Which letter replaces the question mark and completes the puzzle?

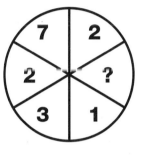

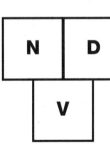

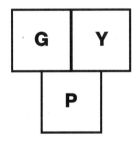

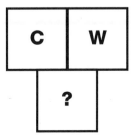

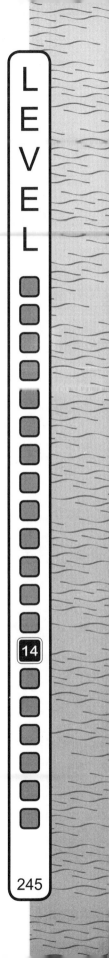

11
PUZZLE

Which number completes the puzzle?

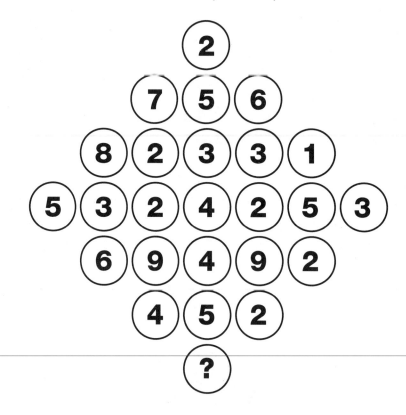

```
              2
          7   5   6
       8   2   3   3   1
     5   3   2   4   2   5   3
       6   9   4   9   2
          4   5   2
              ?
```

(1)(2)(3)(4)(5)(6)(7)(8)

12
PUZZLE

What is missing from this arrangement of circles?

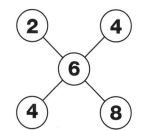
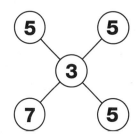
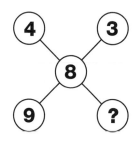

13 PUZZLE

What is missing from the last hexagon?

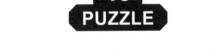

D
L
U
E
P
?

14 PUZZLE

Which number completes the puzzle?

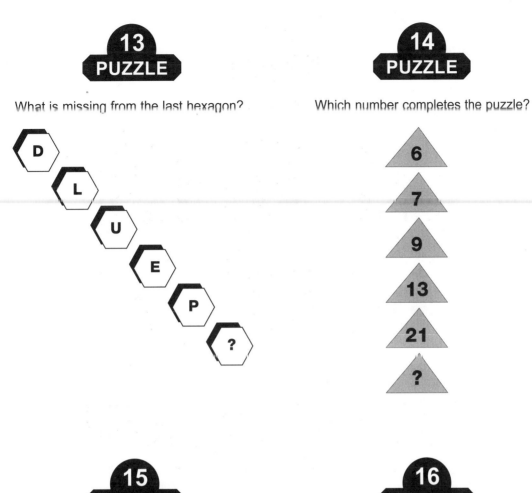

6
7
9
13
21
?

15 PUZZLE

Which letter replaces the question mark and completes the puzzle?

R	T	K	N
X	V	T	Q
M	R	C	G
B	W	O	?

16 PUZZLE

Which letter replaces the question mark and completes the puzzle?

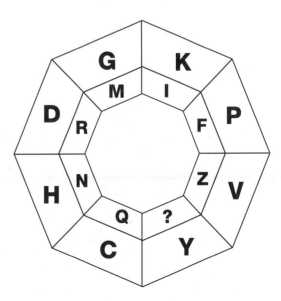

G K
M I
D R F P
H N Z V
Q ?
C Y

Which of the bottom patterns continues the sequence?

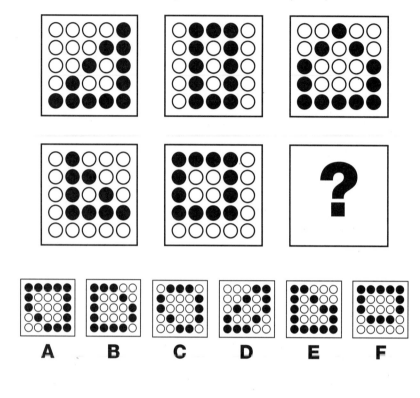

A B C D E F

Which grid fills the missing gap?

PUZZLE 19

What is missing from the last circle?

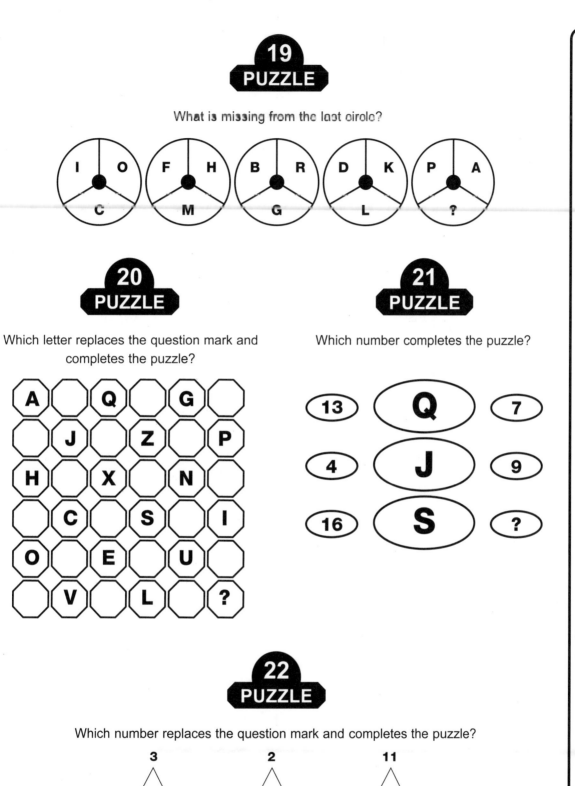

PUZZLE 20

Which letter replaces the question mark and completes the puzzle?

PUZZLE 21

Which number completes the puzzle?

PUZZLE 22

Which number replaces the question mark and completes the puzzle?

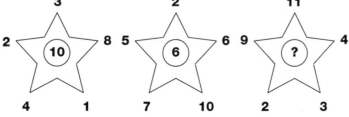

PUZZLE 23

Which three letters need to be added to this puzzle?

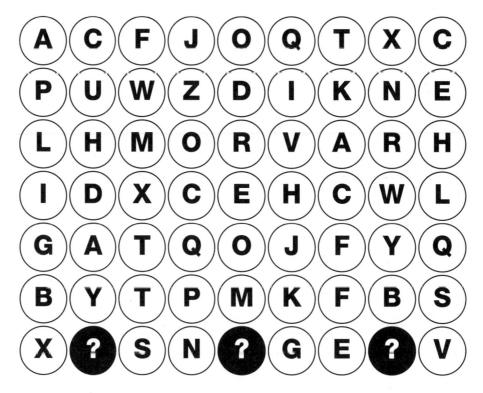

A C F J O Q T X C

P U W Z D I K N E

L H M O R V A R H

I D X C E H C W L

G A T Q O J F Y Q

B Y T P M K F B S

X ? S N ? G E ? V

PUZZLE 24

Following a logical sequence, can you complete this puzzle?

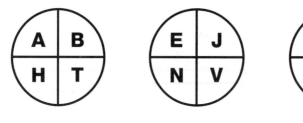

A	B
H	T

E	J
N	V

I	R
T	X

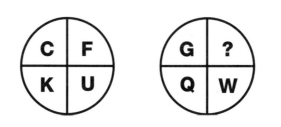

C	F
K	U

G	?
Q	W

Which letter replaces the question mark to complete the puzzle?

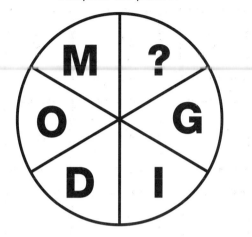

Which number completes the puzzle?

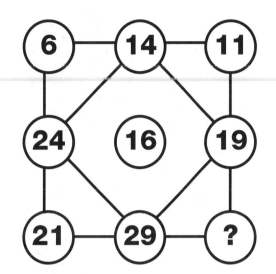

Which of the lower patterns completes the puzzle?

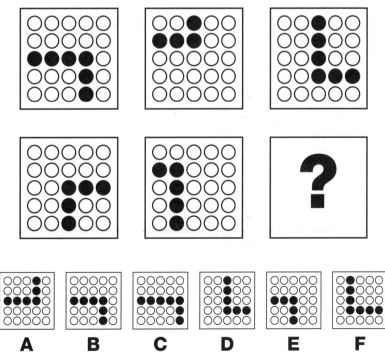

A   B   C   D   E   F

L
E
V
E
L

14

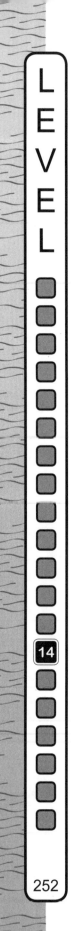

28 PUZZLE

Which number completes the puzzle?

29 PUZZLE

Which number completes this puzzle?

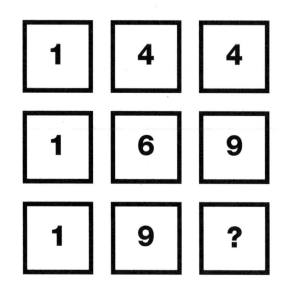

30 PUZZLE

Which number goes in the bottom right hand shape?

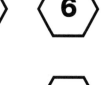

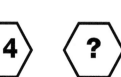

31 PUZZLE

Following a logical sequence, can you complete this puzzle?

| 35 |

| 48 |

| 63 |

| 80 |

| ? |

PUZZLE 32

What is missing from the last oval?

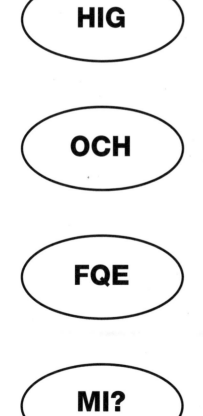

BGK

OFA

HIG

OCH

FQE

MI?

PUZZLE 33

Which number completes the puzzle?

5   7   10   3   ?

PUZZLE 34

Which letter replaces the question mark and completes the puzzle?

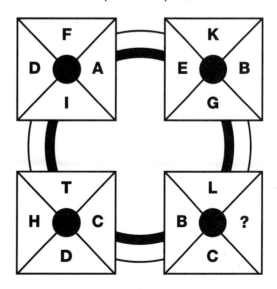

35 PUZZLE

What is missing from the last star?

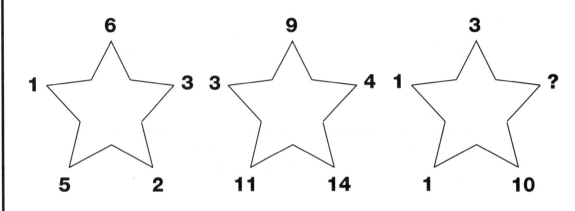

6 · 1 · 3 · 5 · 2
9 · 3 · 4 · 11 · 14
3 · 1 · ? · 1 · 10

36 PUZZLE

Which pattern replaces the question mark to complete the sequence?

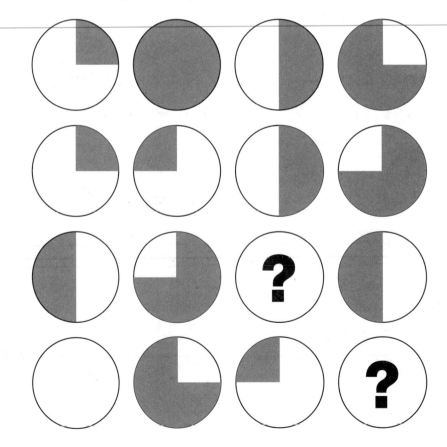

Which letter is missing from the puzzle?

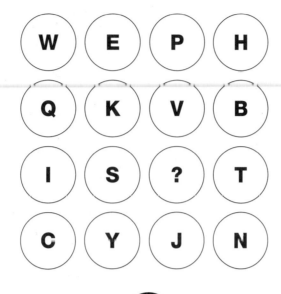

W   E   P   H

Q   K   V   B

I   S   ?   T

C   Y   J   N

Which number replaces the question mark and completes the puzzle?

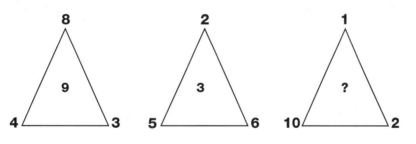

8
9
4   3

2
3
5   6

1
?
10   2

Which letter completes the puzzle?

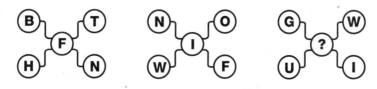

B   T
F
H   N

N   O
I
W   F

G   W
?
U   I

LEVEL

14

255

PUZZLE 40

Which letter completes this wheel?

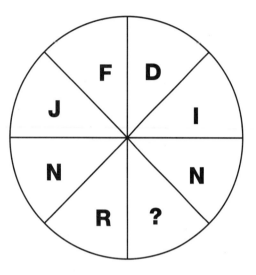

PUZZLE 41

Which letter completes the puzzle?

PUZZLE 42

In this sequence of letters what needs to be added to make the puzzle correct?

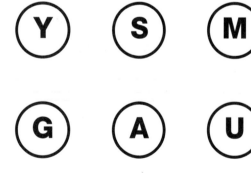

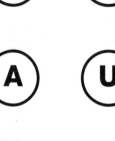

PUZZLE 43

Can you arrange these 12 matches, to form 6 equilateral triangles?

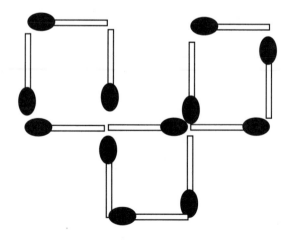

PUZZLE 44

What is missing from the last star?

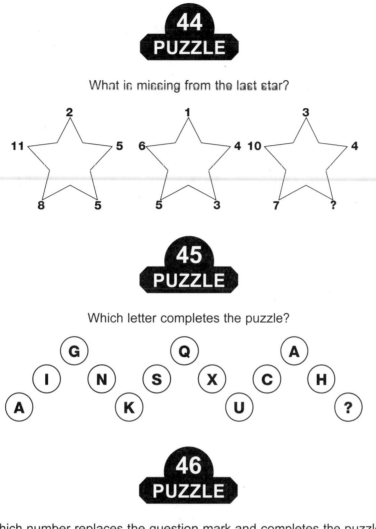

PUZZLE 45

Which letter completes the puzzle?

PUZZLE 46

Which number replaces the question mark and completes the puzzle?

PUZZLE 47

Which number replaces the question mark and completes the puzzle?

48
PUZZLE

Which letter is missing?

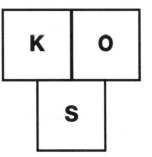

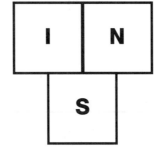

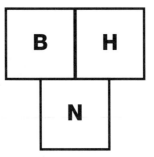

49
PUZZLE

Which grid fills the missing gap?

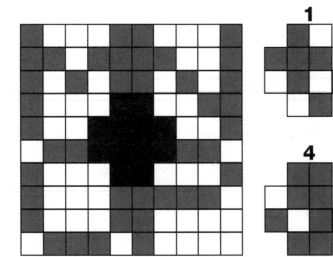

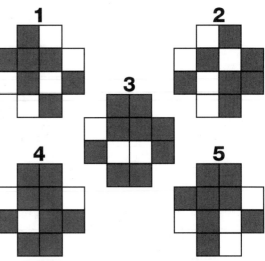

PUZZLE 50

What time would the blank watch show?

4:32	6:35	5:19	7:22	

A	B	C	D	E
8:06	7:54	4:19	6:06	5:32

PUZZLE 51

Which letter replaces the question mark and completes the puzzle?

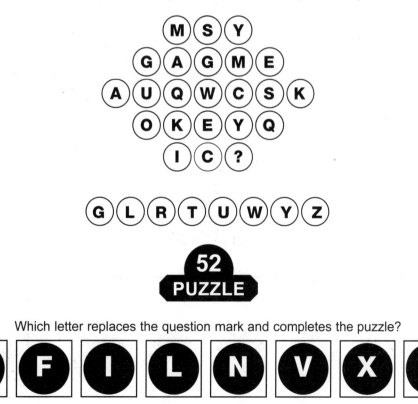

M S Y
G A G M E
A U Q W C S K
O K E Y Q
I C ?

G L R T U W Y Z

PUZZLE 52

Which letter replaces the question mark and completes the puzzle?

A F I L N V X ?

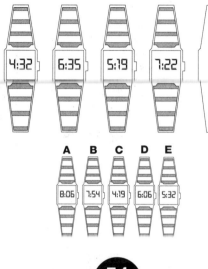

Which of the lower patterns completes this puzzle?

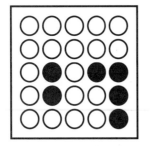
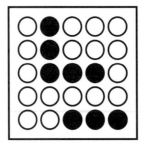
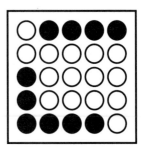

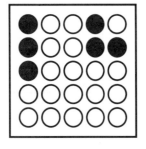
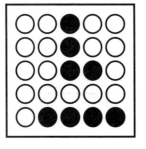

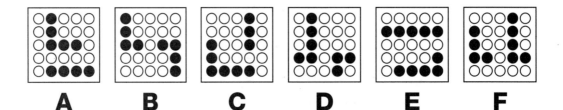

A   **B**   **C**   **D**   **E**   **F**

What is missing from this arrangement of circles?

3 5 4 4 5 3 6 ?

LEVEL

14

1 PUZZLE

Which number replaces the question mark and completes the puzzle?

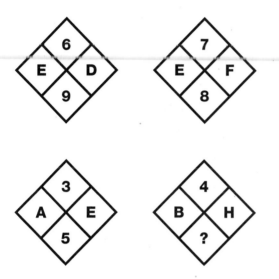

2 PUZZLE

Which letter replaces the question mark and completes the grid?

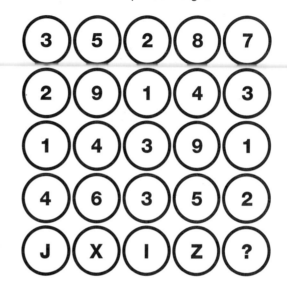

3 PUZZLE

Which letter replaces the question mark and completes the wheel?

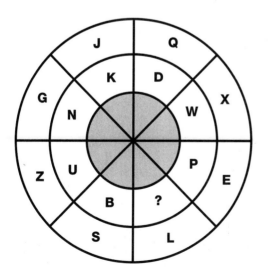

4 PUZZLE

Which number replaces the question mark and completes the sequence?

6	FKM	24
12	LUC	24
20	IRB	9
4	DGQ	24
34	PJH	?

PUZZLE 5

Which number completes the puzzle?

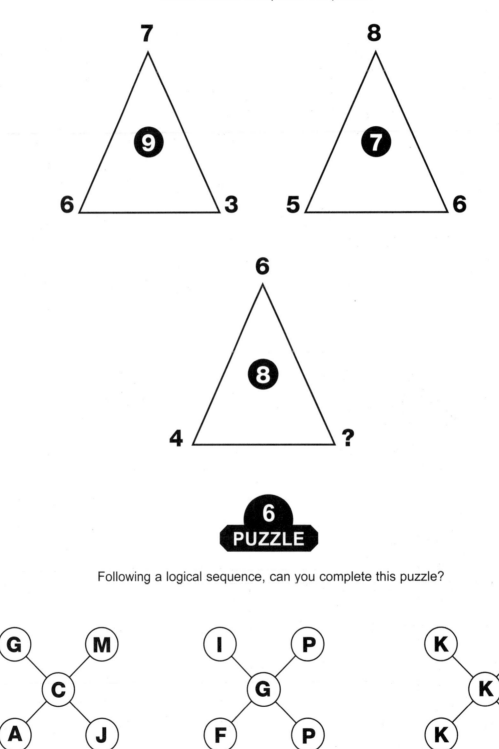

PUZZLE 6

Following a logical sequence, can you complete this puzzle?

PUZZLE 7

What is missing from this puzzle?

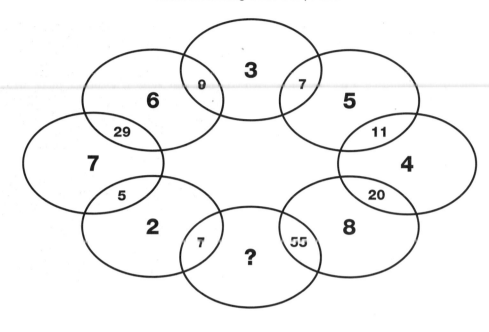

PUZZLE 8

Which letter replaces the question mark and completes the final grid?

D	C	H	G
I	X	M	B
N	S	R	W

R	V	B	F
X	P	H	Z
D	J	N	T

J	S	Z	I
Q	L	G	B
X	E	N	U

O	C	K	Y
W	U	?	Q
E	M	A	I

LEVEL

15

263

PUZZLE 9

What complete this puzzle?

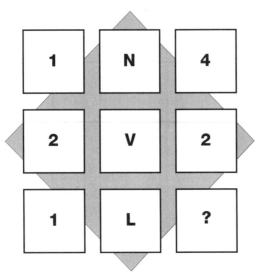

1	N	4
2	V	2
1	L	?

PUZZLE 10

Which number completes the puzzle?

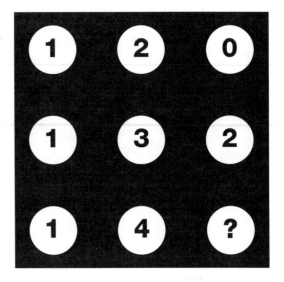

1	2	0
1	3	2
1	4	?

PUZZLE 11

Which of the lower patterns completes the sequence?

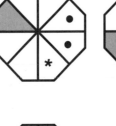
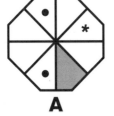

A   B   C   D   E

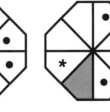
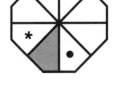
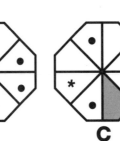
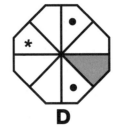

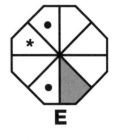

12
PUZZLE

Which number replaces the question mark in the third star?

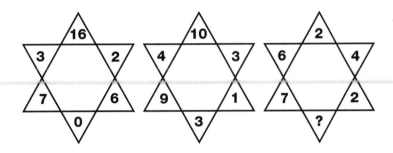

13
PUZZLE

Which letter replaces the question mark and completes the sequence?

J		N
E	P	E
A		W

B		F
W	H	W
S		O

Z		D
U	F	U
Q		M

S		W
N	Y	N
J		?

14
PUZZLE

Which number replaces the question mark on the head of the second figure?

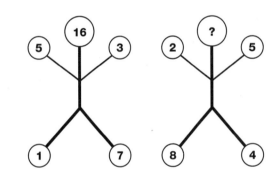

15
PUZZLE

Which number goes on top of the third triangle?

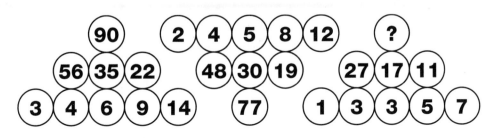

16
PUZZLE

Following a logical sequence, can you
complete this puzzle?

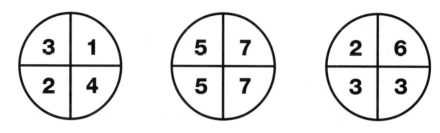

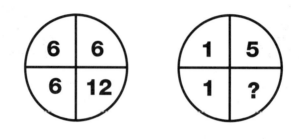

17
PUZZLE

Which of the lower watches fills in the missing space?

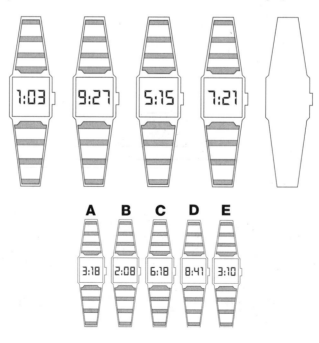

A   B   C   D   E

PUZZLE 18

Which number replaces the question mark and completes the puzzle?

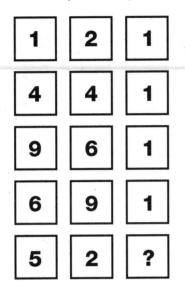

1	2	1
4	4	1
9	6	1
6	9	1
5	2	?

PUZZLE 19

Which number completes this puzzle?

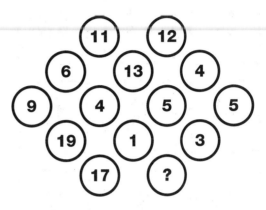

PUZZLE 20

Which number replaces the question mark and completes the puzzle?

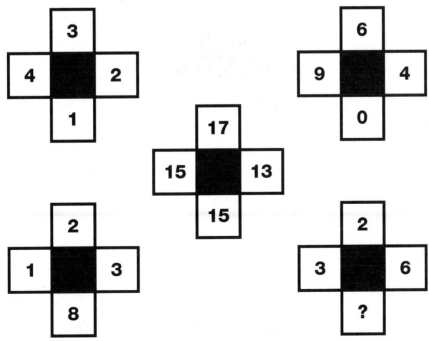

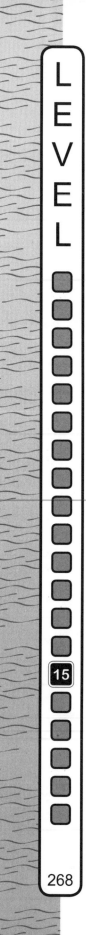

21 PUZZLE

Which letter completes the puzzle?

X	U	Q
H	X	L
Q	Y	?

22 PUZZLE

Which number completes the puzzle?

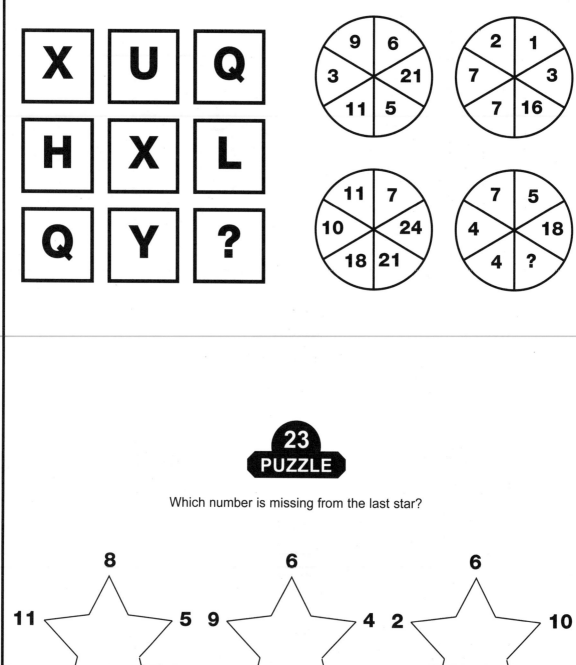

Circle 1: 9, 6, 3, 21, 11, 5
Circle 2: 2, 1, 7, 3, 7, 16
Circle 3: 11, 7, 10, 24, 18, 21
Circle 4: 7, 5, 4, 18, 4, ?

23 PUZZLE

Which number is missing from the last star?

Star 1: 8, 11, 5, 4, 4
Star 2: 6, 9, 4, 2, 3
Star 3: 6, 2, 10, 13, ?

PUZZLE 24

Which letter replaces the question mark and completes the grid?

D			
N	Y		
K	X	L	
A	Q	H	?

PUZZLE 25

Which number replaces the question mark in the middle box?

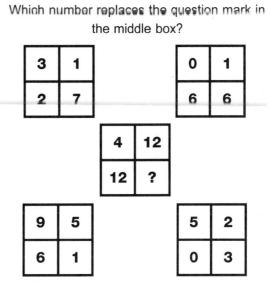

3	1
2	7

0	1
6	6

4	12
12	?

9	5
6	1

5	2
0	3

PUZZLE 26

Which playing card replaces the question mark and completes the puzzle?

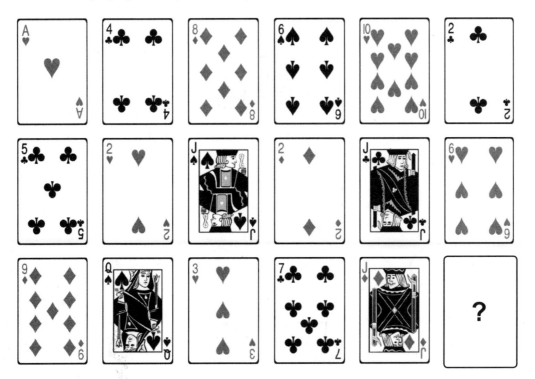

27 PUZZLE

Following a logical sequence, can you complete this puzzle?

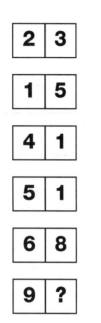

2	3

1	5

4	1

5	1

6	8

9	?

28 PUZZLE

What is missing from this arrangement of circles?

29 PUZZLE

In this sequence of letters what needs to be added to make the puzzle correct?

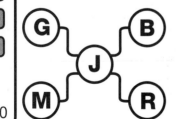

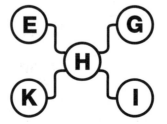

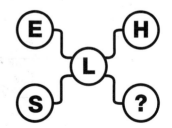

Which letter replaces the question mark and completes the sequence?

V	C
O	D

J	Q
F	X

H	H
A	Z

?	E
S	L

Which letter replaces the question mark in this grid?

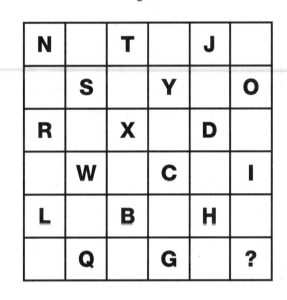

N		T		J	
	S		Y		O
R		X		D	
	W		C		I
L		B		H	
	Q		G		?

What should the missing hand point to on the bottom clock?

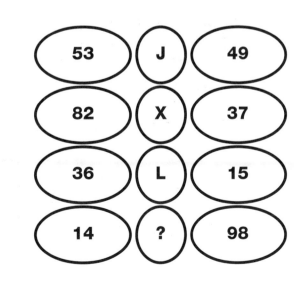

Which letter replaces the question mark and completes the grid?

53	J	49
82	X	37
36	L	15
14	?	98

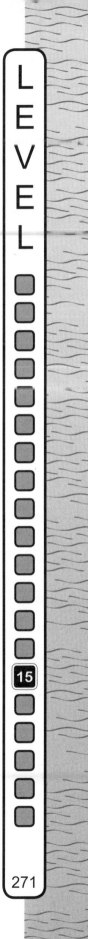

LEVEL

15

271

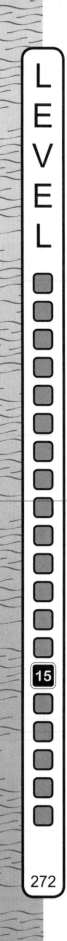

PUZZLE 34

Which number is missing?

PUZZLE 35

Which number completes the puzzle?

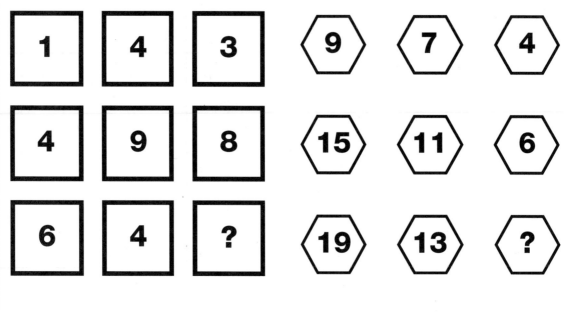

1	4	3
4	9	8
6	4	?

9	7	4
15	11	6
19	13	?

PUZZLE 36

In this sequence of letters what needs to be added to make the puzzle correct?

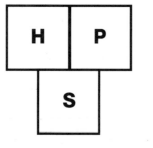

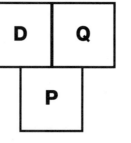

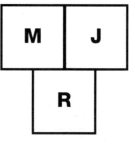

H	P
	S

D	Q
	P

M	J
	R

C	G
	?

272

PUZZLE 37

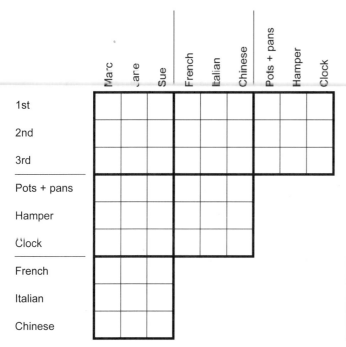

	Marc	Jane	Sue	French	Italian	Chinese	Pots + pans	Hamper	Clock
1st									
2nd									
3rd									
Pots + pans									
Hamper									
Clock									
French									
Italian									
Chinese									

Marc, Jane and Sue were the three finalists in this year's Mastercook competition. The 2nd prize was awarded to the woman who did the Italian dish. The 3rd prize was the kitchen clock, but this didn't go to the person who prepared a grand Chinese meal. Sue won the hamper for her lovely meal, but thought that the Italian dish would probably beat her to the 1st prize. From this information, can you work out which contestant won which prize, and what style of cooking they chose?

Contestant	Position	Style	Prize

PUZZLE 38

Which letter replaces the question mark at the bottom of the grid?

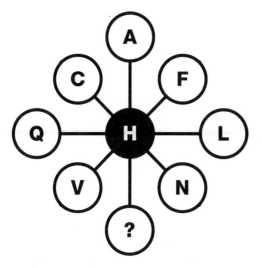

PUZZLE 39

Which letter replaces the question mark and completes the grid?

B	C		E
?			G
Q	M		K

40 PUZZLE

Which letter completes the puzzle?

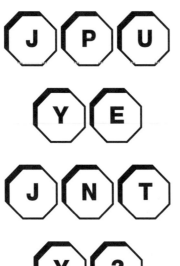

41 PUZZLE

Which number complete this wheel?

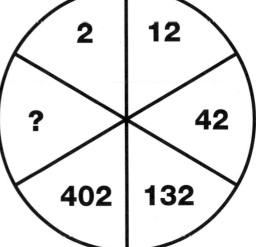

42 PUZZLE

Following a logical sequence, can you complete this puzzle?

43 PUZZLE

What is missing from this arrangement of circles?

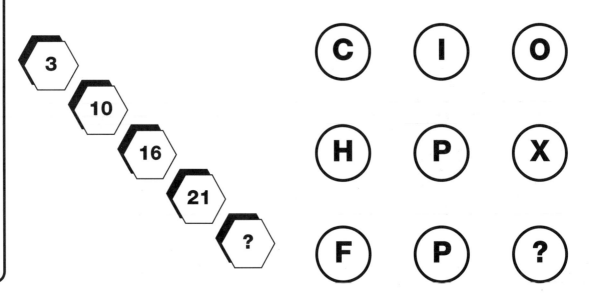

PUZZLE 44

Which picture cube does this shape make?

A

C

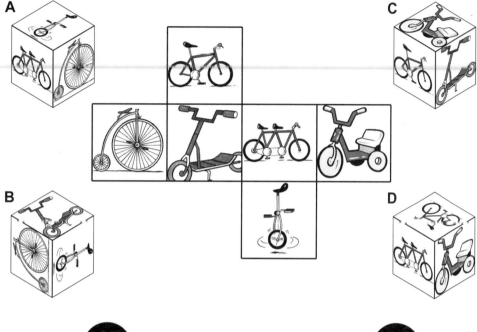

B

D

PUZZLE 45

Which letter replaces the question mark and completes the sequence?

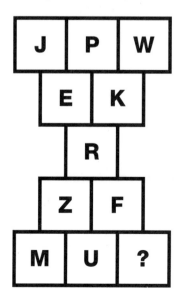

J	P	W
	E	K
	R	
	Z	F
M	U	?

PUZZLE 46

Maria has a large climbing vine outside her house, which doubles in height every year. Since planting the vine six years ago, it has grown to 26 feet. How many years did it take to grow to half this height?

47 PUZZLE

How many jigsaws are needed to balance the bottom scales?

48 PUZZLE

Which number completes the puzzle?

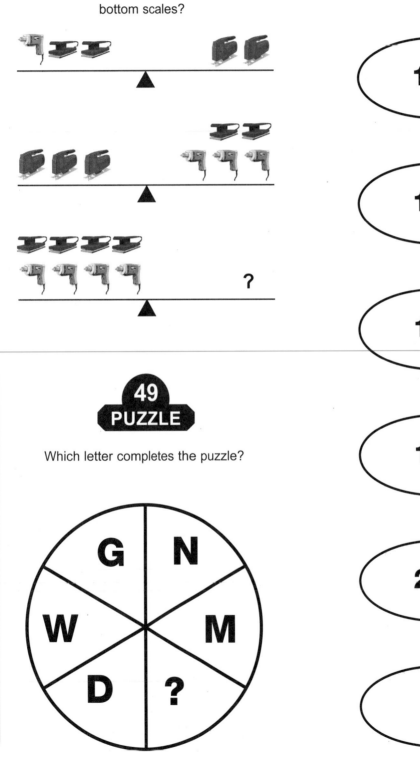

118

141

166

49 PUZZLE

Which letter completes the puzzle?

193

222

?

276

50 PUZZLE

Which letter replaces the question mark and completes the sequence?

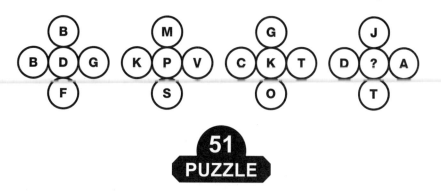

51 PUZZLE

Which number replaces the question mark in the last circle?

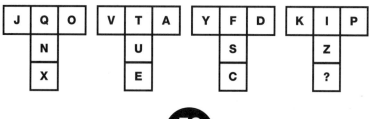

52 PUZZLE

Which letter replaces the question mark and completes the pattern?

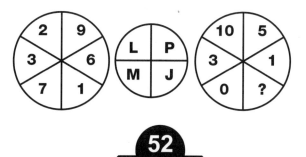

J	Q	O		V	T	A		Y	F	D		K	I	P
	N				U				S				Z	
	X				E				C				?	

53 PUZZLE

Which domino replaces the question mark to complete the puzzle?

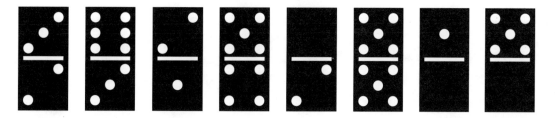

54 PUZZLE

Following a logical sequence, can you complete this puzzle?

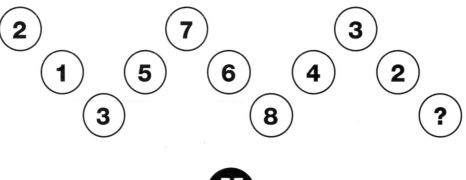

55 PUZZLE

What is the missing pattern?

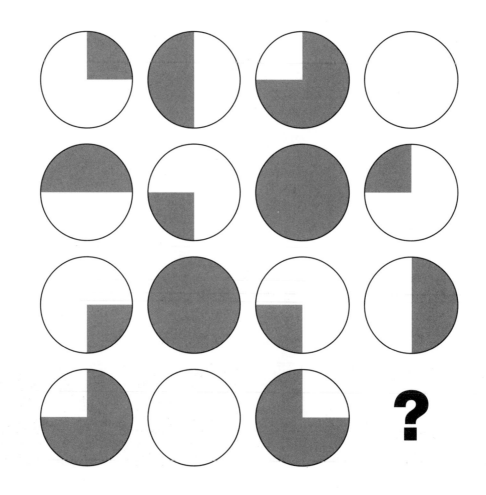

PUZZLE 1

What is missing from this wheel?

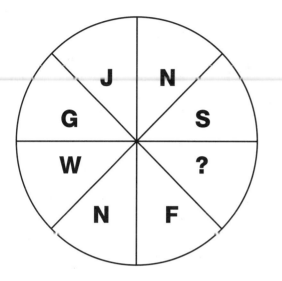

PUZZLE 2

Which letter completes the puzzle?

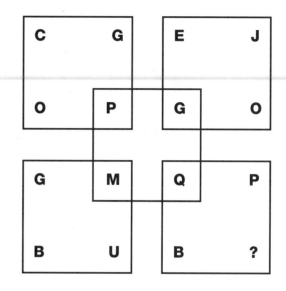

PUZZLE 3

Which symbol is needed to make the scales balance?

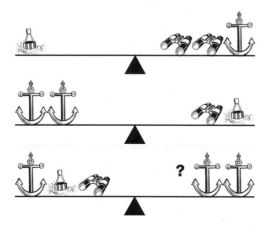

PUZZLE 4

Which number replaces the question mark and completes the puzzle?

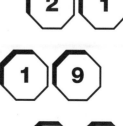

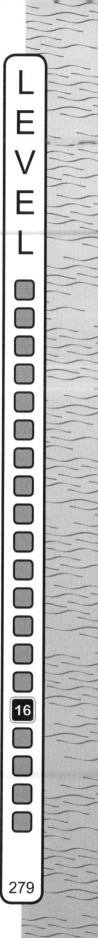

PUZZLE 5

Which of the lower patterns completes the sequence?

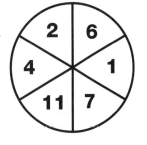

PUZZLE 6

Which number completes the puzzle?

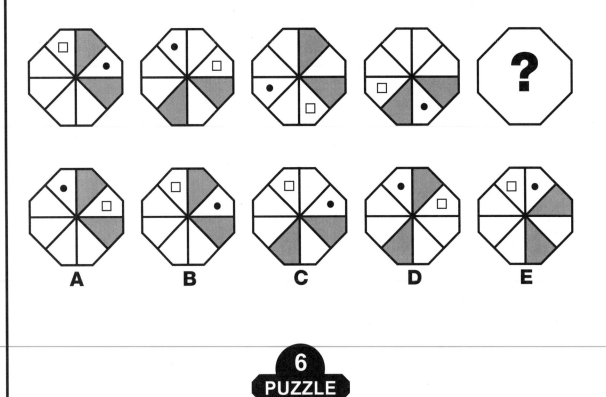

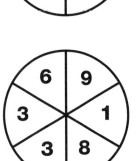
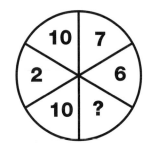
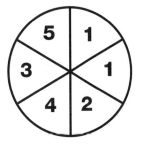
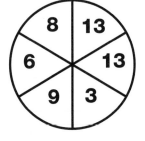

7
PUZZLE

What is missing from the last circle?

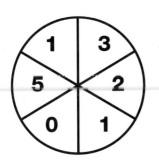 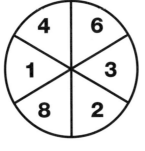 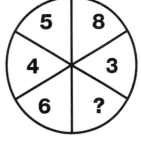

Circle 1: 1 | 3 / 5 | 2 / 0 | 1

Circle 2: 2 | 7 / 1 | 0 / 4 | 1

Circle 3: 2 | 1 / 4 | 4 / 7 | 0

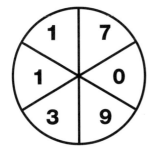 

Circle 4: 1 | 7 / 1 | 0 / 3 | 9

Circle 5: 4 | 6 / 1 | 3 / 8 | 2

Circle 6: 5 | 8 / 4 | 3 / 6 | ?

8
PUZZLE

Which letter replaces the question mark and completes the puzzle?

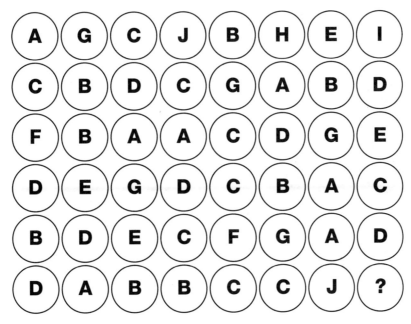

A G C J B H E I
C B D C G A B D
F B A A C D G E
D E G D C B A C
B D E C F G A D
D A B B C C J ?

Which of the lower watches fills in the missing gap?

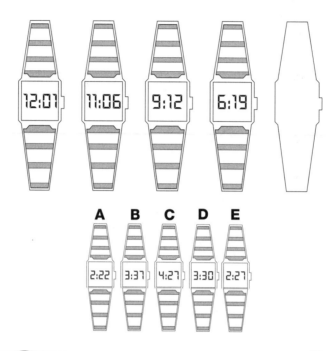

Which letter completes the puzzle?

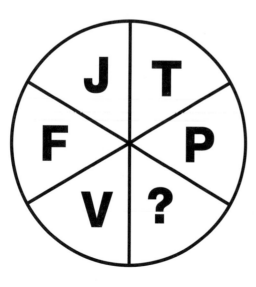

Following a logical sequence, can you complete this puzzle?

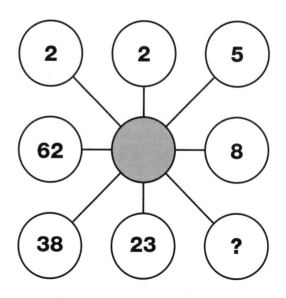

PUZZLE 12

What is missing from the middle circle?

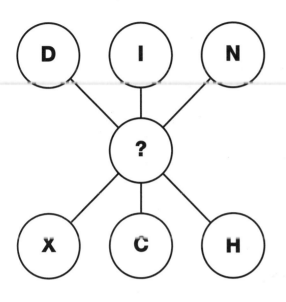

PUZZLE 13

Which number completes the puzzle?

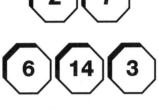

PUZZLE 14

Which number replaces the question mark and completes the puzzle?

PUZZLE 15

Which number replaces the question mark and completes the puzzle?

156	
2	6
3	1
4	5
5	?

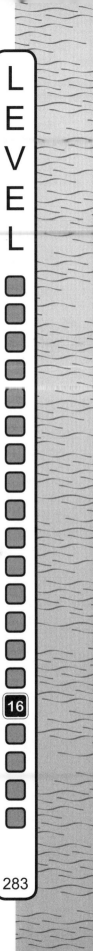

Which of the lower grids replaces the question mark?

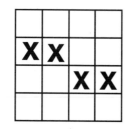
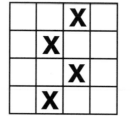
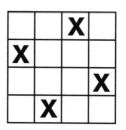

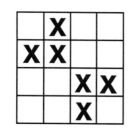
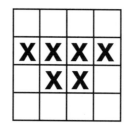
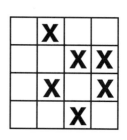

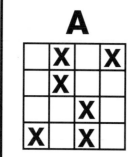
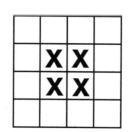

?

A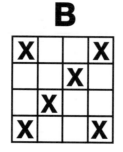

B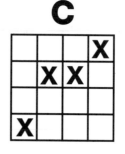

C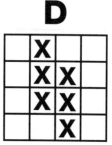

D

L E V E L

16

What is missing from the last circle?

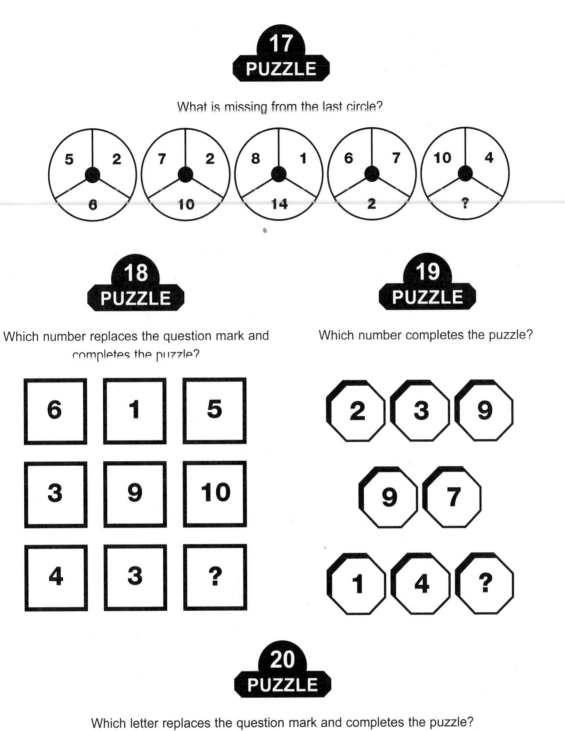

Which number replaces the question mark and completes the puzzle?

6	1	5
3	9	10
4	3	?

Which number completes the puzzle?

2 3 9

9 7

1 4 ?

Which letter replaces the question mark and completes the puzzle?

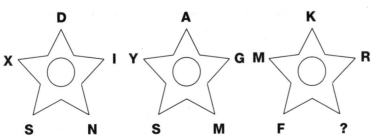

D
X   I Y
S   N

A
G M
S   M

K
R
F   ?

LEVEL

16

285

21 PUZZLE

Which letter completes the puzzle?

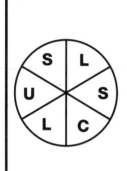

22 PUZZLE

In this sequence of letters what needs to be added to make the puzzle correct?

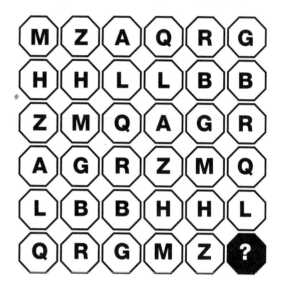

23 PUZZLE

Following a logical sequence, can you complete this puzzle?

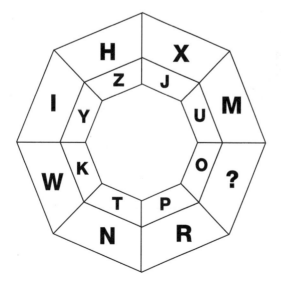

24 PUZZLE

Which number is missing?

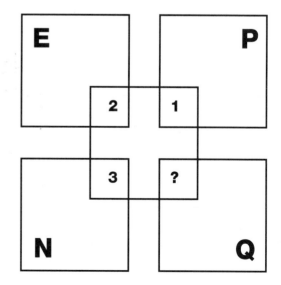

25 PUZZLE

What is missing from the last circle?

(C)   (D)   (K)

(G)   (I)   (F)

(J)   (M)   (?)

26 PUZZLE

Which number completes the puzzle?

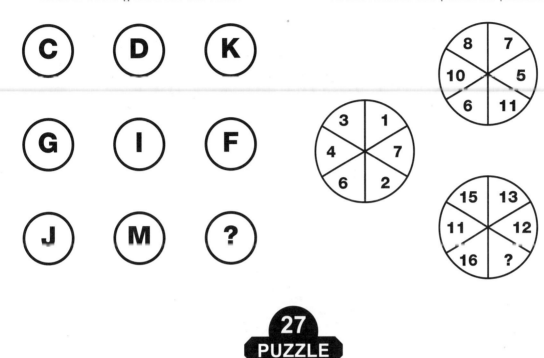

27 PUZZLE

Which number replaces the question mark and completes the puzzle?

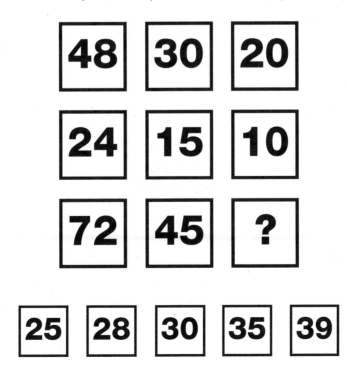

48	30	20
24	15	10
72	45	?

| 25 | 28 | 30 | 35 | 39 |

LEVEL

16

287

PUZZLE 28

Which letter completes the puzzle?

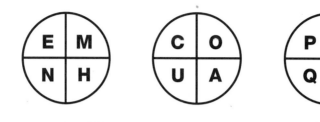

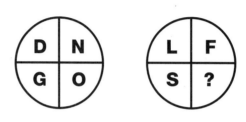

PUZZLE 29

Which number completes the puzzle?

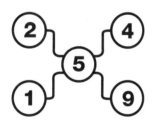
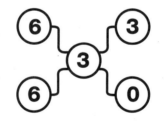
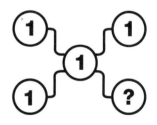

PUZZLE 30

What is missing from the last circle?

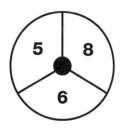
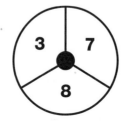

What is missing from the last oval?

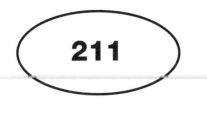

211

621

041

451

861

?

Which letter completes the puzzle?

Which number replaces the question mark and completes the puzzle?

3	8
11	5
16	6
22	10
32	12
44	?

34 PUZZLE

Following a logical sequence, can you complete this puzzle?

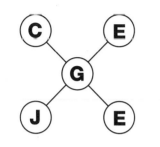

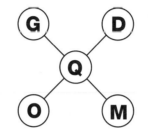

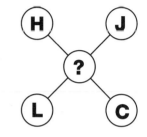

35 PUZZLE

What is missing from this arrangement of circles?

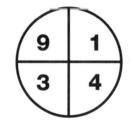

36 PUZZLE

Mr Jones' watch runs 1 second fast every hour, and Mr Brown's loses 1½ seconds every hour. If one day, they both showed 11.00am, how long would it be before they both showed the same time again? And how long would it be before both watches told exactly the right time?

Which of the bottom row of numbers replaces the question mark?

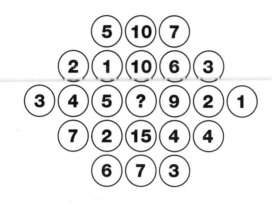

5 10 7
2 1 10 6 3
3 4 5 ? 9 2 1
7 2 15 4 4
6 7 3

10 12 14 16 18 20 22 24

Which letter replaces the question mark and completes the puzzle?

E Q C G   I U K O   M ? S W

Which number completes the puzzle?

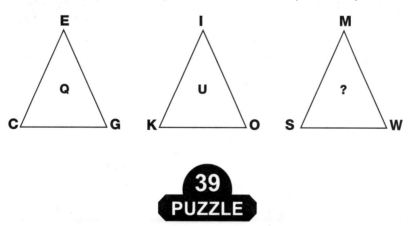

5 — 12 / 3 / 14 — 6

4 — 2 / 4 / 5 — 5

6 — 8 / 1 / 12 — ?

40 PUZZLE

Which letter completes the puzzle?

G	M
Q	

D	R
P	

M	Q
L	

O	E
?	

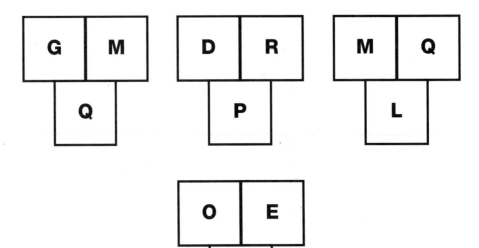

41 PUZZLE

Can you arrange these 6 matches to form 3 perfect squares, all exactly the same size? You may need to break some of them.

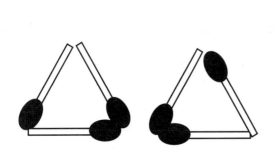

42 PUZZLE

What number continues this sequence?

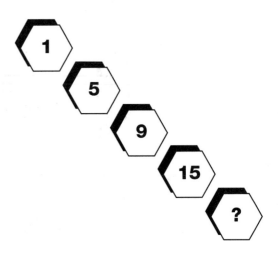

1
5
9
15
?

43 PUZZLE

What is missing from the last star?

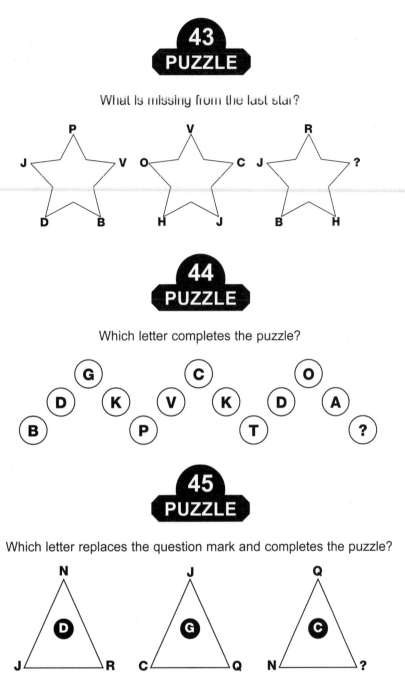

44 PUZZLE

Which letter completes the puzzle?

45 PUZZLE

Which letter replaces the question mark and completes the puzzle?

46 PUZZLE

Which number replaces the question mark and completes the puzzle?

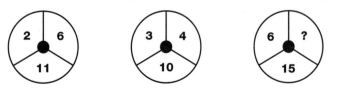

PUZZLE 47

Jane is thinking of two whole numbers, and asks Freddy to work out what they are. The only clue she will give him is that their product is three times larger than their sum.

Can you work out what the two numbers are?

PUZZLE 48

Which number completes the puzzle?

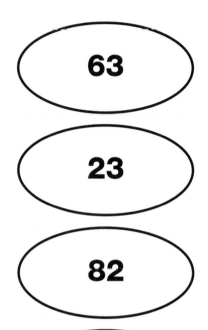

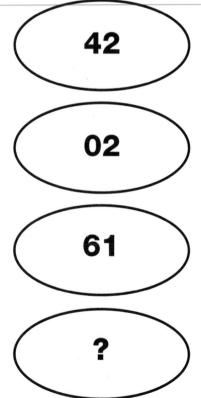

63

23

82

42

02

61

?

PUZZLE 49

Following a logical sequence, can you complete this puzzle?

(J) (F) (M) (A)

(M) (J) (J) (A)

(S) (O) (N) (?)

16

Which segment completes the puzzle?

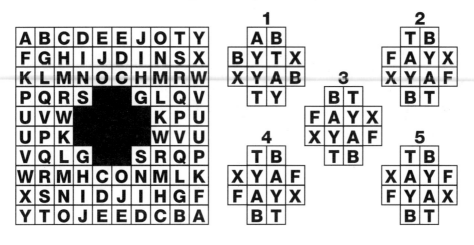

A	B	C	D	E	E	J	O	T	Y
F	G	H	I	J	D	I	N	S	X
K	L	M	N	O	C	H	M	R	W
P	Q	R	S			G	L	Q	V
U	V	W				K	P	U	
U	P	K				W	V	U	
V	Q	L	G			S	R	Q	P
W	R	M	H	C	O	N	M	L	K
X	S	N	I	D	J	I	H	G	F
Y	T	O	J	E	E	D	C	B	A

1
```
A B
B Y T X
X Y A B
  T Y
```

2
```
    T B
F A Y X
X Y A F
  B T
```

3
```
    B T
F A Y X
X Y A F
  T B
```

4
```
  T B
X Y A F
F A Y X
  B T
```

5
```
  T B
X A Y F
F Y A X
  B T
```

Which number replaces the question mark and completes the puzzle?

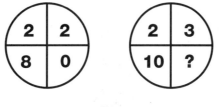

3	1
2	4

1	7
5	1

6	4
5	3

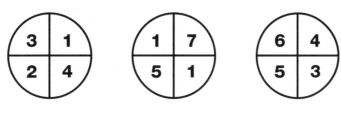

2	2
8	0

2	3
10	?

Which letter replaces the question mark and completes the puzzle?

A H F K K N P ?

Which three numbers are missing from this grid?

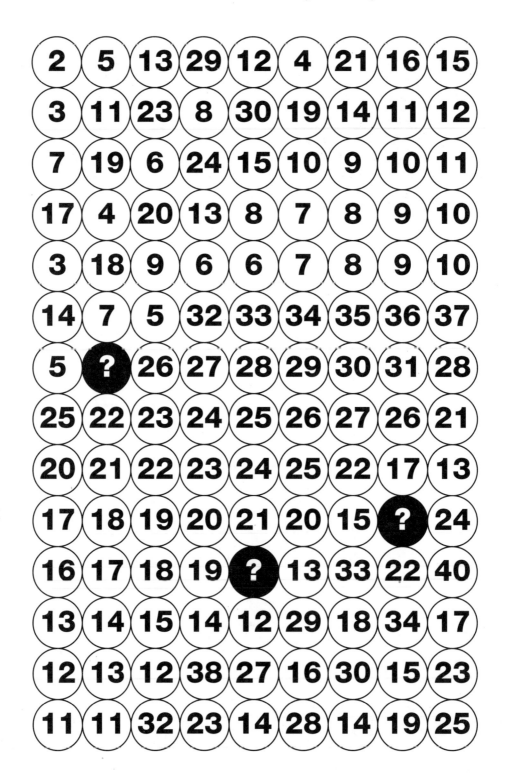

LEVEL

16

Which grid continues the sequence?

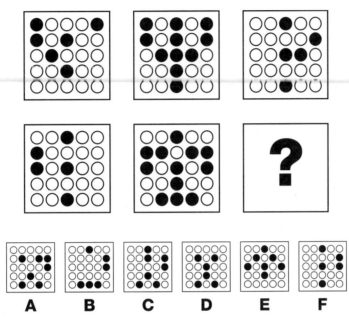

A **B** **C** **D** **E** **F**

Which of the bottom watches fills in the missing gap?

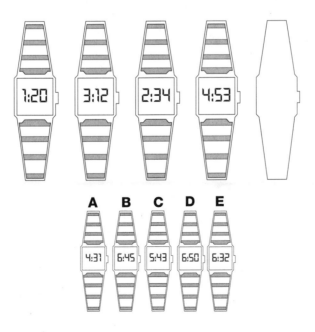

A **B** **C** **D** **E**

Which lower grid replaces the question mark to complete the sequence?

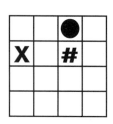
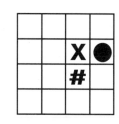
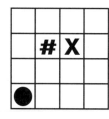
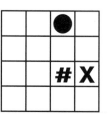

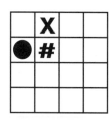
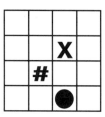
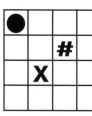
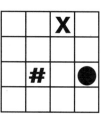

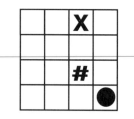
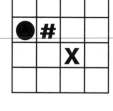
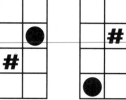
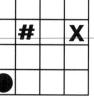

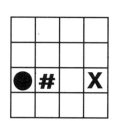
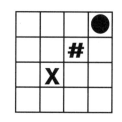
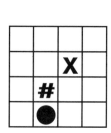

?

A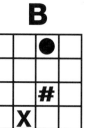

B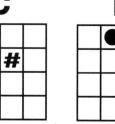

C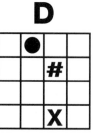

D

4 PUZZLE

Which of the lower letters replaces the question mark to complete the puzzle?

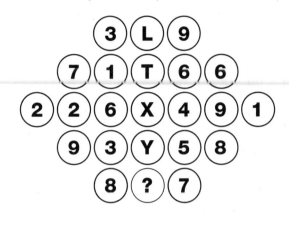

Row 1: 3 L 9
Row 2: 7 1 T 6 6
Row 3: 2 2 6 X 4 9 1
Row 4: 9 3 Y 5 8
Row 5: 8 ? 7

L M N O P Q R S

5 PUZZLE

Which number replaces the question mark and completes the puzzle?

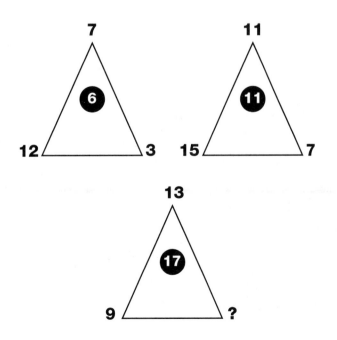

7
6
12 / 3

11
11
15 / 7

13
17
9 / ?

Which letter completes the puzzle?

Following a logical sequence, can you complete this puzzle?

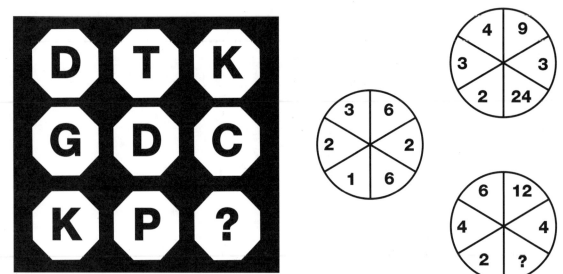

Which of the grids fill the missing gap?

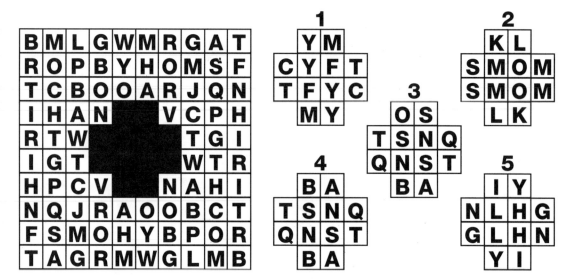

PUZZLE 9

What is missing from the last segment?

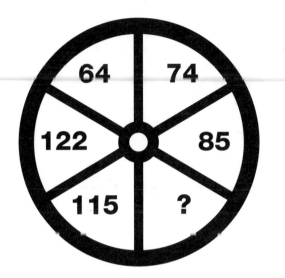

64	74
122	85
115	?

PUZZLE 10

Which number completes the puzzle?

7
8
11
15
22
?

PUZZLE 11

Which letter replaces the question mark and completes the puzzle?

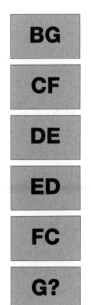

BG

CF

DE

ED

FC

G?

PUZZLE 12

Which letter replaces the question mark and completes the puzzle?

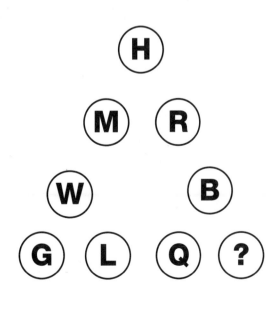

H

M   R

W   B

G   L   Q   ?

Which letters are missing from this arrangement of circles?

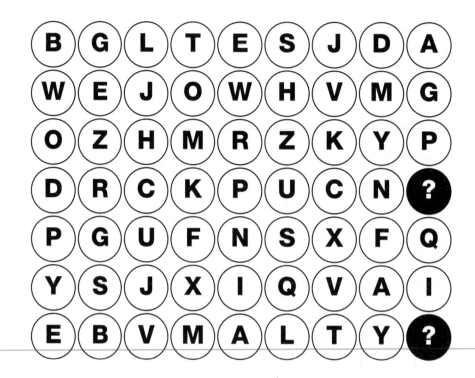

In this sequence of letters what needs to be added to make the puzzle correct?

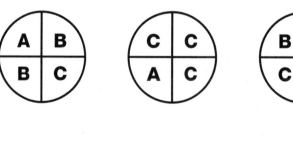

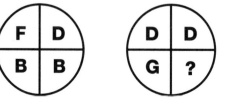

15 PUZZLE

What is missing from the last hexagon?

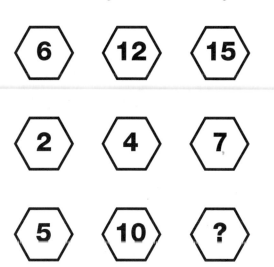

16 PUZZLE

Which letter completes the puzzle?

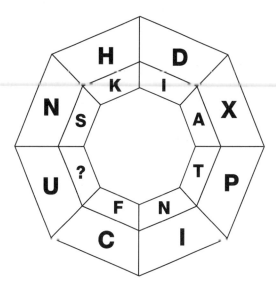

17 PUZZLE

Which letter replaces the question mark
and completes the puzzle?

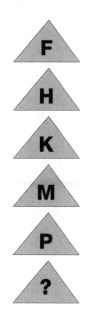

18 PUZZLE

Which number replaces the question mark
and completes the puzzle?

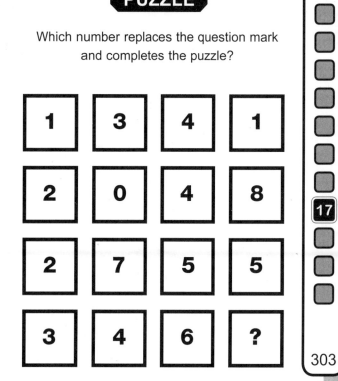

PUZZLE 19

In this sequence of letters what needs to be added to make the puzzle correct?

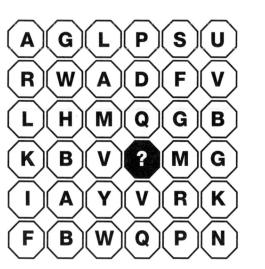

PUZZLE 20

Which number completes the puzzle?

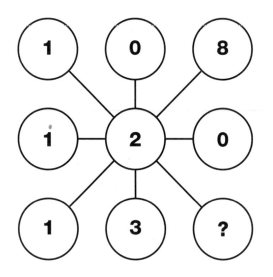

PUZZLE 21

What is missing from this arrangement of circles?

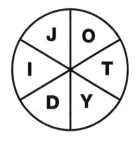
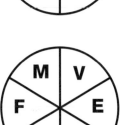
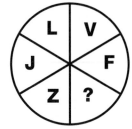

What is missing from the last octogan?

Which letter completes the puzzle?

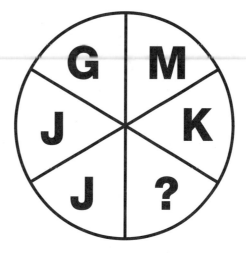

Which number replaces the question mark and completes the puzzle?

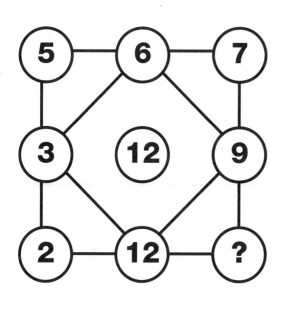

Where should the minute hand point to on the bottom clock?

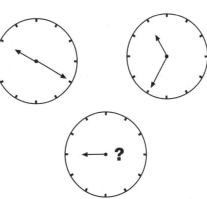

LEVEL

17

305

26
PUZZLE

Which letters complete the puzzle?

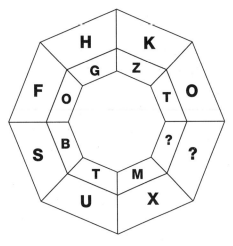

27
PUZZLE

What is missing from this puzzle?

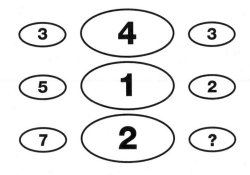

28
PUZZLE

Following a logical sequence, can you complete this puzzle?

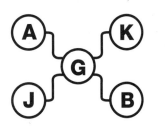 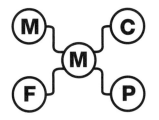 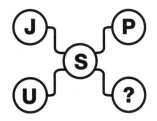

29
PUZZLE

which letter goes in the right hand circle to complete the puzzle?

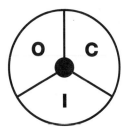  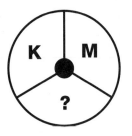

PUZZLE 30

What is missing from the last hexagon?

12 8 14 18 ?

PUZZLE 31

Which number completes the puzzle?

26

22

18

12

?

PUZZLE 32

Which letter replaces the question mark
and completes the puzzle?

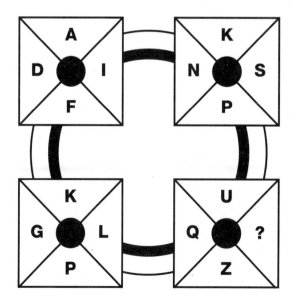

PUZZLE 33

Which number replaces the question mark
and completes the chain?

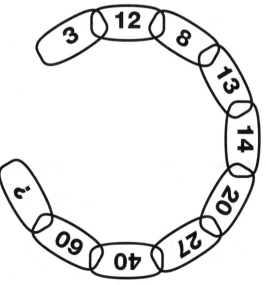

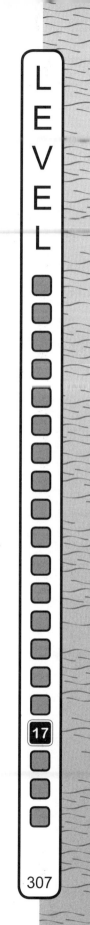

17

Which lower grid replaces the question mark to complete the sequence?

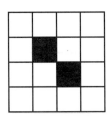
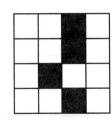
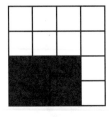
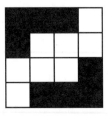

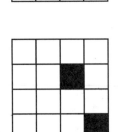
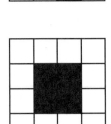
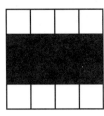
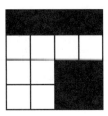

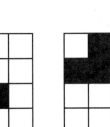
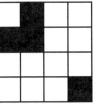
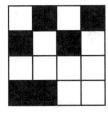
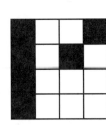

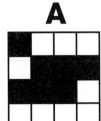
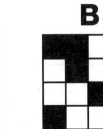

?

A 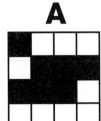   **B**   **C**    **D**

What is missing from the last circle?

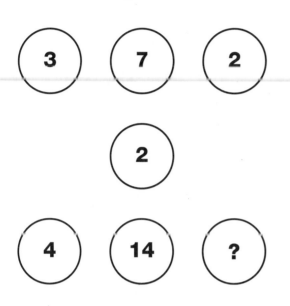

Which letter completes the puzzle?

Which number replaces the question mark and completes the puzzle?

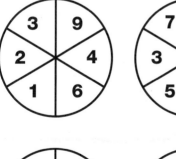

Which number replaces the question mark and completes the puzzle?

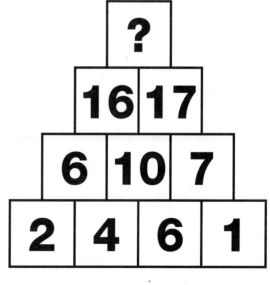

LEVEL

17

39 PUZZLE

Which letter completes the puzzle?

K   T   C

V   E   L

M   D   ?

40 PUZZLE

Following a logical sequence, can you complete this puzzle?

1728

2197

2744

3375

4096

?

41 PUZZLE

Move just 4 matches to create 7 squares. Can you also move the same 4 matches to create 10 squares?

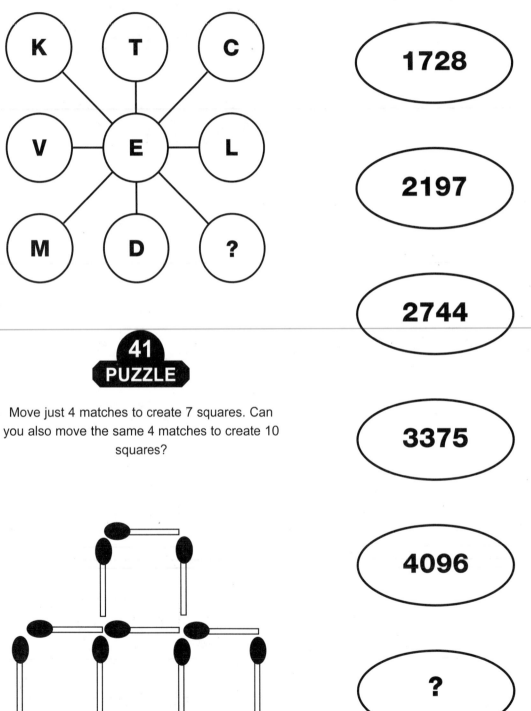

What is missing from the last circle?

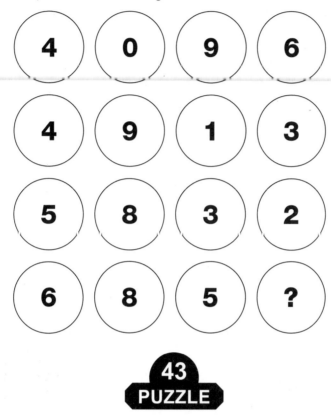

4	0	9	6
4	9	1	3
5	8	3	2
6	8	5	?

Which letter replaces the question mark and completes the puzzle?

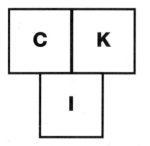

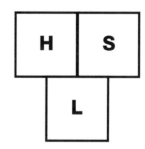

C	K
	I

M	V
	J

H	S
	L

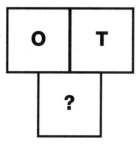

O	T
	?

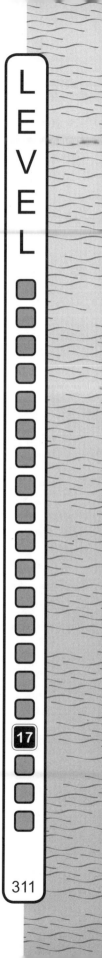

44 PUZZLE

Which letter completes the puzzle?

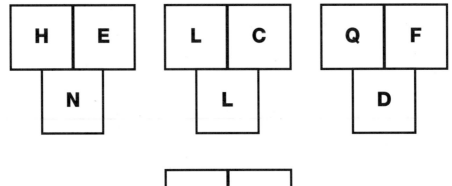

H	E
	N

L	C
	L

Q	F
	D

J	G
	?

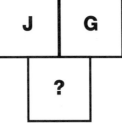

45 PUZZLE

Can you work out
one-half of two-thirds of three-quarters of
four-fifths of five-sixths
of six-sevenths of
seven-eighths of
eight-ninths of nine-tenths of one hundred?

46 PUZZLE

Following a logical sequence, can you complete this puzzle?

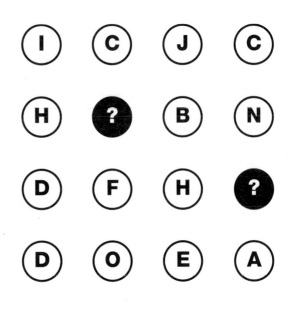

I	C	J	C
H	?	B	N
D	F	H	?
D	O	E	A

What is missing from the last square?

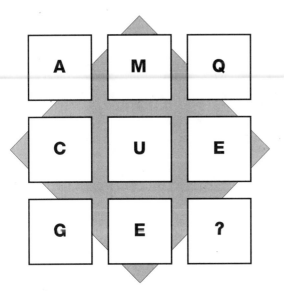

Which number completes the puzzle?

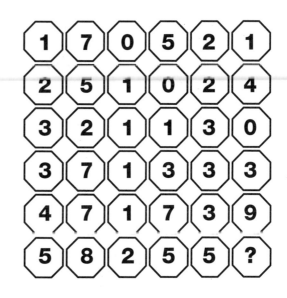

Which two numbers are the odd ones out in these ovals?

Which number replaces the question mark and completes the puzzle?

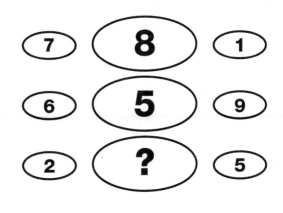

LEVEL

17

313

Which four letters need to be added to this grid?

PUZZLE 1

Which number replaces the question mark and completes the puzzle?

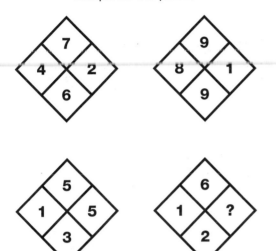

PUZZLE 2

Which number replaces the question mark and completes the grid?

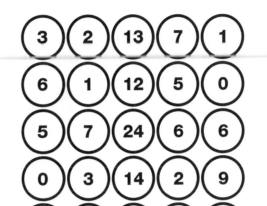

PUZZLE 3

Which number replaces the question mark and completes the wheel?

PUZZLE 4

Which number replaces the question mark and completes the puzzle?

3	GNQ	8
3	RBS	9
4	TUA	2
2	FPC	5
3	OLH	?

Which of the lower grids replace the question mark to complete the sequence?

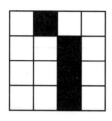
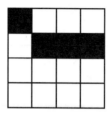
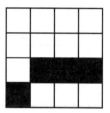

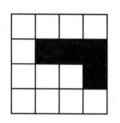
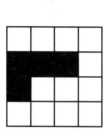
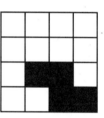

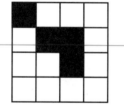
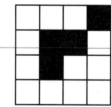
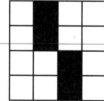
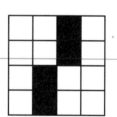

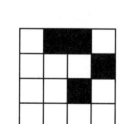
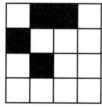
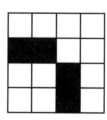

?

A
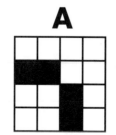

B
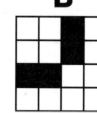

C

D
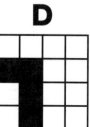

PUZZLE 6

Which letter replaces the question mark and completes the chain?

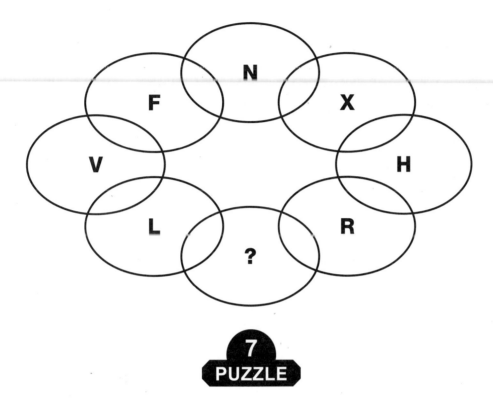

PUZZLE 7

Which number replaces the question mark in the bottom grid?

0	6	4	2
1	7	5	6
2	9	7	1

1	9	5	5
3	0	6	9
4	2	8	4

2	4	6	0
3	5	7	4
4	7	8	9

0	8	4	4
1	9	5	8
3	1	7	?

PUZZLE 8

Which grid fits in the middle?

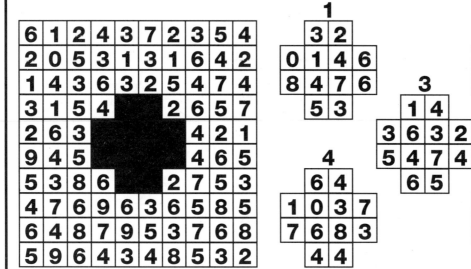

6	1	2	4	3	7	2	3	5	4
2	0	5	3	1	3	1	6	4	2
1	4	3	6	3	2	5	4	7	4
3	1	5	4			2	6	5	7
2	6	3				4	2	1	
9	4	5				4	6	5	
5	3	8	6			2	7	5	3
4	7	6	9	6	3	6	5	8	5
6	4	8	7	9	5	3	7	6	8
5	9	6	4	3	4	8	5	3	2

1
```
    3 2
0 1 4 6
8 4 7 6
    5 3
```

2
```
    2 7
5 3 6 5
8 5 7 6
    8 2
```

3
```
    1 4
3 6 3 2
5 4 7 4
    6 5
```

4
```
    6 4
1 0 3 7
7 6 8 3
    4 4
```

5
```
    5 3
6 3 6 5
8 5 7 9
    2 0
```

PUZZLE 9

Which letter completes the puzzle?

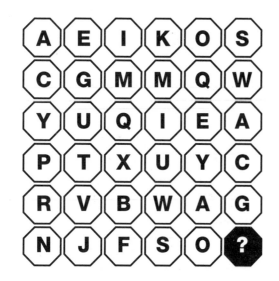

A	E	I	K	O	S
C	G	M	M	Q	W
Y	U	Q	I	E	A
P	T	X	U	Y	C
R	V	B	W	A	G
N	J	F	S	O	?

PUZZLE 10

Following a logical sequence, can you complete this puzzle?

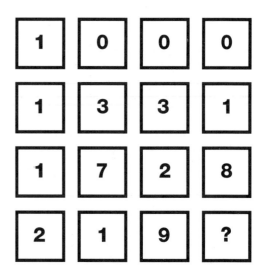

1	0	0	0
1	3	3	1
1	7	2	8
2	1	9	?

11 PUZZLE

What is missing from the right hand star?

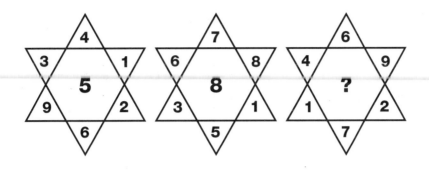

12 PUZZLE

Which letter replaces the question mark and completes the puzzle?

D		H
K	M	X
G		P

M		J
R	B	P
E		F

L		C
S	G	L
G		I

N		U
O	?	W
A		B

13 PUZZLE

Which number replaces the question mark in the second figure?

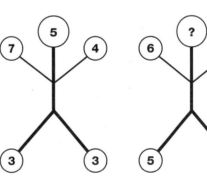

14 PUZZLE

Which letter replaces the question mark in the third triangle?

15
PUZZLE

Which number completes the puzzle?

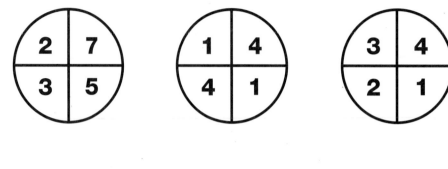

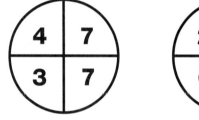

16
PUZZLE

Following a logical sequence, can you
complete this puzzle?

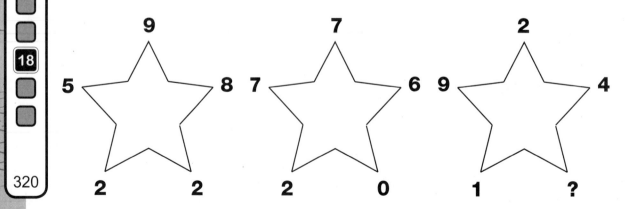

17
PUZZLE

Which letter replaces the question mark and completes the sequence?

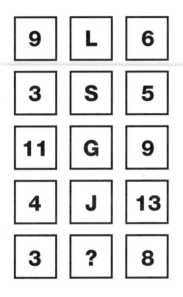

9	L	6
3	S	5
11	G	9
4	J	13
3	?	8

18
PUZZLE

Which letter replaces the question mark in this formation?

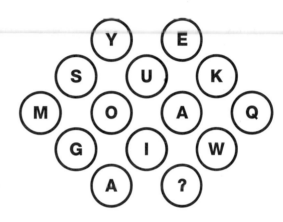

Y   E

S   U   K

M   O   A   Q

G   I   W

A   ?

19
PUZZLE

Which number replaces the question mark and completes the puzzle?

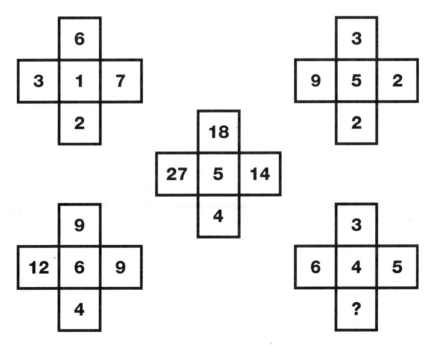

	6	
3	1	7
	2	

	3	
9	5	2
	2	

	18	
27	5	14
	4	

	9	
12	6	9
	4	

	3	
6	4	5
	?	

Which three letters complete the puzzle?

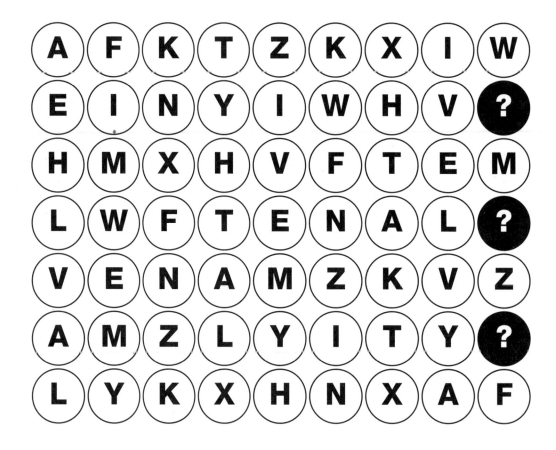

A F K T Z K X I W
E I N Y I W H V ?
H M X H V F T E M
L W F T E N A L ?
V E N A M Z K V Z
A M Z L Y I T Y ?
L Y K X H N X A F

21
PUZZLE

What is missing from this puzzle?

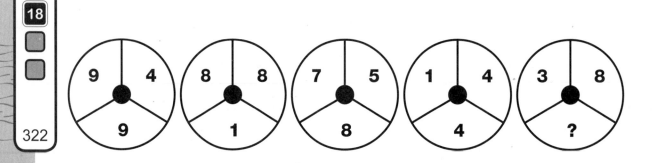

9 4 / 9 — 8 8 / 1 — 7 5 / 8 — 1 4 / 4 — 3 8 / ?

LEVEL

18

22 PUZZLE

Which number replaces the question mark and completes the puzzle?

9			
4	3		
1	8	1	
2	1	7	?

23 PUZZLE

Which letter replaces the question mark and completes the last grid?

A	J
L	R

Q	C
V	M

I	V
F	H

S	D
G	A

Z	V
?	E

24 PUZZLE

Which playing card replaces the question mark and completes the puzzle?

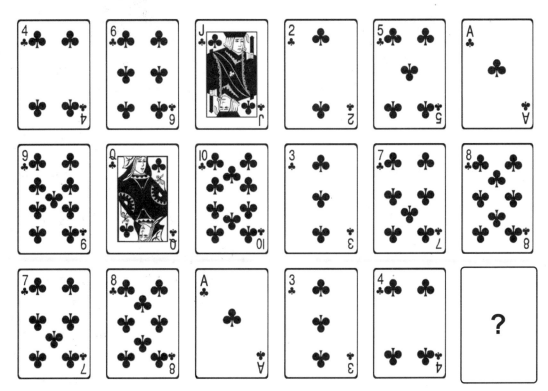

In this sequence of letters what needs to be added to make the puzzle correct?

Which number completes the puzzle?

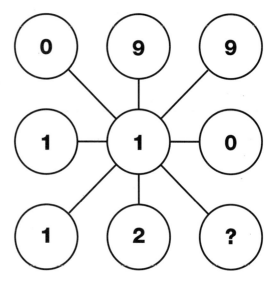

Which letter completes the puzzle?

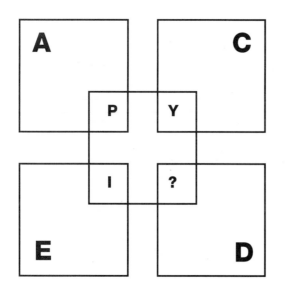

Following a logical sequence, can you complete this puzzle?

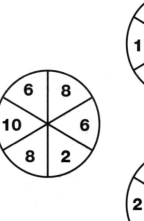

29
PUZZLE

Which number replaces the question mark
and completes the puzzle?

4	2
6	11

7	8
2	3

10	9
7	13

4	7
5	?

30
PUZZLE

Which number replaces the question mark
and completes the pattern?

3		23	6		7
	41			28	
7		8	2		13
4		19	14		3
	45			47	
17		5	11		?

31
PUZZLE

Where should the minute hand point to
on the bottom clock?

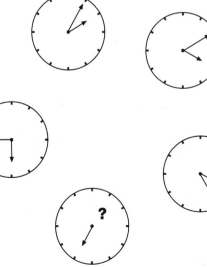

32
PUZZLE

Which letter replaces the question mark
and completes the puzzle?

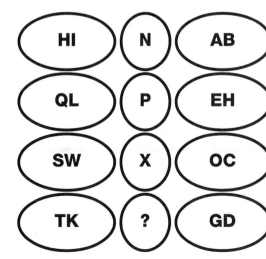

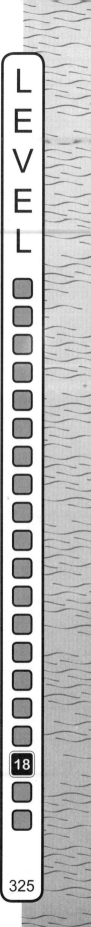

Which of the lower grids replaces the question mark to complete the sequence?

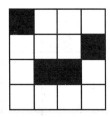
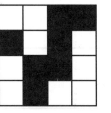
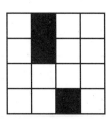

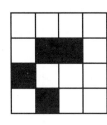
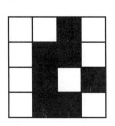
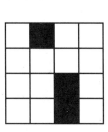

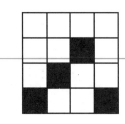
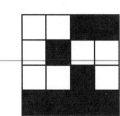
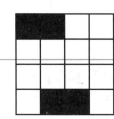

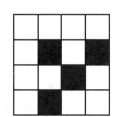

A   **B**   **C**   **D**

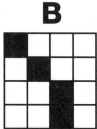
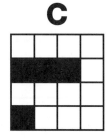
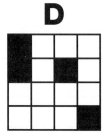
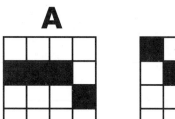

LEVEL

18

	Anne	Beryl	Frank	Pete Shear	Max Morris	Lucy Carr	120 pgs	250 pgs	400 pgs
Thriller									
Biography									
Romance									
120 pgs									
250 pgs									
400 pgs									
Pete Shear									
Max Morris									
Lucy Carr									

Anne, Beryl and Frank are keen readers, and like nothing more than settling down with their favourite books. Beryl likes thrillers the best, but never reads anything which is longer than 300 pages. Anne's book, which is only 120 pages long, features Max Morris as its hero. Frank's book was a good read, but didn't feature Lucy Carr. The romantic novel did not feature Pete Shear. From this information, can you deduce which reader likes which kind of book, who was the central hero of the book they chose, and how many pages long the

Reader	Book type	Hero	Book length

books were?

Which letter replaces the question mark and completes the sequence?

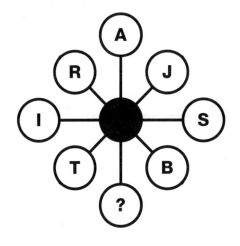

Which number replaces the question mark and completes the grid?

4	8 3 2	8
5 7 4		2 3 3
5	6 1 4	?

37 PUZZLE

Which number completes the puzzle?

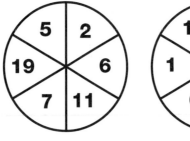
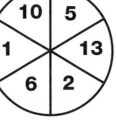
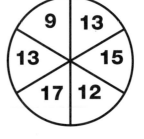

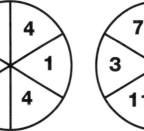

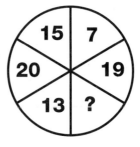

38 PUZZLE

Which letter completes the puzzle?

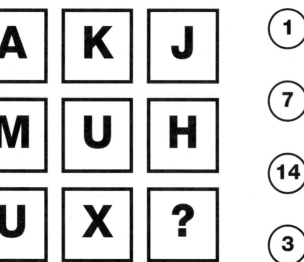

A	K	J
M	U	H
U	X	?

39 PUZZLE

Following a logical sequence, can you complete this puzzle?

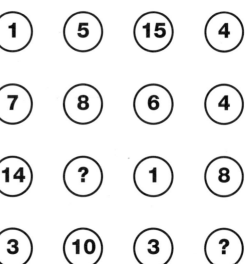

1	5	15	4
7	8	6	4
14	?	1	8
3	10	3	?

Which picture cube does this shape make?

A

C

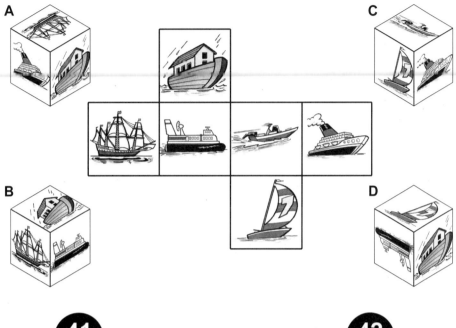

B

D

Which letter replaces the blank and completes the sequence?

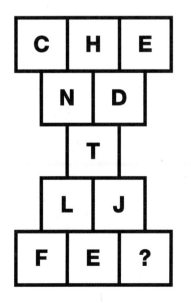

Patrick, Mark and Peter had spent the week decorating their elderly neighbour's house, for which they had earned £500 between them. When it came to dividing up the money, Patrick claimed he had worked 3 times harder than Mark, and Peter had worked twice as hard as Patrick. If the money was to be divided fairly, how much did each worker receive?

Which letters replace the question marks to complete the puzzle?

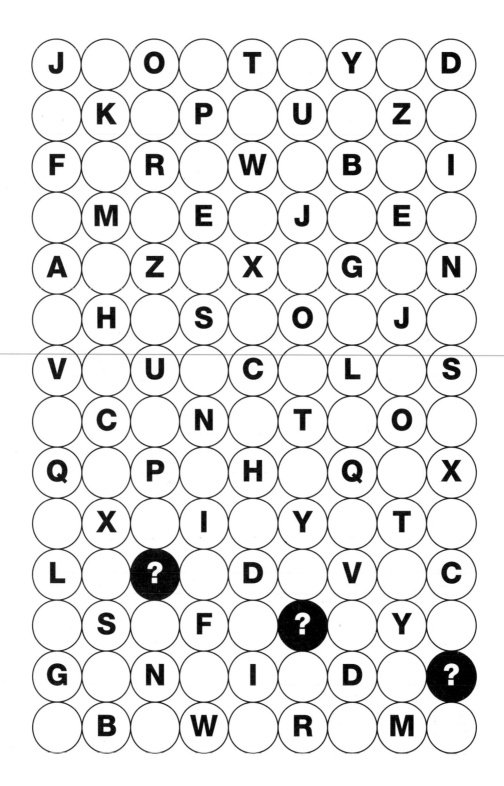

18

330

44 PUZZLE

Which number replaces the question mark and completes the puzzle?

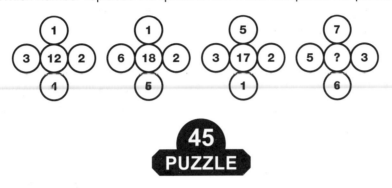

45 PUZZLE

Which number replaces the question mark and completes the puzzle?

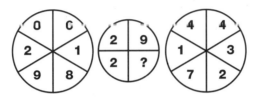

46 PUZZLE

Which number replaces the question mark and completes the puzzle?

3	6	2		4	5	1		6	4	5		3	7	8
	18				20				24				21	
	12				5				20				?	

47 PUZZLE

What should go on the top of the last domino?

48 PUZZLE

Both of these columns of numbers add up to different totals. Can you change just one number to make the totals equal?

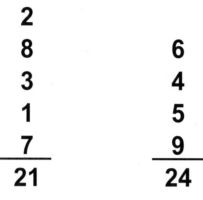

2
8
6
3
4
1
5
7
9
___
___
21
24

49 PUZZLE

Here are 12 matches, arranged to form an equilateral triangle. Can you move just 4 matches to reduce the surface area of the triangle by half?
If you can do that, can you move 6 matches from the original layout to reduce the area to a quarter?

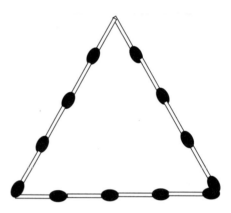

50 PUZZLE

If a group of 6 people have an average age of 21, and each person is half the age of the next person, what are the ages of the 6 people?

51 PUZZLE

Which number completes the puzzle?

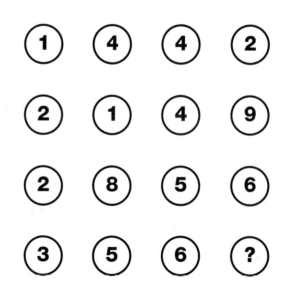

1 4 4 2
2 1 4 9
2 8 5 6
3 5 6 ?

1
PUZZLE

What is missing in the last grid?

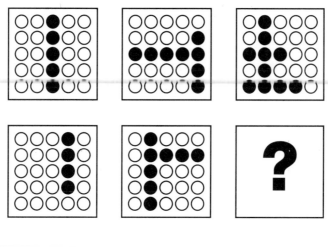

A   B   C   D   E   F

2
PUZZLE

What time should the missing watch show?

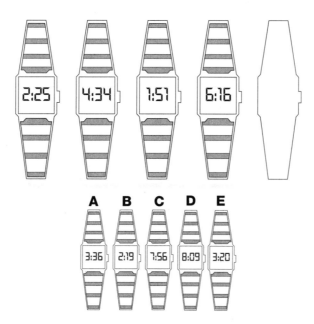

2:25   4:34   7:51   6:16

A   B   C   D   E

3:36   2:19   7:56   8:09   3:20

3
PUZZLE

Which grid completes the puzzle?

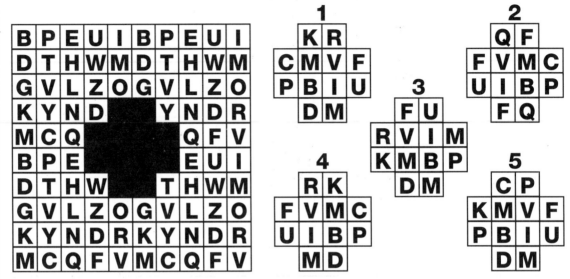

B	P	E	U	I	B	P	E	U	I
D	T	H	W	M	D	T	H	W	M
G	V	L	Z	O	G	V	L	Z	O
K	Y	N	D			Y	N	D	R
M	C	Q				Q	F	V	
B	P	E				E	U	I	
D	T	H	W			T	H	W	M
G	V	L	Z	O	G	V	L	Z	O
K	Y	N	D	R	K	Y	N	D	R
M	C	Q	F	V	M	C	Q	F	V

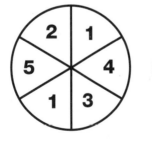

1
K R
C M V F
P B I U
D M

2
Q F
F V M C
U I B P
F Q

3
F U
R V I M
K M B P
D M

4
R K
F V M C
U I B P
M D

5
C P
K M V F
P B I U
D M

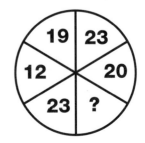

4
PUZZLE

Following a logical sequence, can you complete this puzzle?

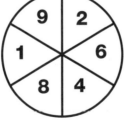

Circle 1: 2, 1, 4, 3, 1, 5

Circle 2: 9, 2, 6, 4, 8, 1

Circle 3: 4, 10, 5, 1, 7, 3

Circle 4: 17, 14, 19, 11, 17, 14

Circle 5: 24, 15, 21, 12, 24, 10

Circle 6: 19, 23, 20, ?, 23, 12

Which of the letters shown below replace the question mark to complete the puzzle?

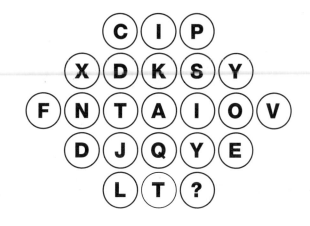

(B)(F)(I)(M)(P)(S)(W)(Z)

6 PUZZLE

Which letter replaces the question mark and completes the puzzle?

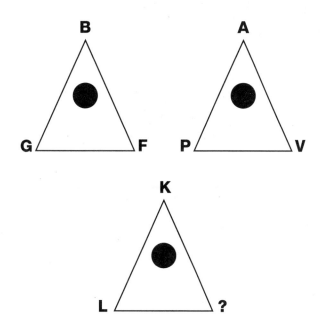

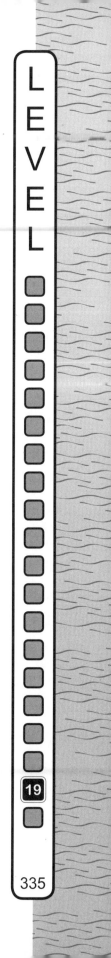

LEVEL

19

7 PUZZLE

Which letter completes the puzzle?

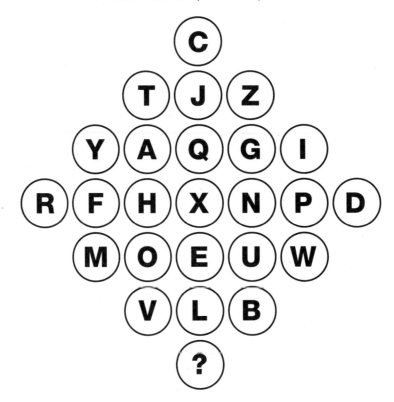

C
T J Z
Y A Q G I
R F H X N P D
M O E U W
V L B
?

K X H T U Z S B

8 PUZZLE

Which number completes the puzzle?

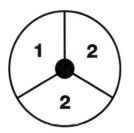

1 2
2

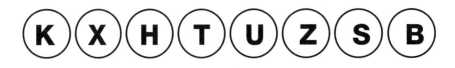

9 2
5

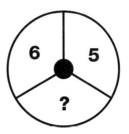

6 5
?

9 PUZZLE

What is missing from the last segment?

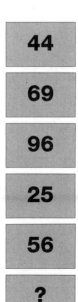

10 PUZZLE

Which number replaces the question mark and completes the puzzle?

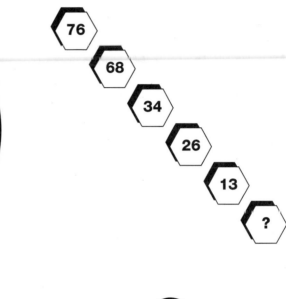

11 PUZZLE

Which number replaces the question mark and completes the puzzle?

44

69

96

25

56

?

12 PUZZLE

Which letter replaces the question mark and completes the puzzle?

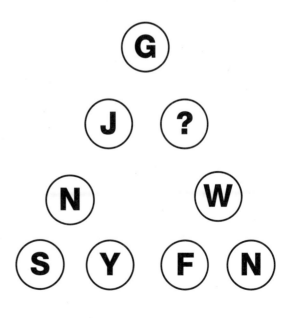

PUZZLE 13

Fill in the empty segments.

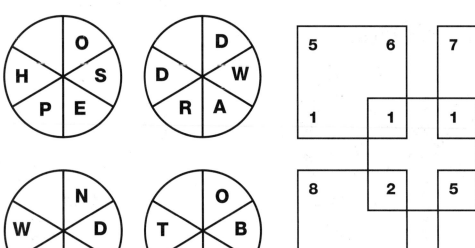

PUZZLE 14

Which number is missing?

5	6	7	9
1	1	1	6
8	2	5	8
1	0	1	?

PUZZLE 15

Following a logical sequence, can you complete this puzzle?

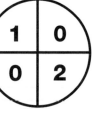
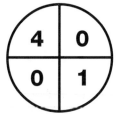

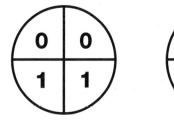
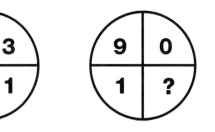

16 PUZZLE

What is missing from the last hexagon?

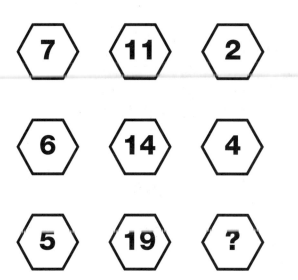

7 11 2

6 14 4

5 19 ?

17 PUZZLE

Which letter completes the puzzle?

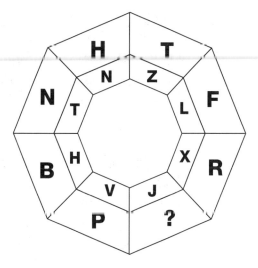

H T
N Z
N T L F
B H X R
V J
P ?

18 PUZZLE

Which number replaces the question mark and completes the puzzle?

8
12
17
23
30
?

19 PUZZLE

Which number replaces the question mark and completes the puzzle?

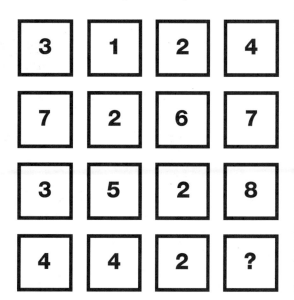

3	1	2	4
7	2	6	7
3	5	2	8
4	4	2	?

PUZZLE 20

Which pattern completes the puzzle?

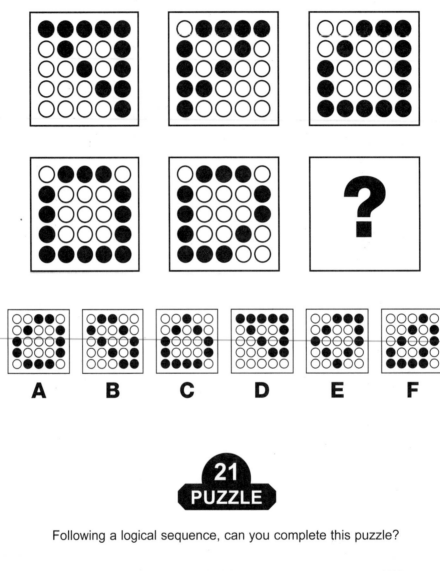

A B C D E F

PUZZLE 21

Following a logical sequence, can you complete this puzzle?

PUZZLE 22

What is missing from the last octagon?

PUZZLE 23

Which letter completes the puzzle?

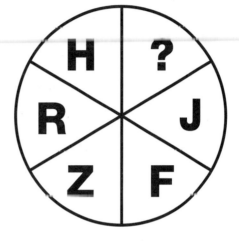

PUZZLE 24

Which number replaces the question mark and completes the puzzle?

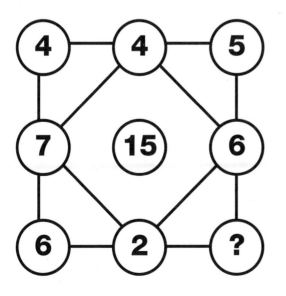

PUZZLE 25

Where should the missing hand point to?

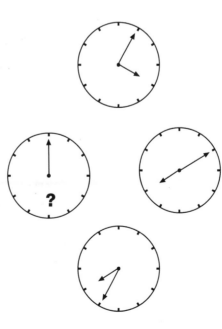

Which of the lower grids replaces the question mark to complete the sequence?

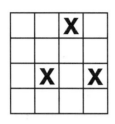
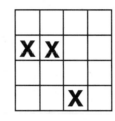
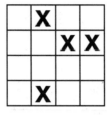
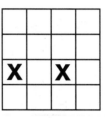

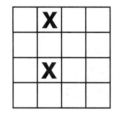
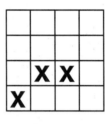
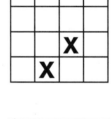
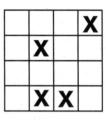

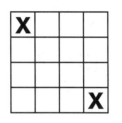
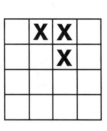
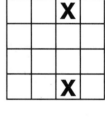

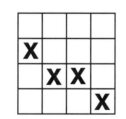
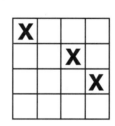
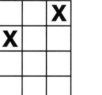

?

A   **B**   **C**   **D**

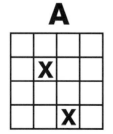
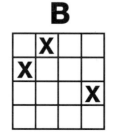
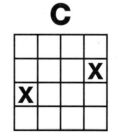
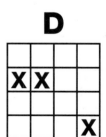

PUZZLE 27

What is missing from the last hexagon?

PUZZLE 28

Which letter completes the puzzle?

A

D

E

I

?

PUZZLE 29

Which letter replaces the question mark and completes the puzzle?

PUZZLE 30

Which number replaces the question mark and completes the chain?

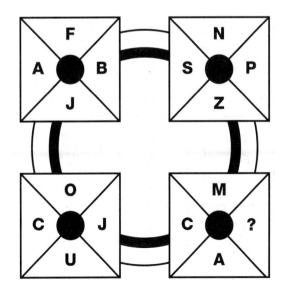

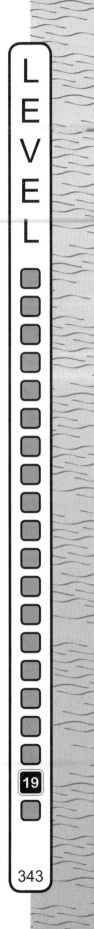

LEVEL

19

343

31 PUZZLE

What is missing from this arrangement of circles?

32 PUZZLE

Which number completes the puzzle?

33 PUZZLE

What is missing?

34 PUZZLE

Following a logical sequence, can you complete this puzzle?

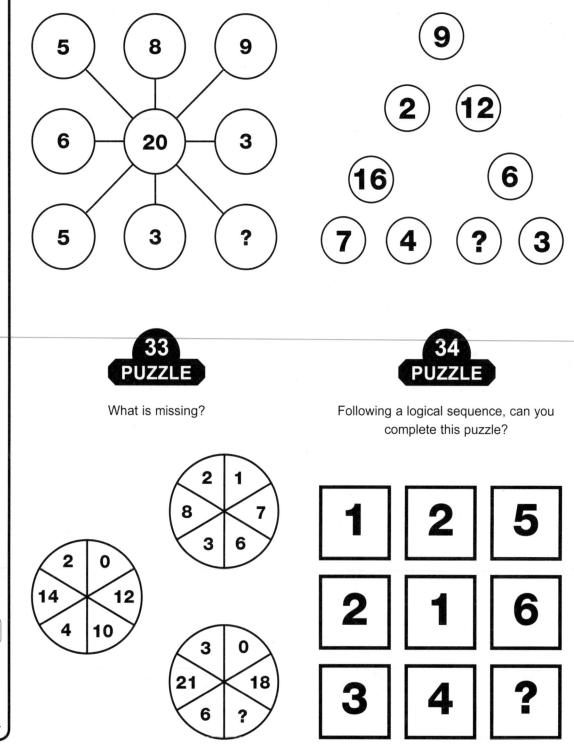

What is missing from the last circle?

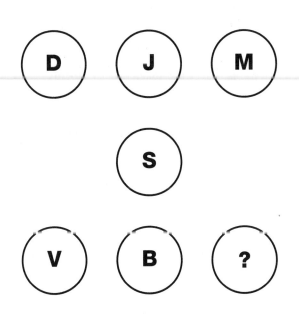

D   J   M

S

V   B   ?

Which letter completes the puzzle?

D   B

A   A   G

G   ?

Which number replaces the question mark and completes the puzzle?

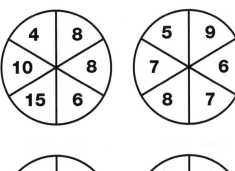

4	8
10	8
15	6

5	9
7	6
8	7

4	1
5	2
3	6

1	8
2	4
5	?

Which number replaces the question mark and completes the puzzle?

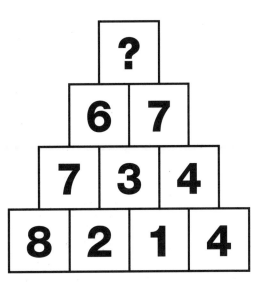

?

6   7

7   3   4

8   2   1   4

LEVEL

19

345

PUZZLE 39

Which number completes this grid?

1	0	0	2	5	6
1	2	1	2	8	9
1	4	4	3	2	4
1	6	9	3	6	1
1	9	6	4	0	0
2	2	5	4	4	?

PUZZLE 40

Out of 100 members of a riding club, 60 were women, 80 were married, 70 wore black boots and 90 wore black jackets.

What is the least number of married women who wear black boots and jackets?

PUZZLE 41

Which letter completes the puzzle?

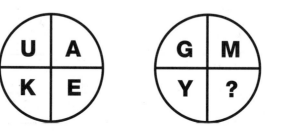

42 PUZZLE

What is missing from the last circle?

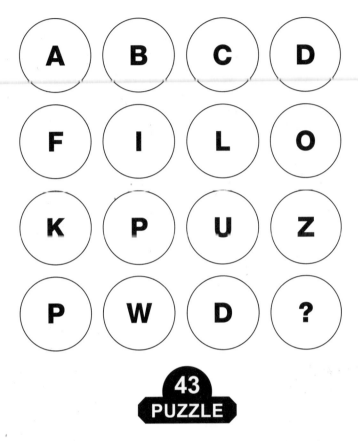

(A) (B) (C) (D)

(F) (I) (L) (O)

(K) (P) (U) (Z)

(P) (W) (D) (?)

43 PUZZLE

Which letter replaces the question mark and completes the puzzle?

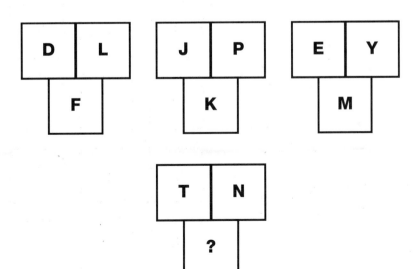

D	L
	F

J	P
	K

E	Y
	M

T	N
	?

44 PUZZLE

Which letter completes the puzzle?

D	F	I	M
C	P	D	R
Q	I	?	X
F	V	M	E

45 PUZZLE

Which number completes the puzzle?

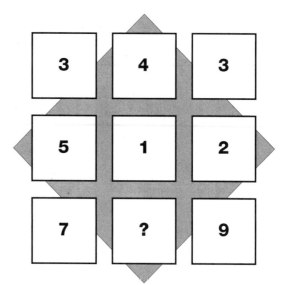

3	4	3
5	1	2
7	?	9

46 PUZZLE

In this sequence of letters what needs to be added to make the puzzle correct?

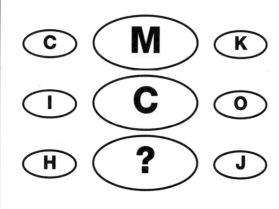

C	M	K
I	C	O
H	?	J

47 PUZZLE

Which number completes this pattern of squares?

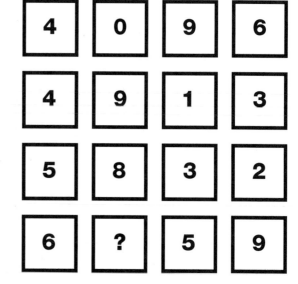

4	0	9	6
4	9	1	3
5	8	3	2
6	?	5	9

PUZZLE 48

What is missing from the last square?

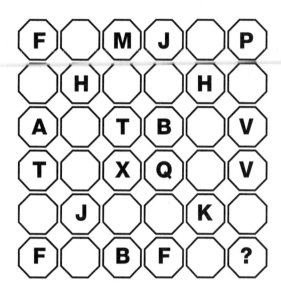

7	2	6
3	9	3
5	4	?

PUZZLE 49

Which letter completes the puzzle?

F		M	J		P
	H			H	
A		T	B		V
T		X	Q		V
	J			K	
F		B	F		?

PUZZLE 50

Which numbers are the odd ones out in these two ovals?

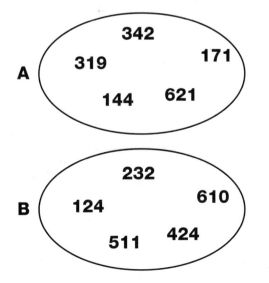

A
342
319   171
144   621

B
232
124   610
511   424

PUZZLE 51

Which letter replaces the question mark and completes the puzzle?

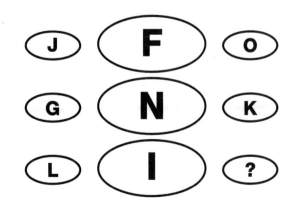

J   F   O
G   N   K
L   I   ?

PUZZLE 52

Which one of the letters given below completes this puzzle?

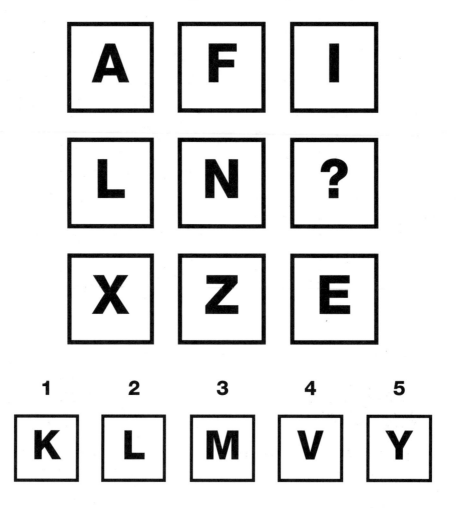

A	F	I
L	N	?
X	Z	E

1 K   **2** L   **3** M   **4** V   **5** Y

PUZZLE 53

Following a logical sequence, can you complete this puzzle?

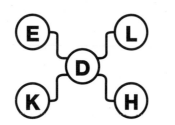

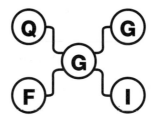

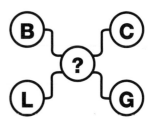

1
PUZZLE

Which letter is missing from this puzzle?

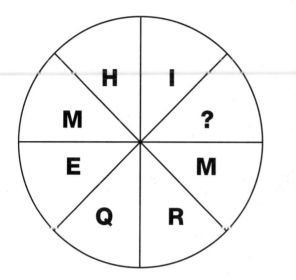

2
PUZZLE

Which letter completes the puzzle?

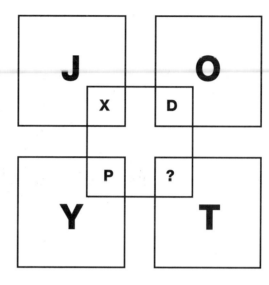

3
PUZZLE

Which number replaces the question mark and completes the puzzle?

71
79
67
80
68
?

4
PUZZLE

Which number replaces the question mark and completes the puzzle?

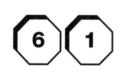

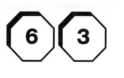

20

351

PUZZLE 5

Which letter completes the puzzle?

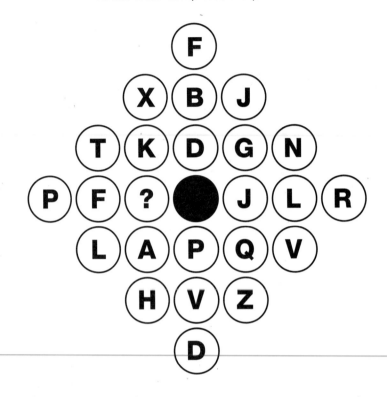

PUZZLE 6

In this sequence of letters what needs to be added to make the puzzle correct?

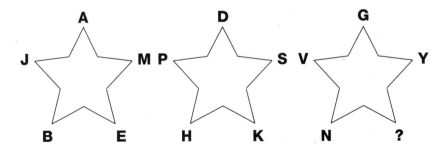

7 PUZZLE

What is missing from the last circle?

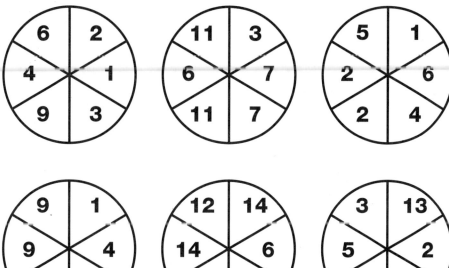

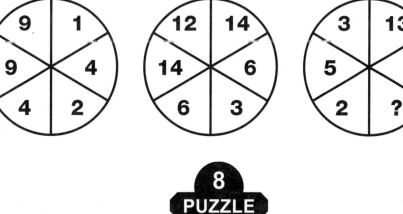

8 PUZZLE

Which letter replaces the question mark and completes the puzzle?

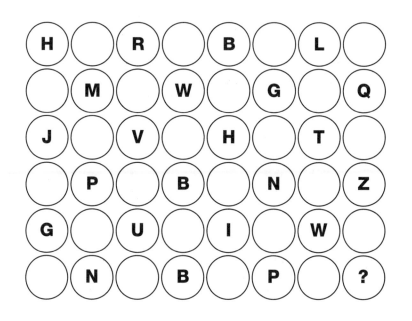

Which of the lower grids will complete this puzzle?

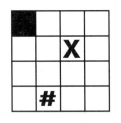
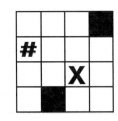
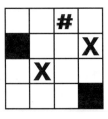
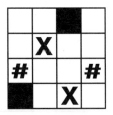

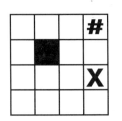
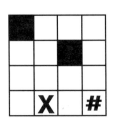
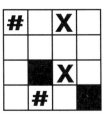

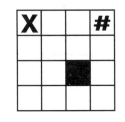
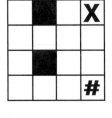
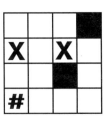
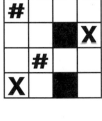

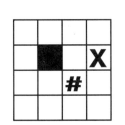
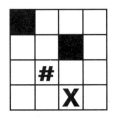
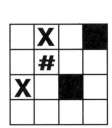

?

A
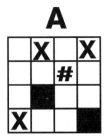

B
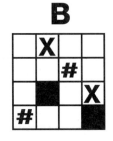

C
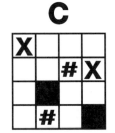

D

10 PUZZLE

What is missing from the middle circle?

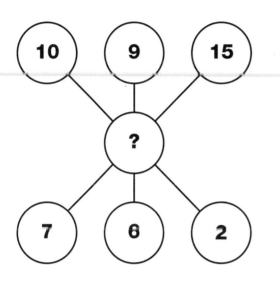

11 PUZZLE

Which letter completes the puzzle?

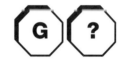

12 PUZZLE

Which number replaces the question mark and completes the puzzle?

| 5 | 6 | 9 | 16 | ? |

13 PUZZLE

Which number replaces the question mark and completes the puzzle?

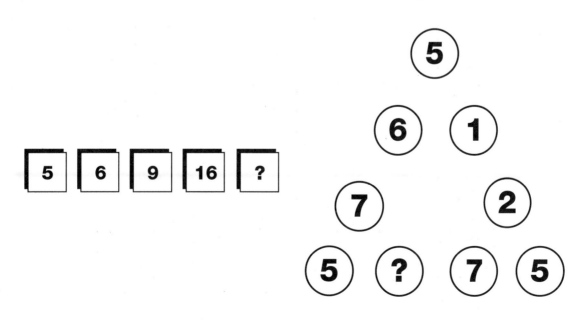

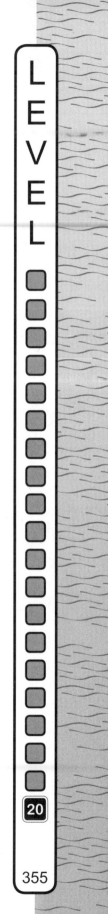

PUZZLE 14

Which watch completes the puzzle?

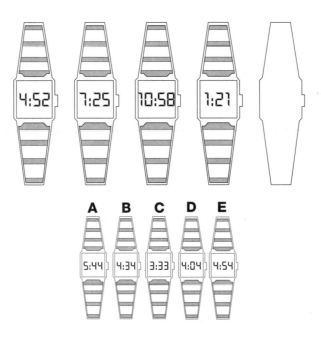

4:52   7:25   10:58   1:21

A   B   C   D   E

5:44   4:34   3:33   4:04   4:54

PUZZLE 15

Which number is missing from the bottom right circle in this puzzle?

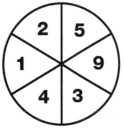

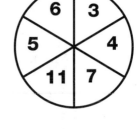

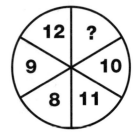

Circle 1: 2, 5, 1, 9, 4, 3

Circle 2: 4, 5, 7, 8, 6, 12

Circle 3: 6, 3, 5, 4, 11, 7

Circle 4: 8, 9, 14, 6, 10, 7

Circle 5: 13, 7, 9, 8, 6, 5

Circle 6: 12, ?, 9, 10, 8, 11

Which number is missing from the last circle?

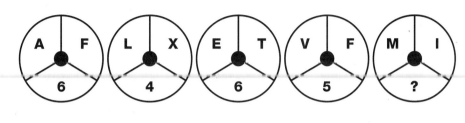

Which number replaces the question mark and completes the puzzle?

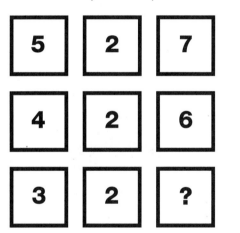

Which letter completes the puzzle?

Which number replaces the question mark and completes the puzzle?

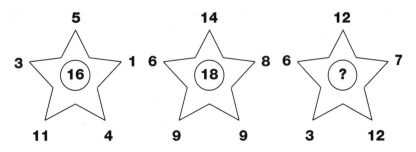

L
E
V
E
L

20

357

PUZZLE 20

Following a logical sequence, can you complete this puzzle?

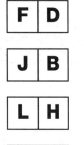

B	C
E	A
F	D
J	B
L	H
?	?

PUZZLE 21

Which number completes the puzzle?

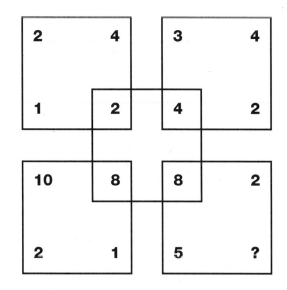

2	4	3	4
1	2	4	2
10	8	8	2
2	1	5	?

PUZZLE 22

Which letters complete the puzzle?

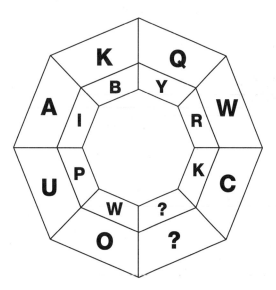

PUZZLE 23

What is missing from these circles?

3	8
18	13

2	8
20	14

 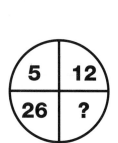

1	9
25	17

5	12
26	?

What is missing from the last circle?

(2) (6) (8)

(3) (7) (3)

(6) (4) (?)

Which letter completes the puzzle?

Which number replaces the question mark and completes the puzzle?

6	2	17
1	4	11
3	7	?

| 9 | 11 | 13 | 17 | 21 |

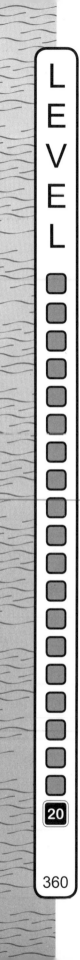

PUZZLE 27

In this sequence of letters what needs to be added to make the puzzle correct?

PUZZLE 28

Which letter completes the puzzle?

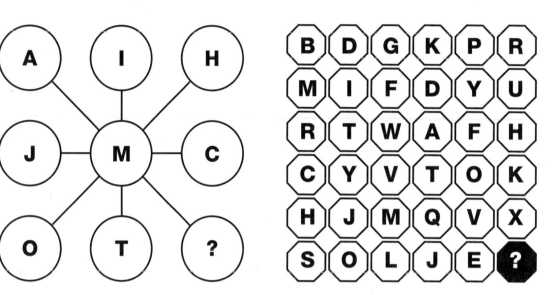

PUZZLE 29

Which number completes this puzzle?

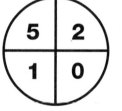

Which letters are missing from the last oval?

AJM

HOT

MVY

TAF

YHK

?

Which letter completes the puzzle?

E	K
W	P

Z	H
S	N

W	B
Q	I

W	D
R	?

32 PUZZLE

Which numbers replace the question mark
and complete the puzzle?

8	11
14	10
19	16
30	21
46	32
?	?

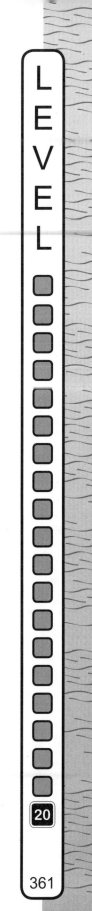

L
E
V
E
L

20

33 PUZZLE

Which number completes the puzzle?

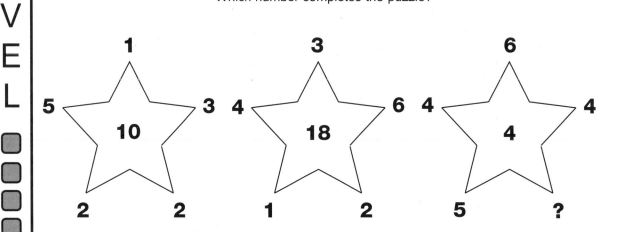

34 PUZZLE

What is missing from this arrangement of circles?

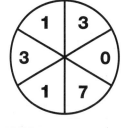

35 PUZZLE

Following a logical sequence, can you complete this puzzle?

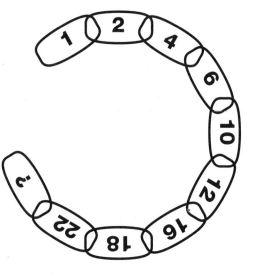

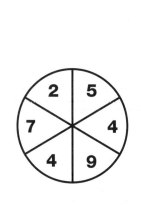

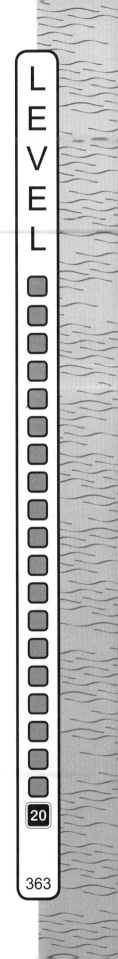

Which of the lower letters replace the question mark to complete this puzzle?

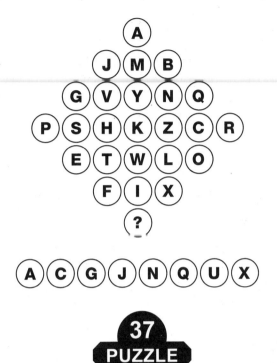

Which number replaces the question mark and completes the puzzle?

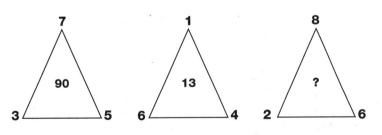

Which letter completes the puzzle?

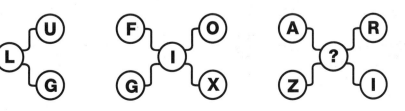

363

PUZZLE 39

Which number completes the puzzle?

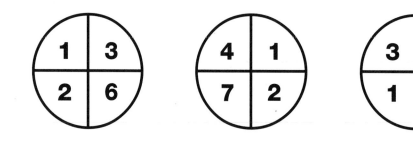

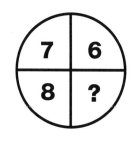

PUZZLE 40

In this sequence of letters what needs to be added to make the puzzle correct?

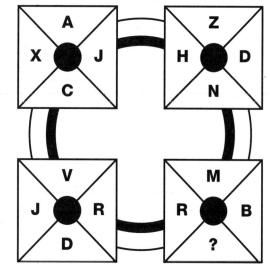

PUZZLE 41

Following a logical sequence, can you complete this puzzle?

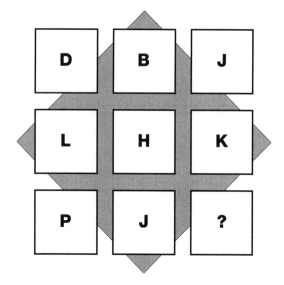

PUZZLE 42

What is missing from the last star?

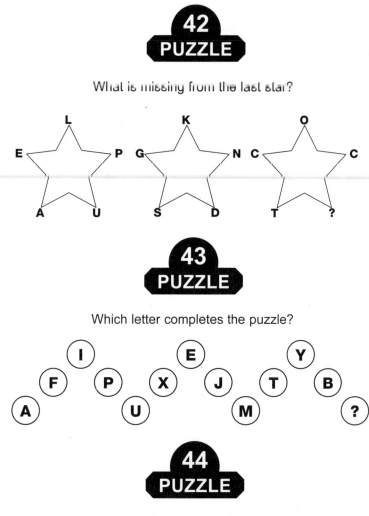

PUZZLE 43

Which letter completes the puzzle?

PUZZLE 44

Which number replaces the question mark and completes the puzzle?

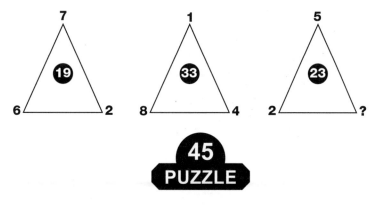

PUZZLE 45

Which letter replaces the question mark and completes the puzzle?

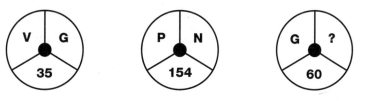

PUZZLE 46

Which letter completes the puzzle?

PUZZLE 47

Which number is missing?

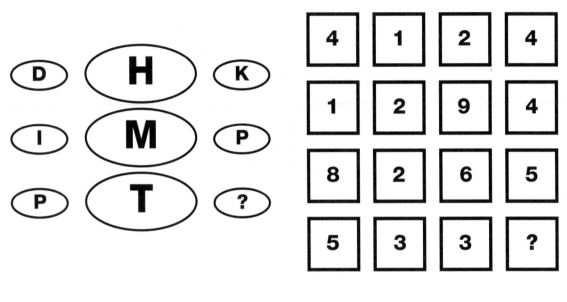

PUZZLE 48

Which of the lower patters replaces the question mark to complete the puzzle?

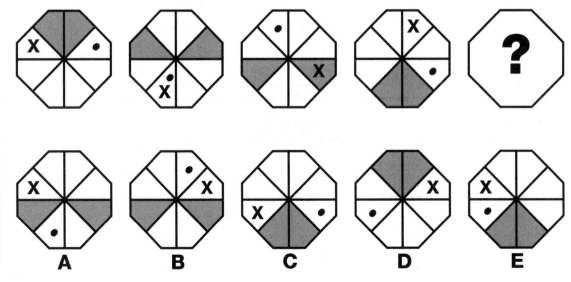

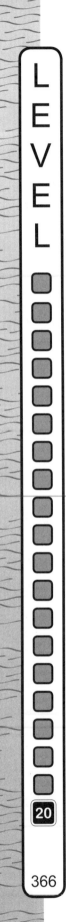

20

366

PUZZLE 49

Which segment fills the missing gap to complete the puzzle?

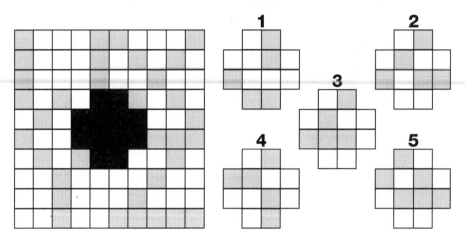

PUZZLE 50

Which number replaces the question mark and completes the puzzle?

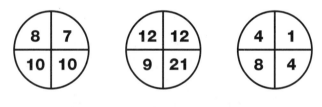

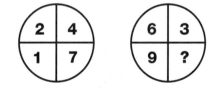

PUZZLE 51

Which number replaces the question mark and completes the puzzle?

LEVEL

20

367

52 PUZZLE

Which pattern completes the puzzle?

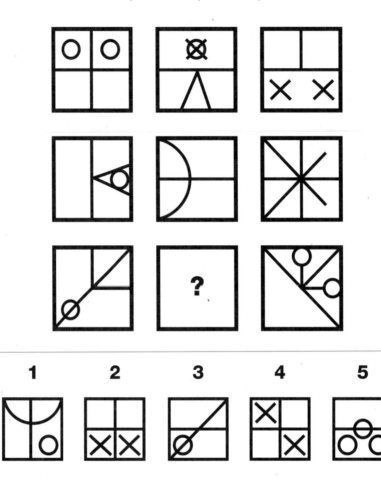

1 **2** **3** **4** **5**

53 PUZZLE

Following a logical sequence, can you complete this puzzle?

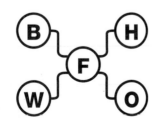 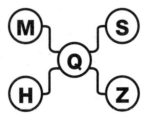 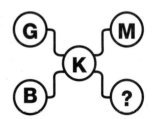

SOLUTIONS

LEVEL 1

1 – D
The number of black dots in each grid increases by 1 each time, starting with the top left grid and working to the right, top row then bottom row.

2 – A
Starting with the watch on the left, add 42 minutes to the time shown to give the time on the next watch to the right.

3 – 7
Starting on the top row, and taking straight lines through the centre, subtract the central number from the upper number, and put the result in the corresponding lower box.

4 – 7
Working in rows, add the left and right hand numbers to give a 2-digit result, and write this in the middle two boxes.

5 – 9
In each row, the central number equals the average of the left and right hand numbers.

6 – G
In each row, multiply the numerical values of the left and right hand letters together to give the value in the centre.

7 – 6
Looking at the diagram in rows, the central circle equals half the sum of the numbers in the other circles to the left and right of the centre.

8 – 9
The number at the centre of each triangle equals the sum of the lower two numbers minus the top number.

9 – 8
In each triangle, divide the top number by the lower left number and add the lower right number to give the value in the centre of the triangle.

10 – 7
In each segment, the difference between the outer and inner numbers is always 9, with the highest and lowest numbers alternating from the inner ring to the outer ring each step.

11 – 5
Working in rows, the central number equals the average of the left and right hand values.

12 – C
In each figure, letters move in sequence, clockwise, in steps given by the numerical value of the central letter.

13 – E
Starting with Y and moving clockwise, letters move backwards through the alphabet in steps of 2 letters, then 3 then 4, etc.

14 – 19
As you move diagonally down, numbers follow the sequence of Prime Numbers.

15 – V
As you move down the diagram, letters move through the alphabet in steps of 4.

16 – 16
Starting bottom left and moving clockwise around the triangle, numbers follow the sequence of Square Numbers.

17 – 25
Starting top left and moving clockwise, numbers increase by 6 each step.

18 – N
Working in rows from left to right, letters advance through the alphabet skipping 1 letter in the top row, 2 letters in the middle, and 3 for the bottom.

19 – 7
All rows and columns add up to 15.

20 – K
Starting at the top left, and working in a Z shape around the circles, letters follow the alphabetic sequence, skipping 1, 2, 3, etc, letters at a time.

21 – M
Working in rows, add together the numerical values of the left and right hand letters to give the numerical value of the central letter.

22 – O
In each segment of the diagram are a pair of letters, one of which is the same distance from the start of the alphabet as the other is from the end.

23 – 39
Working from top to bottom, double each number and subtract 1, then 2, then 3, etc.

24 – 4
Working in columns, the sum of the numbers in each column is always 14.

25 – A
As you move to the right, add 24 minutes to each time value.

26 – G
In each shape, the numbers around the outside are all multiples of the number indicated by the numerical value of the letter in the centre.

27 – V
Starting at the top left, and moving clockwise in a spiral towards the centre, letters move through the alphabet in steps of 5.

28 – K
The numerical values of the letters in opposite segments of the circle always add up to 17.

29 – 6
The numbers in each row and column add up to 15.

30 – Hand pointing to 5
Starting with the top clock and moving anti-clockwise around the others, the hour hand moves back 1 hour, then 2, then 3, etc, while the minute hand moves forward 10 minutes each time.

31 – 9
Working in columns, from top to bottom, double each number and subtract 1 to give the next value down.

32 – 50
As you move to the right, double each number, and subtract 2.

33 – W
Starting on the left, letters advance by 3 places, then 4, 5 and 6.

34 – 28
As you descend, add 3 to the previous number, then 4, 5, 6, etc.

35 – 81
Starting at the top, numbers follow the sequence of Square Numbers of 5, 6, 7, 8 and 9.

SOLUTIONS

36 – 40
Moving from left to right, numbers increase by 2,3,4 and 5.

37 – K
As you move down, the numerical value of the letters follows the sequence of Prime Numbers.

38 – 9
In each square of the diagram, the sum of the numbers is always 22.

39 – 16
Moving clockwise, around alternate segments in the chain, one sequence decreases by 1, 2, 3 and 4 each time, while the other increases by 2, 3, 4 and 5.

40 – A
Starting on the left, and moving right, the 2 shaded segments rotate in opposite directions, 1 space at a time, while the dot moves one segment anticlockwise.

41 – F
Taking each grid of dots in the top row, rotate the pattern by 180° to form the pattern in the bottom row.

42 – 7
Starting with the numbers in the top row, and following straight lines through the centre of the diagram, subtract the middle number from the top number to give the corresponding value on the bottom row.

43 – A
Writing each letter as its numerical value and working in rows, add the top 2-digit number to the bottom 2-digit number to give the 3-digit result in the centre.

44 – 13
In each circle, starting at the top left segment, numbers increase, as you move clockwise, by 2 for the upper left circle, 3 for the upper right, 4 for the lower right and 5 for the lower left.

45 – G
The numerical values of the letters in each row add up to 26 each time.

46 – Four of Diamonds
In each row, the sum of the black cards is always 7, the sum of the red cards is always 8. One card from each suit appears in each row.

47 – 2
Taking the horizontal line of circles through the centre of the diagram, these values equal the sum of the two adjacent numbers in the pattern.

48 – W
Starting at the top left and moving down, then right one column and up, etc in a snakes and ladders pattern, letters move through the alphabet 4 letters at a time.

49 – 3
In each group of 3 numbers, the lower number equals the average of the top two numbers.

50 – 1
Starting in the top left, and moving clockwise, the sum of the digits in each circle follows the sequence 6, 7, 8 and 9.

51 – I
Starting in the top left, and moving clockwise in a spiral, towards the centre, letters move through the alphabet, skipping 1 letter at a time.

52 –

53 – 3
Add the top row of digits together, to give the result on the left hand centre space, and add the bottom row of digits together to give the result on the right hand centre space.

54 – 1
Reading each row as a 3-digit number, the rows follow the sequence of Square Numbers, from 17 to 19.

55 – 8,1
Reading each row as 3 separate 2-digit numbers, the central number equals the average of the left and right hand numbers.

56 – A: 58   B: 86
In the first oval, all numbers are multiples of 8, and in the second, they are all multiples of 7.

57 – B
In each row, add the numerical value of the left and right hand letters together and write the letter with the reverse alphabetical value in the centre.

58 –

Working in columns, top to bottom, the last circle represents the addition of the shaded segments from the top 3 circles. If a shaded segment appears in one of the top 3 circles, it appears in the same position in the bottom circle. If there are 2 shaded segments in the same position in the upper circles, then they cancel out, and become blank in the bottom circle. Shaded squares in all three remain shaded.

59 –

Reading from left to right, the sum of the dots on each domino follows the sequence 2, 4, 6, 8, 10, 12.

LEVEL 2

1 – T
Starting at F and moving anti-clockwise, letters move through the alphabet in steps of 2, 3, 4, 5, etc.

2 – Q
Adding the three numbers in each square together gives the numerical value of the letter at the centre of each square.

3 – Hammer
Hammer = 1
File = 3
Axe = 5

4 – 1
Reading each pair of numbers as a 2-digit number, they follow the sequence of Square Numbers from 6 to 9.

SOLUTIONS

5 – 7
Working in rows, from top to bottom, the sum of the digits in each row follows the sequence 10, 15, 20, 25, 30.

6 – F
All patterns of dots are symmetrical around a central vertical axis.

7 – 7
Taking the top row of circles, numbers in the central circle equal the sum of the numbers in corresponding segments of the left and right hand circles. In the bottom row, numbers in the central circle equal the difference between numbers in corresponding segments of the left and right hand circles.

8 – P
Starting at the top left circle, and moving right, then down one row and moving left, in a snakes and ladders pattern, letters move through the alphabet in steps of 2, 3 and 4, repeating this pattern all the way down

9 – Points to the 2 (6:10)
Starting at the top, and working clockwise around the faces, the time shown increases by 1 hour and 20 minutes each step.

10 – 2
In each circle, add the numbers in the top two segments together, to get a 2-digit number, and write this number in the lower two segments.

11 – H
Starting top left, and moving down, then up the centre, and down the right hand column, to finish bottom right, the letters follow the alphabetic sequence, 6 letters at time.

12 – 4
In each row, square the central number to give a 2-digit value, and write this value in the left and right hand spaces.

13 – 253
Starting at the top left, and moving through the diagram in a Z shape, double each number and add 3 to give the next number along.

14 – U
Multiply the numerical values of the letters in each pair to give the 3-digit result in the spaces above.

15 – 51
Moving to the right, double each number and subtract 3 to give the next number along.

16 – 2
Starting with the 10 at the top, one set of numbers increases by 3 each time, written in alternate boxes as you move down the diagram, and the other set of numbers decreases by 2, written in the boxes remaining.

17 – S
Working clockwise around each shape, letters advance by steps of 3, 4 and 5, working from left to right.

18 – J
Letters in each position on the left triangle increase by steps of 4, 5, 6 and 7 as you move to the next triangle to the right, returning to the start of the alphabet once reaching Z.

19 – I
Working from left to right, letters in corresponding segments of the circles move through the alphabet in steps of 2, 3 and 4, with their relative positions moving one place clockwise at each step.

20 – 6
On each row, add the values of the left hand and central boxes to give the value in the right hand box.

21 – V
Starting at the top left, and moving anti-clockwise around the figure, letters advance through the alphabet 5 letters at a time.

22 – 10
In each star diagram, the number in the centre equals the sum of the top three numbers, subtracting the sum of the bottom two numbers.

23 – J
Working in columns, add the numerical values of the top two letters, to give the numerical value of the lower letter.

24 – 9
Starting with the numbers on the top row, add the central number to each one, giving the results on the bottom row.

25 – A
Starting with the letter L and moving clockwise, letters advance through the alphabet 5 letters at a time.

26 – 3
The sum of the digits on each side of the triangle equals 15.

27 – 23
Starting top left, and moving down in columns from left to right, the numbers follow the sequence of Prime Numbers from 2 to 23.

28 – 10
Numbers in the segments of the left hand circle equal the difference between numbers in corresponding segments of the two right hand circles.

29 – E
Using the numerical value of each letter, in each column, the value of the central letter equals the sum of the values of the top and bottom letters.

30 – 62
Starting at the top, add 1 to the first number, and multiply by 2 to give the next number down.

31 – 2
Working in columns, the numbers in each column add up to 17.

32 – D
The sum of the digits shown on each watch increase by 2 each step.

33 – 1,143
Starting with the top 3-digit number, the first digit increases by 2 as you descend, from 1 to 11. The middle digit decreases by 1 each time, and the right digit alternates between 5 and 3.

34 – 6
Numbers in the lower left circle equal the sum of the numbers in corresponding segments of the top two circles, and numbers in the lower right circle equal the difference of the numbers in corresponding segments of the top two circles.

35 – N
The alphabetical value of the letters in the left hand column follows through the sequence of Prime Numbers, with the letters in the right hand column representing the corresponding reverse alphabetical values.

SOLUTIONS

36 – 5
Working in rows, from left to right, take the outer shape in each box and place it in the centre of the other shapes, moving 1 place to the right each time.

37 – 5
In each diagram, the numbers around the outside increase, in sequence, by value given in the central circle.

38 – I
Starting on the left, and moving down in columns from left to right, letters are written in alphabetical sequence, in steps of 4 letters at a time.

39 – 4
In each triangle, the central number equals the sum of the three outer numbers divided by two.

40 – B
In each diagram, letters are written in sequence, starting in the top left circle and moving clockwise around the other 3 outer circles, in steps given by the numerical value of the central letter each time.

41 – H
Starting top left and working down, then top right and down again, the letters follow the alphabetic sequence, 4 letters at a time.

42 – 40
Each horizontal row of numbers follows the sequence of multiples of 3, 4 and 5.

43 – 49
As you move to the right, the numbers follow the sequence of multiples of 7.

44 – 6
Reading the top line as a 3-digit number, subtract the central number, and write the 3-digit result in the lower circles.

45 – 5
In each star, the central number equals the difference between the sum of the even numbers and the sum of the odd numbers from the points of the star.

46 – U
Starting on the left, and moving along the line to the right, letters follow the alphabetic sequence, in steps of 1,2,3 and then 4, before repeating the sequence.

47 – 5
In each triangle, the number at the apex of the triangle equals the average of the two numbers at the bottom.

48 – 22
In each circle, the lower number equals the product of the top two numbers, subtracting 3 for the left hand circle, 4 for the middle, and 5 for the right hand circle.

49 – H
Starting at the apex of each triangle, and moving around it clockwise, letters skip 3 places for the left hand triangle, 4 places for the middle, and 5 places for the right hand triangle.

50 – Minute hand points to 4.
Starting with the top clock face, and moving clockwise around the other 3, the hour hand advances 3 hours at a time, and the minute hand moves back 20 minutes each time.

51 – X
Starting top left, and moving clockwise around the 4 circles, add 2 to the value of each letter to give the values of the letters in the next circle around.

52 – 2
Splitting the large square into quarters, each quarter features the same pattern of letters.

53 – Y
Starting in the top left circle, and following a W pattern through the others, letters in corresponding segments of the circles follow the alphabetical sequence in steps of 4 letters.

54 – W
Working from left to right, letters move forwards 7 places, then back 2. Repeat this sequence until the end.

55 – 78
Starting on the left, double each number, and add 2.

56 – M
Starting on A and moving clockwise, letters advance through the alphabet 3 at a time.

57 –

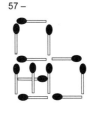

58 – 3
Add adjacent numbers on the bottom row, and put the results in the box directly above, take the difference between adjacent boxes on the next row up, putting the results in the box directly above again. Finally, take the sum of these two boxes, putting the result in the top box.

LEVEL **3**

1 – 4
In each diamond, add the left and right hand numbers together, and subtract this sum from the top number to give the value at the bottom.

2 – 7
In each row of the diagram, the central value equals the sum of the differences between the left hand pair of numbers and the right hand pair of numbers.

3 – 7
The inner digit in each segment equals the sum of the two numbers in the outer part of the opposite segment.

4 – K
In each row, the product of the left and right hand numbers equals the sum of the numerical values of the three letters.

5 – 10:25
Starting at the top, and moving clockwise around the faces, the minute hand moves forward by 10 minutes in each step, and the hour hand moves back one hour.

6 – Top O, P; bottom R, Q
Starting in the top left, take 2x2 squares, with letters of the alphabet written in sequence clockwise, around these groups of 4. Work from left to right, top to bottom, writing in sequence around the block.

SOLUTIONS

7 – 3
Working from left to right, top row then bottom, the sum of the numbers in each circle increases by multiples of 5.

8 – H
Start at the top and move down, taking single letters or pairs of letters that appear on the same horizontal line. The sum of the numerical values of the letters in each line increases by 2 as you go down, from 18 to 26.

9 – 0
In each row of each grid, multiply the left and right hand numbers together to give a digit value, and write this value in the two centre boxes.

10 – 18
Starting at the top, and working down add the first two numbers together, to give the next number down.

11 – 19
In each row of the diagram, the sum of the numbers is 19.

12 – 8
Working in columns, the number at the bottom of each row equals the difference between the upper two numbers.

13 – 1
In each row, the central number is equal to the sum of the right and left hand numbers.

14 – F
In each star shape, the sum of the numerical values of the letters bounded by one triangle is equal to that of the other triangle.

15 – 5
In each H shape, the central number is equal to the difference between the sum of the 3 left hand numbers and the sum of the 3 right hand numbers.

16 – E
In each stick-man diagram, start on the left foot and move around the other limbs in a clockwise direction. The letters advance through the alphabet in steps given by the numerical value of the letter on the head of the diagram.

17 – B
Add together the numerical values of the letters in corresponding positions on the left and right hand triangles, and put the letter with this value in corresponding segments of the centre triangle.

18 – E
Each shape is rotationally symmetrical by 180° around its central point.

19 – 5
In each diagram, the average of the top two numbers, and the bottom two numbers is written in the central circle.

20 – 7
Reading each row of the diagram as a series of 3-digit numbers, the centre 3-digit number equals the sum of the top 2 numbers, and the sum of the lower 2 numbers.

21 – A
Start on the centre left of the diagram, and move in a clockwise spiral towards the centre. Letters advance through the alphabet in steps of 2, 3, 4, etc.

22 – 22
Add together values in corresponding positions of the top two crosses, and put the results in the lower left cross. Calculate the difference between values in corresponding positions of the top two crosses, and put the results in the lower right cross. Finally, add together the values in corresponding positions of the lower two crosses to give the values in the central cross.

23 – 5
In each triangle, subtract the two lower numbers from the number at the top of the triangle to give the value at the centre.

24 – 63
Working in rows from left to right, and from top to bottom, numbers follow the sequence of multiples of 7, 8 and 9.

25 – 4
Working top to bottom, reading each pair of numbers as a two digit value, the values follow the sequence of Square Numbers, from 3 to 8.

26 – T
Working through the diagram in columns, left to right, The sum of the numerical values of the letters in each column follows the sequence 17, 18, 19 and 20.

27 – 2
Start with the top left hand box, and move around the others in a clockwise spiral towards the centre. Read each box as a pair of 2-digit numbers, one above the other. The sum of the 2-digit numbers in each box follows the sequence 55, 60, 65, 70 and 75.

28 – 9 of Clubs
Taking red cards as positive values and black cards as negative values, in each column of the diagram, the lower card value equals the sum of the two upper card values. The suits are used alternately in each column.

29 – 26
Moving clockwise from 5, numbers increase in value by 6, 7, 8, 9, etc.

30 – 4
Working in rows, add the centre and right hand digits together, to give the result on the left.

31 – 3
Working in columns, the sum of the 3 numbers always equals 17.

32 – 5
Taking the top three circles, add together the lower two circles, to get the value in the upper circle, repeat this formula for the three circles on the bottom left and bottom right.

33 – Z
Read the diagram as a whole grid of 4x4 squares. Starting on the bottom left square, move clockwise around the outside of the whole square, with letters written in sequence, skipping 4 letters at a time. Repeat this instruction for the small inner square.

34 – X
Start at the top left and move in alternate boxes from left to right, then down one row and to the left, in a snakes and ladders pattern. Letters advance through the alphabet in steps of 2, 3, 4...8, before repeating this pattern.

35 – To the 4
Start with the top left clock face, and move around the others in a clockwise direction. The value pointed to by the hour hand equals the value pointed to by the minute hand, subtracting 4 for the first clock face, 5 for the next, then 6, etc.

SOLUTIONS

36 – H
In each row, the numerical value of the central letter equals the difference between the sum of the numerical values of the two left hand letters and the sum of the numerical values of the two right hand letters.

37 – 5
Starting with the numbers on the top row, and moving in straight lines through the centre, multiply the top numbers by the central number, putting the results in the lower circles.

38 – 4
In each row, the centre number equals the difference between the left and right hand numbers.

39 – 31
Starting on the bottom row, add adjacent numbers together to give the value in the box above them. Repeat up to the apex of the pyramid.

40 – 343
As you move to the right, the numbers follow the cube values of the numbers 3 to 7.

41 -

Owner	Property	Road	Value
Mavis	Flat	Shangri-La Way	£75,000
Harold	Bungalow	Meadow Rise	£100,000
Bette	Terrace	Honeysuckle Row	£40,000

42 – C
Start on the far left of the diagram and move around it in a clockwise direction. Letters advance through the alphabet in steps of 8 then 9, repeating this pattern all the way around.

43 – 12
The value at each corner of the diagram equals the difference between the sums of the numerical values of the letters in the boxes adjacent to the corner.

44 – C
Working in rows, superimpose the pattern of dots in the left and right hand grids, to form the middle grid.

45 – 57
Starting on the left, and working to the right, add 3 to the first number, then 6 to the next, repeat this sequence, alternately adding 3 then 6.

46 – C

47 – E
Working through the diagram in rows, from top to bottom, the sum of the numerical values of the letters in each row follows the sequence 15, 20, 25, 30, 35.

48 – Joe has 7 marbles, John has 5.

49 –
From left to right: Two of Diamonds, Five of Hearts, Ace of Hearts, Ace of Spades
Working in columns, the sum of the top three cards, and the sum of the lower three cards equals the value of the central card. Also, there are two cards of each suit in each row, apart from spades of which there is only one.

50 – 6
In each group of circles, the centre number equals the average of the four surrounding numbers.

51 – 11
Split the left and right hand circles in half, vertically. The sum of the numbers in the left hand half of the left circle appears in the top left hand segment of the middle circle, and the sum of the numbers in the right hand half of the left hand circle appears in the bottom left hand segment of the middle circle. Repeat this pattern for the right hand circle.

52 – 7
In each diagram, the sum of the upper left and upper middle numbers is written in the centre box, and the sum of the upper right and upper middle numbers is written in the lower central box.

53 – 5
Taking pairs of dominoes, one from the extreme left of the row and one from the extreme right of the row, both show the same point total. Repeat this sequence, working towards the centre.

54 – 13
The boxes follow the sequence of Prime Numbers.

55 –

56 – 1: Q, 2: R
In the first oval, all the letters have even numerical values, and in the second, they are all odd.

57 – 24
Moving clockwise around the circle, numbers follow the sequence of multiples of 6.

LEVEL 4

1 – 6
The number at the centre of each segment equals the sum of the numbers on the outside of the opposite segment.

2 – I
Letters are arranged in each square in alphabetical order, skipping 5 letters at a time. The letter bounded by the central square carries on this sequence, but using the reverse alphabetical value.

3 – Alarm clock
The Alarm clock = 7, the Adaptor = 5 and the Bulb = 2

4 – 23
Looking at the diagram as two columns, numbers in the left hand column increase by 5, 6, 7, etc, and numbers in the right hand column increase by 6, 7, 8, etc.

5 – M
In each segment, the sum of the numerical values of the outer and inner letters equals 26.

6 – 12
Working in rows, add 4 to the left hand digit to give the central value, and add 6 to this digit, to give the right hand value.

SOLUTIONS

7 – E
Starting with the letter Q and moving clockwise, letters move backwards through the alphabet, in steps of 3, then 4, 5, 6, etc.

8 – 4
Working in columns, multiply the top and middle numbers together, and write the result in the lower box.

9 – 5
The numbers in the lower circles equal the numbers in corresponding segments in the upper circles multiplied by two, then subtract 3 for the left hand circle, 4 for the middle and 5 for the right hand circle.

10 – O
In each row, letters follow the alphabetic sequence, in steps of 4 letters each time for the first row, 5 letters for the second, then 6, 7, etc.

11 – D
Working from left to right, top row then bottom, the number of dots in each pattern increases by 1 each time, from 8 to 13.

12 – 4:47
Starting on the left, and moving right, add 1 to each digit and rotate their positions to the left.

13 – 2
The diagram represents a multiplication sum : 128 x 2 = 256

14 – H
In each row of the diagram, the numerical values of the letters add up to 26.

15 – 96
Moving from left to right, numbers follow the sequence of Square Numbers, from 6 to 10, subtracting 4 each time.

16 – 9
Reading each pair of numbers in a row as a 2-digit number, values increase by 6 each time.

17 – 1
Starting on the top row, and moving in straight lines through the central circle, values on the bottom row equal the difference between numbers on the top row and the central number.

18 – W
Starting at the top, add 5 and 3 alternating as you work down.

19 – J
Starting from B and moving clockwise, add the numerical values of the first two letters to give the value of the next letter around.

20 – K
Starting on the left, the numerical values of the letters follow the sequence of Prime Numbers.

21 – X
In each circle, start with the top left segment, and move clockwise around the other segments. The value of each letter increases by 5 for the first circle, 6 for the next, then 7, 8 and 9.

22 – 3
Reading each column as a 3-digit number, moving from left to right, the columns follow the sequence of cube numbers of 5, 6 and 7.

23 – A
Converting each letter to its numerical value, the diagram represents a subtraction sum: 247 – 54 = 193.

24 – 13
In each star, the central value equals the sum of the upper and lower digits on each star, subtracting the sum of the left and right hand digits.

25 – G
Starting with the left hand triangle, letters increase in steps of 2, 3 and 4, as you move to the right, with their positions moving 1 place clockwise around the points of the triangles.

26 – (From top to bottom) 5, 2, 3
Each row contains 4 two-digit numbers, which follow the sequence of multiples of 4 for the top row, 5 for the next, then 6, 7, 8 and 9.

27 – T
Starting on the top left, and moving in an anti-clockwise spiral towards the centre, letters advance through the alphabet by 3 letters at a time.

28 – 6
In each circle, double the numbers on the left hand side and put the result in the opposite segment on the right hand side.

29 – W
Looking at the diagram in columns, letters in the first column are written with 2 straight lines, in the second column they contain 3 straight lines, and letters in the right hand column are written with 4 straight lines.

30 – 12
In each star, add up the digits at each point of the star, and divide by 3 to give the value at the centre.

31 – A
If you take the numerical values of each letter, all columns and rows add up to 15.

32 – T
Starting at the top, and working down through each row, left to right, letters follow the alphabetic sequence, in steps of 5.

33 – 4
Adding up the digits in each oval shape, as you move down the column this total increases by 2 each time, from 12 to 22.

34 – 1
In each circle, the number in the lower left segment equals the sum of the numbers in the top two segments, and the number in the lower right circle equals the difference between the numbers in the top two segments.

35 – C
If you convert each letter to its numerical value, and read pairs of numbers as 2-digit values, the values follow the sequence of multiples of 7.

36 – 5
In each diagram, the top left number minus the central number gives the top right number, and the bottom left added to the central number gives the bottom right.

37 – 25
In each circle, moving clockwise, double the first number and subtract 1 to give the next value.

38 – Q
In each star, letters move clockwise around the points skipping 1, 2, 3 and 4 letters each time.

SOLUTIONS

39 – 2
Working in rows, the sum of numbers in each row follows the sequence 5, 10, 15, 20, 15, 10, 5.

40 – 9
Working from left to right, the sum of the two smaller numbers on each triangle equals the third number.

41 – G
Following lines of circles across all 3 diagrams, letters in the top line follow the alphabetic sequence, in steps of 4 letters at a time. Letters in the central line advance 5 letters, and in the bottom line, 6 letters.

42 – R
Working in columns, letters follow the alphabetic sequence, in steps of 3 for the left hand column, 4 for the middle and 5 for the right hand column.

43 –

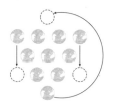

44 – 19
Starting top left, and moving in a Z shape around the circles, the numbers follow the sequence of Prime Numbers.

45 –   A: 15   B: 4
In the first oval, all numbers are even, and in the second all numbers are odd.

46 – 6
The number in the centre of each star equals the average of the surrounding 5 numbers.

47 – F
Moving from left to right, letters move though the alphabet in sequence, skipping 12 letters, then 11, 10, 9, 8, etc.

48 – 43
In each triangle, multiply the lower two numbers together and add the upper number to give the value at the centre.

49 – D
The numerical values of the letters in each circle add up to 20.

50 – 16
Working clockwise, from 2, double each number to give the next one along.

51 – L
Working in rows, from left to right, letters are arranged in consecutive, alphabetical order.

52 – 5
Starting with the top left circle, and moving clockwise around the other 3, double each number and subtract 1 to give the values in the corresponding segments of the next circle around.

53 – Bananas
Bananas = 3
Cabbage = 2
Marrow = 4

54 – 4
Each row of the grid contains each of the 10 digits, 0 to 9, written in a random order.

55 – 6
Numbers in the segments of the lower left circle equal the sum of the numbers in the upper left and central circles. Numbers in the segments of the lower right circle equal the sum of the numbers in corresponding segments of the upper right and central circles.

56 – S
Taking the numerical value of each letter, they follow the sequence of Prime Numbers.

57 –

Starting at the top, and moving clockwise, the minute hand moves back 25 minutes each time, while the hour hand moves forward 3 hours each time.

58 – A
Working in columns, the sum of the numerical values of the letters is written in the lower box.

59 – 2
Splitting the diagram vertically and horizontally, the same 5x5 pattern is displayed in each quarter.

1 – A
Working from left to right, top row then bottom row, the first grid contains a sequence of 2 black dots and a sequence of 3. The next grid contains one of 3 and one of 4. Continue, adding 1 to each sequence every time.

2 – E
The sum of the separate digits on each watch increases by 2 as you move to the right.

3 – 12
Working in columns, the sum of the top two numbers equals the value of the lower number.

4 – D
Starting in the top square, and working clockwise around it, letters advance through the alphabet, skipping 2 letters. Moving clockwise to the next square, the sequence of letters skips 3, then 4, etc.

5 – 11
Starting top left, and taking pairs of adjacent numbers, their total is always 20.

6 – O
Starting at the top left, and working in columns from left to right, letters follow the alphabetic sequence, skipping 4 letters at a time.

7 – N
Starting with the A on the left hand side, move around the shape in a clockwise spiral towards the centre. Letters advance through the alphabet in steps of 4, 5 then 6, repeating this pattern all the way around.

8 – 10
The numbers on the points of the lower triangle equal the sum of the numbers on corresponding points of the upper two triangles.

SOLUTIONS

9 – Seven of Hearts
Working in columns, the sum of the left hand column equals 20, the next along totals 19, then 18, then 17. One card from each suit appears in each row.

10 – 6
In each diagram, multiply the top left number by the central one, to give the lower left number, and subtract the central number from the top right one to give the lower right number.

11 – G
Starting with A and C, as you move clockwise, the numerical value of the next letter equals the sum of the preceding two letters.

12 – O
As you move down, letters appear in alphabetical order, skipping those letters only written with straight lines.

13 – 37
As you move down, subtract 3 from the previous number, then 5, 7, 9 and 11.

14 – 11
Taking any side of the triangle, the sum of the two corner digits is written in one of the circles on that side, and the difference is written in the other circle.

15 – 20
Starting at the top, add 7 to the first number to give the next one, then subtract 2 for the one after that, continue the same sequence for the remaining numbers.

16 – J
Starting in the top left, and moving clockwise in a spiral towards the centre, letters follow the alphabetic sequence, in steps of 8 letters.

17 – B
Working from left to right, add 1 to each digit and rotate from one place to the left.

18 – W
Starting at the top left, and moving to the right, then down one row and to the left, etc in a snakes and ladders pattern, letters advance through the alphabet by 5 steps, then back 2, repeating this pattern for the rest of the diagram.

19 – S
Taking pairs of letters in the inner and outer segments of each eighth of the diagram, the numerical values total 20.

20 – 90
As you move down, the numbers represent multiples of 12, subtracting 1, for the first step, adding 2 for the second, subtracting 3 for the third, adding 4 for the next, etc.

21 – 9
Reading each horizontal line as a 4-digit number, add together the top two rows to give the result in the third row, and subtract the first row number from the second to give the result in the fourth row.

22 – 2
In each circle, the sum of the segments always equals 13.

23 – A
Working in rows, from left to right, the number of dots in each pattern increases by 2 each time.

24 – K
Working in columns, add together the numerical values of the first and second letters, and put the letter with the reverse alphabetical value of this sum in the bottom space.

25 – S
Starting with the G, move clockwise around the circle, in steps of 3 letters, then 4, 5, 6 and 7.

26 – 3
In each row, the sum of the digits is 10.

27 – Hour hand is pointing to 2.
Multiply the hour hand value by 2 and add the minute hand value. This total is always 15.

28 – 23
In each triangle, the value at the centre equals the sum of the square roots of the three numbers at each corner.

29 – 80
As you move right, numbers show the sequence of Square Numbers, from 5 to 9, subtracting 1 each time.

30 – A: Odd = 28, B: Odd = 74
In the first oval, all numbers are multiples of 3, and in the second, all numbers are a multiple of 4.

31 – 21
Each number represents the numerical value of the vowels in the alphabet.

32 – I
As you move down, letters are written in alphabetical order, skipping any letters written with curved lines.

33 – F
Starting with the top segment of the top left square and moving clockwise around the other 3 squares, letters move through the alphabet in steps of 2, with the positions moving one place clockwise each time. Letters in the next segment of the top left square follow the same pattern, in steps of 3 letters, etc.

34 – 26
Moving clockwise around the chain, numbers increase by 4, then 3, then 2, before repeating this pattern.

35 – 5
The value in each corner circle equals the sum of the values in the two adjacent circles.

36 – 2
Working in columns, the top number equals the sum of the lower two numbers.

37 – N
Working in rows, add the numerical values of the left hand and central letters, to give the value of the right hand letter.

38 – J
Starting with the letters on the top row, and moving in straight lines through the centre, add the numerical values of the top and central letters to give the value of the letters on the bottom row.

39 – 42
Starting in the top left and moving in a Z shape around the diagram, each number equals the sum of the previous 2 numbers.

40 – D
Starting with the bottom right letter and moving in a clockwise spiral around the diagram towards the centre, letters advance through the alphabet six letters at a time.

SOLUTIONS

41 – 2
The numbers in the segments of the top left circle equal the sum of the numbers in corresponding segments of the lower two circles, and the numbers in the top right circle equal the difference between numbers in corresponding segments of the lower two circles.

42 – 1
Starting with the bottom line of the triangle and moving up, the sum of the digits in each line decreases by 5 each time, from 20 to 5.

43 – 4
In each square, the average of the three outer numbers is written in the centre square.

44 – D
Working in columns, the sum of the numerical values of the letters in each column equals 22.

45 – 4
All columns and rows add up to 15.

46 – 43
The numbers increase by 7 each step.

47 – C
Converting each letter to its numerical value, and reading pairs of circles as 2-digit numbers, arranged in two vertical columns, numbers follow the sequence of multiples of 7, starting with 14 and ending with 63.

48 – 2
Numbers in the squares of the top middle figure equal the sum of the numbers in corresponding squares of the other 3 figures.

49 – 3
In each circle, the sum of the 4 numbers equals 16.

50 – Pencil sharpener
Calculator = 6
Pencil sharpener = 8
Tape dispenser = 9

51 – Jack of Spades
Starting at the top left, and working in rows, top to bottom, cards follow sequence, in steps of 1, 2, 3, etc., until 8, then 7, 6, 5, etc., There is 1 card of each suit in each line.

52 – Left to right, 28, 40, 54
In each row, numbers increase by 2, then 3, 4, 5, etc, as you go down.

53 – 13
Starting at the top left and working down, then to the right and up, and finally to the right and down in a zigzag shape, numbers follow the repeated sequence, subtracting 1 then adding 3, etc.

54 – 4
Working in rows from top to bottom, the sum of the digits in each row increases by 2 each time, from 20 to 30.

55 –   A: 15   B: 38
In the first oval, all numbers are Prime Numbers.
In the second oval, all numbers are Square Numbers.

56 – 3
Working in rows, the number in the central oval equals the sum of the left and right hand numbers, divided by 3.

57 – 1
Working in rows, starting on the left, reflect the first box around the vertical axis, to give the central box, and invert the colours of this box, to give the one on the right.

58 – M
Working from left to right, add 2 to the value of the first letter to give the next, add 4 to get the one after that, repeat this sequence, alternately adding 2 then 4.

bottom row, with the letters written in alphabetical order in steps of 5 letters at a time.

2 – L
Moving down the first column, up the second, down the third, etc letters increase by 7 in each alternate circles.

3 – 7
In each segment of the circle, multiply the outer 2 numbers together and subtract the sum of the outer 2 numbers in the opposite segment to give the value in the inner grey segment.

4 – Q
Converting all letters to their numerical values, the middle section of each row of the diagram contains a list of letters which are common multiples of a number, given by the value of the letter in the right hand box. One letter In each row does not follow this sequence, and is put in the left hand box.

5 – E
If you superimpose the top row of grids onto the corresponding grids in the bottom row, the resulting pattern of dots form the letters X, Y and Z.

6 – 22
Square the two numbers at the bottom of each triangle, add them together and subtract the number at the top, to give the value in the middle of the triangle.

7 – S
Join pairs of letters at opposite sides of the diagram, with lines which run through the centre. The sum of the numerical values of the pairs of letters is always 25.

8 – 1
Values in the lower left table equal the sums of the values in corresponding positions of the top two tables, and values in the lower right table equal the difference in values in corresponding positions of the top two tables.

9 – 18
Starting at the top and moving clockwise, add the first two numbers together, and subtract 2, to give the next number in the sequence.

1 – M
The 4 diagrams as a whole contain 2 sequences of letters.
The first starts at the top of the top left hand diamond, and goes vertically downwards, then up to the top of the top right hand diamond and down again. Letters in this sequence are written in alphabetical order, in steps of 4 letters at a time.
The second sequence starts on the left hand segment of the upper left diamond and moves in horizontal lines from left to right, top row then

SOLUTIONS

10 – 1
In each row, the sum of the odd numbers equals the even number.

11 – H
Taking pairs of letters from corresponding positions on the left and right hand stars, add their numerical values together, and put the result in the central star.

12 – N
In each star, start at the bottom and move anti-clockwise around the points. Letters follow the alphabetic sequence, in steps of 8 letters, for the left hand circle, 9 for the central one and 10 for the right hand circle.

13 – 3
In each diagram, the numerical value of the left hand letter equals the product of the upper and lower left hand numbers, and the right hand letter equals the product of the upper and lower right hand numbers. The numerical value of the central letter equals the sum of the numerical values of the left and right hand letters.

14 – 5
In each diagram, the sum of the three upper numbers equals the product of the two lower numbers.

15 – P
Start at the top of the left hand triangle and move in horizontal lines, from left to right, across all the triangles at once, top to bottom. Letters are written in sequence, skipping 2 letters, then 3, then 4, before repeating this sequence.

16 – 8
In each diagram, the difference between the sum of the odd numbers and the sum of the even numbers is written in the central circle.

17 – 9
In each diagram, the number in the centre equals the difference between the sum of the upper and lower pair of numbers.

18 – 5
In each circle, numbers in opposite segments add up to the same value 10 for top left, 11 for top right, 12 for bottom left and 13 for bottom right.

19 – S
Working in columns, add the numerical values of the top two letters together to give the value of the lower letter.

20 – B
In each row of the diagram, the reverse alphabetical value of the central letter equals the sum of the left and right hand digits.

21 – 12
The diagram contains two diamonds of 3x3 circles, arranged side by side, with the central 4 circles overlapping. Starting in the central left circle of each diamond, the numbers from 1 to 9 are written in lines, moving up and to the right. In the circles where the diamonds overlap, the values are added together to give the ones shown on the final diagram.

22 – 1
Add up the four outer numbers and place your answer in the centre square of the shape one place clockwise.

23 – 26
In each circle, multiply the lowest number by two, and add two, to give the next number.

24 – 1
In each triangle, multiply the bottom two numbers, and subtract the top number, to give the result in the centre of the triangle.

25 – N
Working in columns from top to bottom, left to right, letters are written in alphabetic sequence, in steps of 3 letters, then 4, then 5, etc.

26 – I
Starting with the letters in the top left square, and moving around the other squares in a clockwise spiral towards the centre, letters advance through the alphabet in steps of 4 letters at a time, with the relative positions of each letter moving 1/4 turn clockwise at each step.

27 – King of Clubs
Start at the top left of the diagram and move to the right, then down one row and to the left, etc. in a snakes and ladders pattern. The value of each card increases by 5 each time, with their suit following the sequence of hearts, clubs, diamonds and spades.

28 – 6
Reading each row as a 3 figure number, the top row minus the middle row equals the bottom row.

29 – X
Working top to bottom, left to right, letters follow the alphabetic sequence, skipping 1 letter, 2 letters, 3, 4, 5, etc.

30 – 17
Values in each box equal the sum of the two numbers in the boxes directly underneath, minus 1.

31 – D
Taking pairs of letters in opposite segments, one is the same distance from the start of the alphabet as the other is from the end.

32 – B
Start with the top left square and move clockwise around the others. The sum of the numerical values of the letters in each square follows the sequence 20, 25, 30 and 35.

33 – 1
Split the grid in half vertically, to give two columns, 3 squares wide. Working from top to bottom, left then right, and reading each 3 square row as a whole 3-digit number, the columns follow the sequence of Square Numbers, from 10 to 21.

34 – Five minutes to Ten
Start with the top left clock face, and move around the others clockwise. The minute hand moves backwards by 15 minutes, then 20, then 25, etc, while the hour hand moves forward 2 hours, then 3, then 4, etc.

35 – G
Convert each letter to its numerical value, and read each pair of values as 2-digit numbers. In each row, the number in the centre equals the difference between the 2-digit values on the left and right.

36 – G
Starting at the apex of the triangle, and moving clockwise, letters advance through the alphabet 6 at a time.

37 – 18
Working from top to bottom, subtract 5 from the first number to give the next one down, then subtract 7, 9, 11 and 13 to give the rest.

SOLUTIONS

38 – 10
Starting with the top two rows, add the numbers on the top together to give the lower left value, and multiply them together to give the lower right value. Repeat this sequence for the third and fourth row.

39 – Q
Letters on opposite sides of the central circle are the same number of letters away from the letter given in the central circle.

40 –

Theatre group	Play	Opening month	Ticket price
Piecrust	Macbeth	June	£10
RSC	Othello	October	£3
CAD	Julius Caesar	March	£6

41 – 1
Taking any series of 3 numbers in a straight line in the diagram, their total is always 19.

42 – Y
Start in the top left hand corner and move anti clockwise around the perimeter of the square. Letters are written in alphabetical order, skipping 1 letter, then 2 letters, then 3, etc.

43 – R
Starting at the top, letters advance through the alphabet, in steps of 5, 6, 7 and 8.

44 – A, Q
In the outer circle, starting at C and moving clockwise, letters advance through the alphabet in steps of 2, 3, 4, etc. In the inner circle, starting at M and moving anti-clockwise, letters also advance through the alphabet in steps of 2, 3, 4, etc.

45 – K
Starting bottom left, and moving to alternate squares clockwise around the triangle, letters advance in steps of 3.

46 –

47 – A

48 – 1
Working from the top row, add the values in adjacent boxes and put this sum in the box directly below, working towards the centre. Repeat this pattern starting at the bottom row as well.

49 – The bottle is worth 50p, and the perfume is worth £9.50

50 – 1: N, 2: O
In the first oval, the numerical values of the letters are all multiples of 3, and in the second, they are all multiples of 4.

51 –

In each clock face, the hour hand points to the number which is double the minute hand's number.

52 – 109
Working from left to right, multiply each number by two, and add 3 to get the next number along.

53 – E
Divide the circle, horizontally and vertically, into quarters. The numerical values of letters in adjacent segments in each quarter add up to 20.

54 – S
Start with the top left circle, and move in horizontal lines from left to right, top to bottom, across all 4 shapes. Letters are written in alphabetical order, in steps of 5 letters at a time.

55 – H
Start at the top left segment of the left hand circle and move clockwise, then to the middle circle and move anti-clockwise, and finally to the right hand circle and move clockwise again. Letters are written in alphabetical order, in steps of 4 letters at a time.

56 – V
Starting with the upper left box of the left hand diagram, and moving to the right, letters follow the alphabetical order, 5 letters at a time. A second sequence starts from the middle of this row and goes down, with letters following the alphabetical order, 6 at a time. Repeat this pattern for the other diagrams, using steps of 6 and 7, 7 and 8, and 8 and 9 letters.

57 – 5
Take each half of the dominoes separately, add together the spots shown on the first two pieces to get the third domino, then add together the spot from the second and third to get the fourth, etc. Return to 0 whenever the spot total exceeds 6.

58 – 2
The four numbers at the corners of the diagram, and the four numbers at the centre of each side, add up to 20.

59 – 251
Starting at the top, and working down, double each number and add 5 to give the next value down.

60 – Lion
Lion = 3
Whale = 5
Goat = 9

1 – E
In each row, the left hand grid is symmetrical around a vertical axis, the central grid is symmetrical about a horizontal axis, and the right hand grid is symmetrical about a diagonal axis, running bottom left to top right.

2 – A
As you move from left to right, the time shown on each watch decreases by 12 minutes, then 24, 36 and 48.

3 – N
Starting with the letters in the top row, subtract the numerical value of the central letter to give the letters on the bottom row.

4 – J
Starting at the top and moving anti-clockwise letters advance through the alphabet, 8 letters at a time.

5 – D
Starting on the left, and moving to the right, the dot moves from one segment to the one directly opposite, and back again. The # moves 1 place anticlockwise each time, as does the shaded segment.

SOLUTIONS

6 – 4
Working in rows, from top to bottom, the sum of the digits in each row increases by 2 each time, from 8 to 16.

7 – 9
Working clockwise around the 3 triangles, the sum of the outer digits in each triangle is written in the centre of the triangle one place clockwise.

8 – 11
The value of the numbers in the lower triangle equals the sum of the numbers, in corresponding positions on the upper two triangles.

9 – 7
Find the difference between corresponding pairs of numbers, on the left and central stars, and put the result in the same position on the right hand star.

10 – N
Starting with B and moving clockwise, letters advance through the alphabet in steps of 2, then 4, 6, 8 and 10.

11 – 72
Numbers follow the sequence of Square Numbers, from 1 to 6, multiplying each one by 2.

12 – 68
As you move down, multiply each number by 2 and subtract 4.

13 – 2
The sum of the numbers along each side of the triangle is always 15.

14 – G
Starting on the left, and working down in columns, if possible, and moving to the right, letters follow alphabetic sequence, in steps of 2, 3 and 4, 2, 3 and 4, etc.

15 – N
Starting on the left, and moving to the corresponding segment on the right, letters increase in value by steps of 4, 5 and 6.

16 – I
Convert each letter into its numerical value, and read each row as a 3-digit number. Rows follow the sequence of Square Numbers from 15 to 17.

17 – W
Starting with the top left outer segment and moving clockwise, letters advance through the alphabet in steps of 4, then 5, 6, 7, etc. The letters in the inner segments follow the same pattern, but move anti-clockwise.

18 – 16
As you move downwards, numbers increase by 3, then 2, then 1, before repeating this pattern.

19 – 7
The numbers in each row of the diagram add up to 18.

20 – 89
Starting top left and working down, then up the central column and down the right hand column, add the first two numbers together, to give the next along.

21 –

On each clock face, the numbers pointed to by the hour and minute hands add up to 9.

22 – J
Starting on the left, the letters follow the alphabetic sequence, skipping letters written with only straight lines.

23 – 100
For the left hand column, double each number, and subtract 3 to give the next number down, for the right hand column, double each number and subtract 4 to give the next number down.

24 – G
Starting at the top left and working anti-clockwise towards the centre in a spiral, letters advance through the alphabet in steps of 8 at a time.

25 – F
Taking pairs of letters in adjacent segments, their numerical values always add up to 10.

26 – 2
The sum of the 4 digits at the corners of the diagram is 17, as is the sum of the 4 digits in the middle of each side of the diagram.

27 – Hour hand points to 8
Starting with the top clock face, and moving clockwise around the others, the minute hand moves forward 15 minutes, while the hour hand moves back 2 hours each time.

28 – 6
Values on the lower triangle equal the difference between corresponding numbers on the upper two triangles.

29 – 9
In each triangle, the value in the centre equals the sum of the odd numbers around the points of the triangle, minus the sum of the even numbers.

30 – V
Each hexagon is filled with the letter of the alphabet you find one place after the vowels.

31 – J
Adding 1 to the numerical values of each letter gives the sequence of Prime Numbers.

32 – 9
Starting with the top left square, and moving clockwise around the other 3, the sum of the digits in each square follows the sequence 20, 19, 18, 17.

33 – 71
As you move clockwise around the diagram, add the previous 2 numbers together and subtract 3 to give the next number in the chain.

34 – 3
Splitting the diagram into 3 smaller triangles one at the top and two at left and right, each containing 3 numbers, the sum of the number is always 15.

35 – Z
Starting top left, and moving clockwise around the outer squares, and then the inner squares, letters advance through the alphabet, skipping 3 letters at a time.

36 – 18
Starting at the top, multiply the two digits of each number together and subtract this total, to give the next value down.

37 – E
In each row the sum of the numerical values of each letter is always 20.

SOLUTIONS

38 – 9
Starting with the numbers in the top row, and following straight lines through the centre of the diagram, subtract 3 from the number and put the result in the corresponding lower circle.

39 – 2
Reading the top and bottom lines as 2-digit numbers, multiply these together to give the 3-digit result, written in the middle.

40 – 1
Numbers in the segments of the lower left circle equal the sum of the digits in corresponding segments of the upper circles. Numbers in the lower right circle equal the difference between numbers in corresponding segments of the upper circles.

41 – F
Starting with the B on the lower right of the triangle, and following the diagram round in a clockwise direction, letters move through the alphabet in steps of 5.

42 – 18
Starting top left, and moving clockwise, subtract 3 from an odd number to give the next value, and subtract 5 from an even number in the same way.

43 – M
Starting top left, and moving clockwise around the diagram. Letters follow the alphabetic sequence, skipping any letters written with curved lines.

44 – 10
Working from top to bottom, add the first two numbers together, and subtract 3 to give the next value down.

45 -

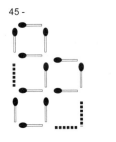

46 – A
In each column of the diagram, the sum of the numerical values of the letters is always 25.

47 – W
In each group of 3 squares, starting on the upper left and moving clockwise around the other 2 squares, letters follow the alphabetic sequence in steps of 6 for the left hand diagram, 7 for the upper middle, 8 for the right hand diagram and 9 for the lower one.

48 – 6
Add the numerical values of the letters in each row together, and put this 2-digit value in the line underneath.

49 – J
In each row, add numerical values of the left and right hand letters, and write the letter with the reverse alphabetical value in the centre square.

50 – 11
Working in rows, from left to right, multiply each number by 2 and add 1 to give the next number along.

51 –

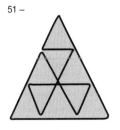

52 – 56
Starting at the top left and moving down, then to the right and up, in a snakes and ladders pattern, add the first two numbers together and subtract 1 to get the next in the sequence.

53 – 6
Divide the whole diagram into 4 equal quarters, each comprising of a 3x3 square. The sequence of numbers in the top left quarter is repeated in each of the other quarters, but increasing by 1 each time as you move clockwise.

54 – A: 11   B: 16
In the first oval, each number represents the numerical value of the vowels in the alphabet. In the second oval, each number represents the numerical value of letters of the alphabet written with only straight lines.

55 – 4
In each row of the diagram, the sum of the left and right hand digits, minus the central digit is always 8.

56 –

Start in the top left, and move in rows to the right, then down a row and to the left, etc in a snakes and ladders pattern, using the repeated sequence of symbols:

X X > > > 0 0 < + + <.

LEVEL 8

1 – 8
Divide the circle, horizontally and vertically, to give 4 quarters. The sum of the numbers in the segments of each quarter equals 11.

2 – K
Add 6 to the numerical value of each of the larger letters, and write the letter with this value in the smaller square diagonally opposite.

3 – Carriage
Carriage = 2
Car = 3
Bus = 6

4 – D
Converting each letter to its numerical value and reading each line as a 2-digit number, the numbers follow the sequence of multiples of 6, from 36 to 54.

5 – W
Follow lines of letters, from the middle left, diagonally up to the right, then diagonally down to the right, etc, letters follow the alphabetic sequence, in steps of 2, 3, 4, etc.

6 – 20
In each diagram, the central number equals the sum of the 4 surrounding numbers.

7 – O
Starting with the left hand circle in the top row, add 4 to the numerical value of

each letter and write the letter with this value in the corresponding segment of the lower left circle. Continue this pattern, adding 5 to the letter values in the central circle, and 6 in the right hand circle.

8 – A
Start at the top left of the diagram, and work down the left hand column, then along one space to the right and up the next column, in a snakes and ladders pattern, write the following repeated sequence of letters: A C P R F D U.

9 – 4
In each triangle, the central number equals the average of the 3 surrounding numbers.

10 – 11
Numbers on third star are the difference between corresponding numbers on first two.

11 – 6
Working through the diagram in rows, and reading each row as a whole number, the diagram represents a subtraction sum: 203 – 7 = 196

12 – C
Convert each letter to it's numerical value, and read horizontal lines as 2 or 3-digit numbers. Add the top 3-digit number to the 2-digit number below to give 200, repeat this pattern for the 3 and 2-digit numbers underneath.

13 – 39
Moving from left to right, add 6 to the first number to get the next, then 8, 10 and 12 to complete the sequence.

14 – 16
Starting with the top left number, and working down one row at a time, alternating between left and right, double the number each time. Repeat this sequence, starting with the top right number.

15 – O
In each set of 3 boxes, the sum of the numerical values of top two letters equals the numerical value of the lower letter.

16 – E
As you move to the right, subtract 1 from the hour value, and add 12 to the minute value. If the minutes exceeds 60, the hour value increases by 1.

17 – 1
Numbers in segments of the central circle equal the difference between the sum of the numbers in corresponding segments of the left two and right two circles.

18 – 10
Working in columns, starting with the top number, add 4 to give the next value down, and add 5 to give the one under that.

19 – Z
Starting at the top left of the diagram, and moving around it in a Z shape, letters follow the alphabetic sequence, in steps of 6 letters at a time.

20 – 11
In each star, add together the top 3 numbers, and subtract the lower 2 numbers, to give the value in the centre of each star.

21 – H
Starting top left, and moving clockwise, letters move forward by 6 places, then 7, 8, 9, etc.

22 – H
In each row, add the numerical values of the left and right hand letters, to give the reverse alphabetical value of the central letter.

23 – (top to bottom) A, H
Working in rows, from left to right, letters move through the alphabet in steps of 4 for the top row, 5 for the next, then 6, 7, 8, etc.

24 – T
Working in rows, the numerical value of the letter in the right hand column equals the sum of the numerical values of the letters in the left and central columns.

25 – T
Starting with the top left segment of each circle, and moving clockwise, letters follow the alphabetic sequence, in steps of 3 letters for the top circle, 4 letters for the left hand circle, and 5 letters for the bottom circle.

26 – 3
In each row of the diagram, add the left and right hand digits together and add 2 to give the result in the centre.

27 – 9
Working in columns, starting at the top, double each number and subtract 1 to give the next number down.

28 – Z
Starting top left, and working in columns, from left to right, letters move through the alphabet 5 places at a time.

29 – D
Working from left to right, one shaded section moves 1 segment clockwise at each turn, while the other moves two segments anticlockwise at each turn.

30 – 601
Starting at the top, double each number and add 7 to give the next number down.

31 – L
In each circle, the numerical value of the letter in the lower left quarter equals the sum of the numerical values of the upper 2 letters, and the numerical value of the letter in the lower right quarter equals the difference between the numerical values of the upper 2 letters.

32 – 92
Working from top to bottom, left to right, add together the first two numbers and subtract 3 to give the next value along.

33 – 4
In each triangle, multiply the lower two numbers together, and subtract the top number, to give the result in the middle.

34 – Q
Starting on the left, letters advance 10 places in the alphabet as you move to the right, returning to the start of the alphabet after reaching Z.

35 – Q
Starting at the top, add 6 to the numerical value of the top letter to give the value of the next one down. Then 7, 8, 9, etc for the rest.

36 – E
Start at the top of the diagram, and work through each row from left to right. Letters move through the alphabet, In steps of 3 letters, then 4, 5 and 6 letters, repeating this sequence.

SOLUTIONS

37 – 47
Starting at the top on the left, and working in rows across the 3 triangles, values increase by 2, then 3, then 4, etc.

38 – P
In each diagram, starting on the top left and moving clockwise in a spiral towards the centre, letters increase in value by 3 for the left hand diagram, 4 for the middle, and 5 for the right hand diagram.

39 – 9
Working in rows, the central value equals half the sum of the other digits in each row.

40 –

41 – 9
In each star, the average of the outer 3 numbers is written in the centre of the star.

42 – V
Starting with the B in the top left, and moving left to right across the diagram in horizontal lines, letters advance through the alphabet in steps of 6 letters at a time.

43 – 21
In each triangle, add the lower 2 digits together and multiply by the upper digit to give the result in the centre.

44 – 1
In each circle, add together the numbers in the left and right hand segments, and subtract 2 to give the result in the lower segment.

45 – Y
Starting at the top and working down, the numerical value of each letter follows the sequence of Square Numbers, from 1 to 5.

46 – 159
Starting top left and moving clockwise, double each number and add 1 to give the next number round.

47 – 23
The reverse numerical value of each letter is written in the inner square is on the opposite side.

48 – 16
Starting from the top, add the left and right hand numbers together, to give the lower left hand number, and calculate their difference to give the lower right hand number.

49 – 1
Start at the top left and move down, then along one space to the right and up the next column, in a snakes and ladders pattern. Letters are written in alternate squares, in steps of 2 letters at a time.

50 – 1
Using the numbers in the segments of the lower two circles, the numbers in the upper left circle equal the sum of the numbers in corresponding segments of the lower 2 circles, the numbers in the upper central circle equal the difference between numbers in corresponding segments of the lower 2 circles, and the numbers in the upper right circle equal the product of the numbers in corresponding segments of the lower 2 circles.

51 – 0
Working from left to right and reading each pair of numbers as a 2-digit value, these values represent the sequence of multiples of 7, starting at 49 and finishing on 70.

52 – 35
Starting on the left, double each number, and subtract 3, to give the next number along.

53 – 13
Starting bottom left, and working clockwise, in a spiral, numbers increase by 5, then decrease by 2 alternately.

54 – 7
Starting in the top left circle and moving clockwise add 2 to each number, and rotate their positions 90° clockwise to give the values in the next circle.

55 –

Starting with the top clock face, and moving clockwise around the others, the minute hand moves forward by 1 division, then 2, then 3, while the hour hand moves forward by 2 divisions, then 3, then 4.

LEVEL 9

1 – K
In each square, start with the left hand segment, and move clockwise around the others. Letters are written in alphabetical order in steps of 10 for the top left square, 11 for the top right, 12 for the lower left and 13 for the lower right.

2 – 3
Work through the diagram in columns. The value in the centre of each column equals the difference between the sum of the top 2 numbers and the bottom two numbers.

3 – 2
In each slice of the circle, the difference between the outer and middle numbers is written in the inner segment of the opposite slice.

4 – J
Start on the top left of the diagram and work from top to bottom in columns, from left to right. Letters are written in alphabetic order, in a repeated sequence of steps of 5, 6 and 7.

5 – 1
Starting with each odd number, multiply by 2 and add 4 to give the number in the opposite segment.

6 – V
Working from left to right, letters represent the vowels in the alphabet, displaced 1 letter forward.

7 – 2
In each row, multiply the left and right hand numbers together, and subtract 5 to give the central number.

8 – U
Starting at the top left and working in rows, left to right, the letters follow the alphabetic sequence skipping 1 letter, then 2 letters, then 3, 4, etc.

9 – 4
Calculate the difference between adjacent numbers in the centre of each

oval and put the result in the space between the two ovals in the opposite side of the diagram.

10 – 11
Numbers in the top right hand grid equal the sum of the numbers in corresponding positions in the upper and lower left hand grids, and numbers in the lower right hand grid equal the difference between numbers in corresponding positions in the upper and lower left hand grids.

11 – 16
Using pairs of numbers in corresponding positions on the upper two triangles, calculate their difference, and put the result in the corresponding position on the lower triangle.

12 – C
In each diagram, starting with the right hand point, and working clockwise, letters advance through the alphabet in steps given by the numerical value of the top letter.

13 – Q
Treat each star as 2 intersecting triangles, and start on the top or the left of each triangle in each star and move clockwise around it. Letters are written in alphabetical order in steps of 6 for the left hand star, 7 for the central one and 8 for the right hand star.

14 – 6
In each diagram, the central value equals the difference between the sums of the numbers in the left hand column and the sums of the numbers in the right hand column.

15 – 14
In each diagram, the number at the top equals the average of the four smaller numbers.

16 – 11
In each triangular group of circles, start with the longest row and add together 3 adjacent values and put this sum in the circle directly above or below the centre of the 3 values. Continue this sequence towards the apex of each triangle.

17 – 5
Split the diagram twice, along a vertical axis, to give three columns, two spaces wide. Starting at the top

of each column, reading each row as 2-digit numbers, add the top two numbers together to give the next 2-digit number down. Continue this pattern for each column.

18 – 51
Working from top to bottom, multiply each number by 2 and subtract 3 to give the next value down.

19 – 5
Split the diagram into quarters, of 5x5 squares. There is a random pattern of numbers in the top left square, which is rotated 90° anticlockwise around the other three quarters.

20 – 6
Calculating the sum of the 3 numbers in each row, from top to bottom, the rows follow the sequence of 11, 13, 15, etc.

21 – 5
Start with the row of 4 numbers in the centre of the diagram, and add adjacent pairs of numbers together, putting the results in the circles directly above. Repeat this pattern for the next row up. Next, calculate the difference between adjacent numbers in the middle row, putting the results in the circles directly below. Repeat this pattern for the next row down.

22 – F
Two sequences are used in these five grids, both only using the lines containing three letters. Firstly, move along the horizontal lines from top left to bottom right in steps of four, starting with the A. Secondly, move down the vertical lines in steps of six, starting with the E. Whenever two numbers cross add the numerical values together and put the solution in the middle of each cross.

23 – C
On each watch face, the digits add up to 15.

24 – C
Working from left to right, the X moves clockwise, one segment at a time, while the • moves anticlockwise. One shaded segment moves two spaces clockwise each time, while the other moves three spaces anticlockwise.

25 – 6
Start with the numbers along the top

right diagonal of the diagram, and add pairs of adjacent numbers together, putting the result in the square to the lower left of the original pair of numbers. Continue in this way towards the lower left hand corner.

26 – 14
Add together numbers in corresponding segments of the upper 2 squares, and put the results in the middle square. Numbers in the lower left square equal the product of the upper left and central squares, and numbers in the lower right square equal the product of the upper right and central squares.

27 – 7 (any suit)
Taking the value of Aces as 1 and all court cards as 10, In each column of the diagram, the value of the sum of the 3 cards is always 21.

28 – R
Working from top to bottom, double the numerical value of each letter, and subtract two, to give the next letter down.

29 – 6
The sum of each outer number and the inner number of the opposite segment is always 15.

30 – 29
In each triangle, multiply the lower two numbers and subtract the number at the top, to give the value at the centre.

31 – K
Start with the top left hand segment of the top left hand square, and move around the other squares in a clockwise direction. Letters are written in sequence in steps of 5 letters at a time for the top left segment, 6 letters for the top right, 7 for the bottom right and 8 for the bottom left. The relative positions of the letters in each sequence move 1 segment clockwise at every step.

32 – S
Split the diagram into 3 rows, each 2 boxes high. In the top double row, letters are written in sequence, from left to right, alternating between the upper and lower row, in steps of 6 letters at a time. The middle row follows the same sequence, in steps of 7 letters at a time, as does the bottom row, in steps of 8 letters.

SOLUTIONS

33 – To the 5
Start with the top left clock face, and move around the others in a clockwise direction. The sum of the numbers pointed to by the hour and minute hand follows the sequence 14, 15, 16, 17 and 18.

34 – B
In each row, the value in the centre equals the difference between the sum of the numerical values of the pair of letters to the left and the pair of letters to the right.

35 – J
In each row, the difference between the sum of the left hand numbers and the sum of the right hand numbers equals the numerical value of the letter in the centre.

36 – 6
In each star, add the top 3 numbers together to give a 2-digit number, and write these two digits on the lower points of the star.

37 –

Gardener	Injury	Crop	Day
Bob	Back	Roses	Wednesday
Mike	Knee	Apples	Friday
Sandra	Elbow	Potatoes	Monday

38 – K
The sum of the letters in the three adjacent circles on each side of the diagram is always 30.

39 – D
The diagram contains 3 sets of 4 letters – one set of outer corner letters, one set of inner corner letters, and one set of letters on each side of the square. The numerical values of the letters in each set add up to 40.

40 – N
The difference between the numerical values of the bottom letters is written at the top of each triangle.

41 – 9
The numbers in the segments in the central circle equal the sum of the numbers in corresponding segments of the left and right hand circles.

42 – C

43 – D
Start with the C at the centre of the diagram and follow 2 sequences of letters, both clockwise from the C, one around the upper half of the diagram, and one around the lower half. Letters in the upper half advance through the alphabet in steps of 7 letters at a time, and letters in the lower half advance in steps of 9.

44 – 7 people

45 – 0
In each diagram, reading the top and bottom pair of numbers as two digit values the centre number is the difference between them.

46 – 4
Working in columns, the sum of the even numbers equals the sum of the odd numbers.

47 -

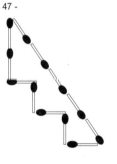

48 – X
In each diagram, the central letter falls midway between the left and right hand letters, and the top and bottom letters.

49 – 4
Split the left and right hand circles into 2 halves vertically. The numerical value of the letter in the upper left segment of the central circle equals the sum of the numbers in the left half of the left hand circle, and the letter in the lower left equals the sum of the numbers in the right half of the left hand circle. Repeat this pattern for the right hand circle.

50 – I
Start on the upper left of each diagram, and move to the right, then down the last 2 boxes in the centre. Letters are written in alphabetical order, in steps of 5 for the left hand diagram, 6 for the next, then 7, then 8.

51 – 3
Starting on the left and working to the right, take pairs of dominoes and calculate the sum of the dots they are displaying. This sum follows the sequence 3, 6, 9 and 12.

52 – 12
In each shape, starting top left and moving clockwise, numbers increase by 3, then 4.

53 – R
Moving clockwise around the circle, in alternate segments, one group of segments follows the alphabet in steps of 5, the other group in steps of 6.

54 –

8	3	4
1	5	9
6	7	2

LEVEL 10

1 – K
Split the circle into 4 quarters, horizontally and vertically, with 2 segments each. Starting with the top left segment, the sum of the numerical values of the letters in the 2 segments equals 15. The sum of the next pair of segments clockwise equals 16, then 17, then 18.

2 – 9
Taking numbers in diagonally opposite squares, calculate their sum, and put the answer in the small, inner square of the upper number. Calculate their difference, and put this answer in the small, inner square of the lower number.

3 – Doughnut
Doughnut = 4, Eclair = 6, Bun = 7

4 – Q
Taking each pair of letters in each row, the numerical value of one letter equals the inverse numerical value of the other letter.

5 – E
In each diagram starting at the top left and moving clockwise, letters follow the alphabetic sequence, skipping the number of letters each time, as indicated by the numerical number of the central letter.

SOLUTIONS

6 – 10
Take the numerical value of each letter, and add 5 to give the numerical number in the opposite segment.

7 – L
Working in rows, the sum of the numerical values of the left and centre letters equals the numerical value of the right hand letter.

8 – 39
Starting on the left, double the value in each segment; and add 1 to give the values in the circle to the right.

9 – 1
Starting with the 3 circles in the top row, add together values in corresponding segments of the left and right hand halves of the left hand circle, and put the results in corresponding segments of the left hand half of the central circle. Repeat this pattern for the left and right hand segments of the right hand circle.
For the lower row, follow the same pattern, but calculating the differences between values in the left and right hand halves of the left and right hand circles, putting the results in the central circle.

10 – H
Start on the top left of the diagram, and move clockwise in a spiral towards the centre. Letters advance through the alphabet in steps of 5.

11 – 3
In each triangle, the number in the centre is a common denominator for the three surrounding numbers.

12 – H
In each triangle, add up the numerical values of the letters around the outside, to give the reverse numerical value of the letter at the centre.

13 – I
Start at the top left, and work through the diagram in a Z shape, letters move through the alphabet in steps of 6, then 7, then 8, etc.

14 – 1
Taking the top 3 numbers, add them together, and write the 2-digit result in the spaces below. Repeat this pattern for the next set of numbers.

15 – 6
Working from left to right, numbers represent the reverse alphabetical values of the vowels in the alphabet.

16 – 6
Working from top to bottom, and reading each pair of boxes as a 2-digit number, add 10 to the first number to give the next one down, then add 15, and 20 to complete the sequence.

17 -

Starting at the top, and working clockwise around the faces, the minute hand moves back 5, 10 then 15 minutes, while the hour hand moves forward 2 hours then 3 then 4.

18 – Y
Starting at top left, and working in rows to the right, top to bottom, the letters follow the alphabetic sequence, skipping 1, 2 then 3 letters before repeating the sequence.

19 – 15
Working from left to right, top row then bottom, the sum of the two digits in the left hand segments of the circles follow the sequence of multiples of 6, and the sum of the right hand segments follow multiples of 4, starting at 8.

20 – 13
As you move from left to right, the sum of the digits in each circle forms a sequence of multiples of 6, from 6 to 30.

21 – 6
Working in rows, the central value equals the difference between the left and right hand values.

22 – 18
Starting on the top left, and moving clockwise around the diagram, add the first two values together to give the next value along. Repeat this sequence.

23 – 6
For each star, add the outer numbers together and divide by 3 for the left hand, 4 for the centre, and 5 for the right hand, putting the result in the centre.

24 – F
Starting with A in the bottom left, and moving clockwise around the triangle letters follow the alphabetic sequence, jumping 12 letters, then 11, 10, 9, etc.

25 – 17
Starting top left, and moving clockwise in a spiral, towards the centre, add the first two numbers together, then add 1 to give the next number in the sequence.

26 – I
Working in rows, the numerical value of the central letter equals the sum of the numerical values of the left and right hand letters.

27 – 29
Working top to bottom, numbers follow the sequence of Prime Numbers.

28 – O
Start on the top left and move down, then right one space and up, etc in a snakes and ladders pattern. Letters advance through the alphabet in steps of 5.

29 – U
Start with the letters in the left hand circle. Subtract 3 from the numerical values of each letter, and put the letter with this value in the corresponding segments of the upper circle. Repeat this pattern, adding 3 to the numerical values of the letters, and putting the results in corresponding segments of the lower circle.

30 – N
Moving from left to right, top to bottom letters follow alphabetical order, skipping any written with curved lines.

31 – B
If the watch is viewed upside down, the digits appear to be the same.

32 – L
In each star, starting with the top letter and moving clockwise, letters increase in value by 4, 5, 6 and 7.

33 – S
Working from top to bottom, the numerical values of the letters follow the sequence of Prime Numbers, adding 1, then 2, then 3, etc.

SOLUTIONS

34 – 12
Add numbers in corresponding segments of the upper two and lower left circles to give the values in corresponding segments of the lower right circle.

35 – 3
Starting at the top and moving down, reading each pair of boxes as a 2-digit number, add the separate digits to the 2-digit number as a whole, and put the result in the 2 boxes below. Continue this sequence as you move down.

36 – B
Starting with the outer ring, add 5 to the numerical value of each letter and put the result in the inner, 1 place clockwise from the starting letter.

37 – 35
Working from top to bottom, double each number and subtract 3.

38 – 38
Start top left, and working down in columns from left to right, add the first two numbers together and subtract 1 to give the next value down.

39 – 4
In columns, the sum of the even numbers, minus the odd number is 15.

40 – L
Start at the top of the diagram and work in rows, from left to right, top to bottom. Letters move through the alphabet in steps of 4, 5, 6, 7, 8, 9 and 10, before repeating this sequence.

41 – 6
In each triangle, add together the lower two digits and subtract 2 for the left hand triangle, 3 for the middle and 4 for the right hand triangle, putting the result at the apex of the triangle.

42 – 9
Add together the four outer numbers in each diagram. Divide this answer by two to get the middle number.

43 – 10
Starting on the bottom row, the sum of the numbers in each row increases by 1 each time, from 15.

44 – Y
Starting with J, and moving clockwise, letters move through the alphabet in steps of 4, 5, 6, etc.

45 – 89
Starting with 1 and moving clockwise, double each number, and add 1, 2, 3, etc.

46 – U
Work in rows, from left to right, letters follow the alphabetic sequence, skipping 1 letter, then 2 letters.

47 – X
Starting with the top letter in each star, and moving clockwise around the others, letters advance through the alphabet in steps of 8 for the left hand star, 9 for the central star, and 10 for the right hand star.

48 – V
Working from left to right, following the zigzag pattern of the line, letters move through the alphabet skipping 15 letters, then 14, then 13, etc.

49 – 12
In each triangle, the central value equals the average of the 3 values around the outside.

50 – 27
In each circle, multiply the top two numbers together, and divide by 2 for the left hand circle, 3 for the centre, and 4 for the right hand circle, putting the result in the lower segment.

51 – N
Starting in the top left segment of the top left circle, move clockwise around the segments, before moving onto the next circle clockwise, letters move through the alphabet in steps of 2, 3, 4, 5, etc.

52 – M, W, I
Starting at top left, move clockwise around the outer circles. Letters follow the alphabetical sequence in steps of 5. Moving to the next set of circles in, the letters are in steps of 7, and the final central circles, in steps of 9.

53 –

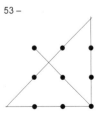

54 –

17	1	15
9	11	13
7	21	5

55 – 2
Split the diagram horizontally and vertically into 4 quarters. A sequence of letters is written in each quarter, following the alphabetic order, 3 letters at a time, starting with the upper left quarter. Add 2 to the values of each letter to give the letters in the next quarter clockwise, then 3, then 4.

56 – 5
Take values in the top left and centre circles and put their sum in corresponding segments of the lower left circle. Take values in the middle and right hand circles, and put their difference into corresponding segments of the lower right circle.

57 – 22
Working from left to right, add numbers in the first two boxes together, and subtract 4, to give the next value along.

58 – Nine of Hearts, Seven of Spades, Nine of Diamonds
Starting top left, and moving clockwise in a spiral to the centre, cards increase in value by 3 each time. The suits of the cards follow a repeated pattern, moving in an anti-clockwise spiral of hearts, clubs, diamonds, spades / spades, diamonds, clubs, hearts.

LEVEL 11

1 – F
In each diagram, the black circles join together to make straight sided polygons. Working from left to right, top row then bottom row, the number of sides in each polygon increases by 1 each time, from 3 to 8.

2 – D
On each watch, the sum of the digits shown equals 8.

3 – 8
In each row and column, add the two even numbers, and subtract the odd, to always give the answer 11.

SOLUTIONS

4 – L
Starting at any corner and moving clockwise, add 4 to the letter value to give the next letter, then add 5 to get the one after that. Repeat this sequence for the other two corners.

5 – 16
Working in rows, multiply the left hand column by 2, and the middle column by 3, add these together, to give the result in the right hand column.

6 – I
In each circle, starting with the top left letter, follow the alphabetic sequence, in steps of 5 letters for the top circle, 6 letters for the left hand circle, and 7 letters for the lower one.

7 – F
Working in rows, from top to bottom, the sum of the numerical values of the letters in each row starts at 12, and increases by 2 as you go down each row.

8 – 32
In each triangle, add together the lower 2 digits, and multiply this by the top digit, to give the value written in the centre of the triangle.

9 – 5
In each triangle, the difference between the lower two numbers equals the difference between the top and middle numbers.

10 – 12
In each diagram, multiply the left hand pair of numbers, then subtract the central number to give the upper right hand value, and add the central number to give the lower right hand value.

11 – G
The numerical values of the letters in opposite segments of the circle add up to 16 each time.

12 – H
Working from top to bottom, letters are written in pairs. Take the 2-digit numerical value of the first letter and add the 2 digits together. Write the letter with this numerical value in the next space down. Continue in this way down the line.

13 – 71
As you move down, numbers follow the sequence of Square Numbers, from 36 to 121, subtracting 10 for the second number, 20 for the next, then 30, etc.

14 – T
Starting in the bottom left corner of the diagram, and moving clockwise, letters follow in alphabetic order, skipping 1 letter, then 2, then 3, etc.

15 – Outer ring, Q, inner ring, M
The letters in the outer rings are the same number of places in from the start of the alphabet as the number in the opposite inner ring are from the end of the alphabet.

16 – 15
Working in columns, the difference between the two odd numbers equals the even number.

17 – 3
In the top row, numbers in the central circle equal the sum of the corresponding segments from the left and right hand circles. On the bottom row, numbers in the central circle equal the difference between the numbers in corresponding segments from the left and right hand circles.

18 – 1
Working in columns, start with the top number, and subtract the number in the centre, to give the result in the bottom row.

19 – V
Starting with the top left outer segment and moving clockwise, alternating between the inner and outer segments, letters advance through the alphabet 5 letters at a time. Starting with the top left inner segment, follow the same pattern, using every sixth letter.

20 – 849
Working from top to bottom, add 1 to each number and multiply by 3 to give the next value down.

21 – 6
Working in rows, from top to bottom, and reading each row as a 4-digit number, rows follow the sequence of Cube Numbers, from 13 to 16.

22 – P
Starting at the bottom of the diagram, and moving clockwise in a spiral, letters follow the alphabetical order, skipping out the vowels.

23 – 7
In each star, the value in the centre equals the average of the five surrounding values.

24 – 8
Starting in the top left and working in columns, add the first two numbers together and add 1 to give the number at the bottom of each row.

25 – L
Starting with the A in the top left segment of the circle, and moving clockwise, letters follow a modified alphabetic sequence. To make the sequence, write the alphabet, removing all letters written with any curved lines, then take alternate letters from this sequence.

26 – 1
The four numbers in the corners of the square, and the four numbers in the middle of each side of the square add up to 21.

27 – The hour hand points to the 4.
The sum of the values pointed to by the hands on each clock equals 12.

28 – 8
In each circle, multiply the top two numbers, and subtract the lower right number, to give the result in the lower left segment.

29 – B
Moving from left to right, the two shaded segments move 1 place around each time, in opposite directions. The circle moves between one segment, and the one directly opposite it, and the star moves 1 place anticlockwise each time.

30 – Y
From left to right, the numerical value of the letters represents the sequence of multiples of 5, from 5 to 25.

31 – M
Working downwards, add the numerical values of the first two letters together, and put the letter with this value in the next box down. Continue in this way down the diagram.

SOLUTIONS

32 – 4
Add up numbers in corresponding segments of each square. The sum of the digits in the left hand segments equals 20, the sum of the upper segments equals 22, the right hand segments equals 24 and the lower segments equal 26.

33 – 22
There are two repeated sequences in the circle. Starting with the first segment and moving clockwise, add 1 to the first number, then 2, 3, and 4, writing the results in alternate segments. Starting with the second segment, add 3 to this number, then 4, 5 and 6, writing these results in the alternate segments left.

34 – Y
Starting at the top left of the left figure, and working to the right in rows across all three diagrams, letters advance through the alphabet, five letters at a time.

35 – M
Reading down each column, letters are ten spaces apart.

36 – Create a tetrahedron (a triangle based pyramid) in 3D

37 – 17
Starting with the bottom left number and moving along the chain, add two, then four and then subtract three. Repeat this sequence until the end.

38 – D
Starting at the top left and moving in a Z shape around the diagram, the numerical value of the letters increases by 6, then 7, then 8, etc.

39 – 2
Reading each row as a whole number, multiply the top 2-digit number by the lower 2-digit number to give the result represented by the middle 3-digit number.

40 – 13
Starting with the top circles, multiply each value by 2 and subtract 3, writing the result in the corresponding segment of the lower circle.

41 6
Numbers in boxes from the second row up equal the average of the 2 numbers in the boxes directly below. Continue to the apex of the triangle.

42 –

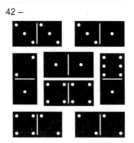

43 - A: 77 B: 18
In the first oval, all numbers are even multiples of 7, in the second, all numbers are odd multiples of 9.

44 – O
Starting at the top, and moving down, letters move forward 3 places, then back 7, etc.

45 – O
Working in rows, from left to right, in the top row add 3 to the numerical value of the first letter to give the next one along, then 4, then 5. In the next row, add 5 to the first letter, then 6, then 7. In the third row, start by adding 7, then 8, then 9, and in the bottom row, add 9, then 10, then 11.

46 – O
In each group of 3 boxes, the numerical value in the lower box equals the average of the numerical values of the letters in the top 2 boxes.

47 – 6, 9, 8
Work in rows, from top to bottom, the sum of the digits in each row follows the sequence 45, 46, 47, etc.

48 – 2
Reading each line of the diagram as a 3-digit number, add the top and middle lines together to give the result on the bottom line.

49 – Y
Split the diagram into equal quarters of 3x3 squares. In each quarter, move around the spaces in a clockwise spiral towards the centre, starting on the top left. Letters follow the alphabetic sequence, in steps of 2 letters, then 3, then 4, etc.

50 – 1: Q 2: D
The first oval contains letters with even numerical values, and the second oval contains letters with odd numerical values.

51 – 1
In each row, add the left and right hand numbers together and subtract 2 to give the number in the centre of the row.

52 -

The group of dominoes is symmetrical around the centre.

LEVEL 12

1 – B
In each square, the sum of the numerical values of the top and bottom letters equals the sum of the left and right hand letters.

2 – 11
Working through the diagram in columns, the value at the bottom of each column equals the sum of the top 2 numbers, minus the sum of the next 2 numbers.

3 – F
Add together the numerical values of the letters which appear in the outer segments, and put the letter with this value in the inner segment, one place clockwise.

4 – Z
In each row, multiply the numerical values of the left and right hand letters, putting the result in the centre.

SOLUTIONS

5 – E
From left to right, the shaded segment moves 1 space anticlockwise each time, as does the star. The square moves two places clockwise, and the black dot moves from one segment to the segment opposite each turn.

6 –

Starting with the top diagram, and moving clockwise around the others, the hour hand advances by 1, 2 and 3 segments, while the minute hand advances by 3, 2 and 1 segment.

7 – 8
Working in rows, the sum of the digits in each row follows the sequence of the Square Numbers, 16, 25, 36.

8 – Y
Start on the left hand of the diagram, and move clockwise. Letters are written in alphabetical order, in steps of 10 letters at a time.

9 – 8
In each grid, working in columns, add the top and bottom numbers together, and put this sum in the centre square in the grid underneath the original (for the top grids), or the grid above (for the lower grids).

10 – 9
Start with the numbers in the upper left circle, and add 2 to each one to give the values in the lower left circle, add 3 to the upper middle circle values to give the values in the lower middle circle, and add 4 to the upper right circle to the lower right.

11 – 10
In each line, multiply the left and right hand numbers together, then subtract their sum from the result, to give the central number.

12 – I
Starting at the bottom left, and working clockwise, in a spiral, letters move through the alphabet in steps of 2, then 3, 4, 5, etc.

13 – 5
In each star, the value at the centre equals the difference between the sum of the top 3 numbers and the sum of the bottom 3 numbers.

14 – F
In each diagram, convert each letter to its numerical value, and read the top and bottom pairs of letters as complete 2-digit values. Multiply these values together to give the 3-digit result written in the centre spaces.

15 – 4
In each diagram, read the upper and lower pairs of numbers as 2-digit values and add these together to give the result written at the top.

16 – X
In each triangular shape, start on the extreme left and move in a clockwise spiral towards the centre. Letters are written in alphabetical order, in steps of 6 letters for the left hand shape, 7 letters for the centre, and 8 letters for the right hand shape.

17 – N
Starting at the top of the diagram, and moving clockwise in a spiral, letters move through the alphabet 5 letters at a time.

18 – 8
In each diagram, reading the top two numbers as a two digit number, multiply this by the central number, and write the two digit result in the lower two spaces.

19 – 4
Working in rows, add the left and right hand values together and subtract 3 to give the number in the centre of each row.

20 – B
Start on the left of the diagram, and work in columns, top to bottom, from left to right. Letters are written in sequence, in steps of 2, then 4, then 6, then 8, before repeating this pattern.

21 – 4
Add together the four outer numbers of each grid. This answer is the central number of the grid one place further clockwise.

22 – 1000
Working from top to bottom, follow the sequence of cube numbers from 5 to 10.

23 – 10
Working in rows, the central value in each row equals the average of the left and right hand numbers.

24 – 60
In each circle, starting with the top left segment and moving clockwise, double the first number to get the next value, then add two to get the one after that. Repeat, doubling then adding two for, the rest of the circle.

25 – 26
Starting with the top two left hand numbers, add them together and subtract 1 to give the next number down. With the right hand numbers, add the first two numbers together and add 1 to give the next number down.

26 – 10
Working in columns, the sum of the numbers in each column equals 23.

27 – 5
Add together numbers in corresponding segments of the outer four squares. The answer is placed in the diagonally opposite segment of the middle square.

28 – Jack of Spades
There are 2 sequences in the grid – one determining the value of the card, and one determining the suit of the card. Starting on the top left and moving right, then down one row and to the left, then down the final row and to the right, cards are arranged in order, with their value increasing by 4 each time. To calculate the suit of each card, start on the top left and move down, then right one row and move up, etc cards are arranged in the order Hearts, Clubs, Diamonds, Spades.

29 – I
In each set of boxes, working through the alphabet from the top left to the top right letter, the lower box represents the vowel you find in this sequence.

30 – 11
In each shape, subtract the sum of the even numbers from the sum of the odd numbers, putting the result in the centre.

SOLUTIONS

31 – Y
Work in rows, across the 4 squares as a whole. Start at the top left and move to the right, then down one row and to the left, etc in a snakes and ladders pattern. Letters advance through the alphabet in steps of 5 letters at a time.

32 – 6
Split the diagram into 2 halves vertically, each 3 columns wide. Numbers in the left hand half follow the sequence of cubed numbers, from 64 to 729, and numbers in the right hand half follow the sequence of squared numbers, from 121 to 256.

33 – To the 6
Starting with the top left clock face and working clockwise around the others, the sum of the numbers pointed to by the 2 hands starts at 3 and increases by 2 each time.

34 – W
In each row, take the reverse alphabetical value of the left hand letter and the alphabetical value of the right hand letter and calculate the difference, putting this result in the central square.

35 – H
Starting on the top row, and working down in columns, letters follow the alphabetic sequence, in steps of 5, 4, 3, 2 and 1.

36 – 8

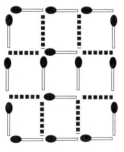

37 –   1:Z
            2:K
In the first oval, the letters are those which come one place after the vowels in the alphabet, and in the second oval, the letters all come one place before the vowels.

38 – 25, 32
Starting in the top left segment and moving clockwise around the outer ring add the first two digits together and add 1 to give the next number around. Move anticlockwise around the inner ring, adding the first two digits together and subtract 1 to give the next number around.

39 –

Child	Mother	Costume	Age
Andrew	Paula	Carrot	8
Daisy	Jane	T.V.	7
Lily	Mary	Martian	9

40 – F
Taking pairs of letters at opposite sides of the diagram, the sum of their numerical values equals 21 each time.

41 – T
Start at the top left, and move clockwise around the square. Letters follow the alphabetical order, skipping 4 letters, then 5, 6, 7, 8, 9 and 10, before repeating this sequence.

42 –

Split the diagram in to four quarters. Starting in the top left corner, repeat the pattern of circles in the other quarters, rotating the relative positions of the circles 90° anticlockwise. The colours are inverted each step.

43 – Z
Working left to right, alternately subtract 2 from the numerical value of the first letter, then add 5.

44 – C

45 – O
Start at the centre letter, and move around the upper triangle in a clockwise direction. Letters follow the alphabetical order in steps of 9 letters at a time. Repeat the same pattern, moving clockwise around the lower triangle, with the letters written in steps of 7 letters at a time.

46 – 30 men.

47 – Z
Starting top left and working down, then to top right, and down again, numbers follow the alphabetic sequence, skipping 6 letters each time.

48 – U
Starting at the top, and working down, letters move through the alphabet, skipping 1 letter, then 2, 3, 4, etc.

49 – E, L, W
Starting in the top left, and working down in columns, from left to right, letters move through the alphabet in steps of 2, 3, 4, etc.

50 – 2
In each diagram, the central value equals the sum of the left and right hand digits, minus the sum of the upper and lower digits.

51 – J
Start on the upper left hand segment of the left hand circle and move anti-clockwise around it. Then move to the upper left of the central circle and move clockwise, then on to the right hand circle, and again move anti-clockwise. Letters are written in sequence along this path, skipping 3 letters, then 4, 5 and 6, before repeating this sequence.

52 – 4
In each shape, use the left and right hand numbers as a source. The upper central number equals the sum of the left and right hand numbers, the middle central number equals the product of the left and right hand numbers, and the lower central number equals the difference between the left and right hand numbers.

53 – 3
As you move from left to right, the spot total on each domino increases by 3 then decreases by 1 alternately.

54 – 124
The numbers follow the sequence of cube numbers, from 1 to 5, subtracting 1 each time.

55 – K
Starting in the top left and moving down, in columns, from left to right, the letters move forward, in steps of 4, 6, 8, 10, etc.

SOLUTIONS

56 – 1
Starting in the top left, and moving clockwise in a spiral, letters are written in alternate squares in steps of 7.

LEVEL 13

1 – B
Working in rows, left to right, top row then bottom, one black circle is added each time, with the positions of the circles moving 1/4 turn clockwise each time.

2 – E
Taking the hour and minute values on each watch separately, as you move to the right the hour value increases by 1, 2, 3 and 4, and the minute value decreases by 11, 22, 33 and 44.

3 –
Z	D	F
F	X	L
L	R	R

Starting top left, and moving down the first column, then up the next, etc, letters follow the alphabetical sequence in steps of 6.

4 – 1
The number enclosed in each square equals the sum of the small numbers in the centre of the other three squares.

5 – I
Working downwards, letters are placed in alphabetical order, skipping letters written with curved lines.

6 – 5
Working in rows, in each row the central number is equal to the difference between the sum of the even numbers in the row and the sum of the odd numbers in the row.

7 – V
Starting with the top left triangle, and moving clockwise around the other 2, letters advance through the alphabet in steps of 4, 5 and 6, with their relative positions moving 1 place clockwise around each triangle.

8 – 1
Working from left to right, top row then bottom, the sum total of the numbers in each circle follow the sequence 14, 15, 16, 17, etc.

9 – 6
Using the central column, square each number, to give a 2-digit result, and write these digits, using the spaces on the right and left of the central number in each row.

10 – 23
Starting top left, and moving down, alternately right and left, numbers increase by 4 each time. Following the same pattern for the top right, numbers increase by 5.

11 – 196
Starting with the top left segment, and moving clockwise around the circle, numbers follow the sequence of Square Numbers, from 121 to 256.

12 – M
As you move down the line of letters, alphabetical values increase by 7, then 4, then 7, etc.

13 – 57
As you work down the column, numbers follow the sequence of Square Numbers from 16 to 81, subtracting 4, then 8, then 12, etc.

14 – 1
Splitting the diagram into 3 smaller triangles, with 3 circles each, the sum of the numbers in each smaller triangle is always 21.

15 – B
Starting at the bottom left, and working right, then up one row, and to the left, etc, letters follow the alphabetic sequence, in steps of 3 then 4, 5, 6, etc, towards the apex.

16 – Q
Taking pairs of letters in opposite segments of each circle, one letter is the same distance from the start of the alphabet, as the other is from the end.

17 – E
In each group of 3 squares, the difference between the numerical values of the top two letters equals the numerical value of the lower letter.

18 – D
Starting on the top left, and moving to the right, then down one row and to the left, etc. in a snakes and ladders pattern, letters advance through the alphabet in steps of 5, then 2, then 5, etc.

19 – N
Take pairs of letters, one from an outer segment and one from the inner segment in the opposite position. The sum of the numerical values of these letters is always 20.

20 – 69
Starting at the top and working down, double each number and subtract 5 to give the next number down.

21 – 5
Working in columns, the sum of the numbers in each column equals 18.

22 – 8 and 20
Starting at the top of the diagram, and moving down to the left, in diagonal lines, numbers increase by steps of 2 for the first diagonal line, 3 for the next, 4, 5, 6, etc.

23 – K
In each diagram, starting top left and moving clockwise to end up in the centre, letters follow the alphabetic sequence, skipping the same number of letters each time.

24 – C
In each row, the numerical value of the central letter equals the sum of the values of the left and right hand letters.

25 – B
Starting with the top left segment and moving clockwise, letters advance through the alphabet in steps of 4, then 5, then 6, etc.

26 – 16
Starting on the top left, and moving clockwise in a spiral towards the centre, numbers increase by 7, then decrease by 2. Repeat this pattern all the way around.

27 – Minute hand pointing to 6
Starting with the top clock face and moving clockwise around the others, the hour hand moves forward by 1 hour, then 2, then 3, while the minute hand moves forward 10 minutes, then 20, then 30.

28 – 12
Working from left to right, starting at the top of each star, and moving clockwise, double each number and subtract 2 for the left hand star, subtract 3 for the middle, and 4 for the right hand.

SOLUTIONS

29 – H
Starting top left, and working clockwise, in a spiral, letters follow the alphabetic sequence, skipping letters written with any curved lines.

30 – M
Working from top to bottom, the numerical values of the letters follow the sequence of Prime Numbers.

31 – 10
Working from left to right numbers follow the sequence of Prime Numbers, subtracting 1 each time.

32 – J
Working from top to bottom, letters appear in alphabetical order, skipping any letters written with only straight lines.

33 – Q
Starting with the top left square, and moving clockwise around the other squares, the numerical values of each letter increase by 2, with their relative positions in each square rotating 1 place clockwise at each turn.

34 – 24
Working clockwise around the diagram, add the first two numbers together and subtract 3 to give the next number along.

35 – 6
In each set of boxes, the lower number equals the average of the top numbers.

36 –

Working from left to right, the sum of the dots in each column equals 12, then 13, 14, 15, etc.

37 – G
Starting with the letters in the top row, and following straight lines through the middle circle, subtract the numerical value of the middle letter (G) and write the letter with the corresponding numerical value in the lower circle.

38 – Y
Starting with the bottom left letter and moving in a clockwise spiral towards the centre, letters advance through the alphabet in steps of 4, 5, 6, etc.

39 – 3
In each circle, the sum of the numbers in the left hand half of the circle equals double that of the numbers in the right hand half of the circle.

40 – E
Starting with the bottom row and moving up, one row at a time, the sum of the numerical values of the letters starts at 26 for the bottom row, then 24, 22 and 20 as you move up.

41 –

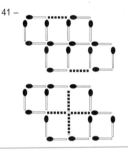

42 – 9
Starting on the top, and moving down, alternately subtract 2 and add 4 to give the next numbers in the sequence.

43 – W
Starting on E and moving clockwise, letters increase in value by 3, 5 and 7, before repeating this sequence.

44 – 4
Reading the top and bottom rows of numbers as 2-digit numbers, multiply them together to give a 3-digit number, written on the middle row.

45 – X
Starting with the bottom right hand corner, and moving in a clockwise spiral towards the centre, letters advance through the alphabet, skipping 4 letters at a time.

46 – 11
Starting with the diagram in the top left, and moving to the right, ending up with the bottom diagram, average the values in the top two boxes and put the result in the lower box, adding 1 for the first diagram, 2 for the next, then 3, then 4.

47 – 6
All columns and rows in the diagram add up to 15.

48 – 891
Take each three digit separately. Square the centre digit and write the answer either side of it.

49 – 12 apples.

50 – 9
Working in rows, top to bottom, reading each row as a 3-digit number, rows follow the sequence of Square Numbers from 11 to 13.

51 – P
Starting in the top left corner and moving clockwise in a spiral towards the centre, letters follow the alphabetic sequence, skipping 5 letters at a time, written in alternate squares of the diagram.

52 –   A: 42   B: 52
In the first oval, all numbers are multiples of 4.
In the second oval, all numbers are multiples of 3.

53 – 5
In each row, add together the left and right hand numbers, then add 2 to give the central value.

54 – From top to bottom, Five of Hearts and Ace of Spades.
In each row, the value of the right hand card equals the difference between the sum of the red cards, and the sum of the black cards on that row. The suit of the right hand card is always the same as the far left hand card.

1 – 156
Start with 1 and move clockwise. Multiply the previous number by 2 and add 4 to give the next number around.

2 – 1
In every row of the diagram, if you subtract the odd numbers from the even number, you always get 10.

SOLUTIONS

3 – To the 4
The sum of the numbers the hour and minute hands point to is always 11.

4 – C
The sum of the numerical values of pairs of letters, opposite each other in the diagram, is always 20 (the numerical value of the central letter).

5 – 7
In each square, the sum of the three outer numbers is written in the central square, 1 place clockwise from it.

6 – K
In each pair of boxes, the first letter is the same distance from the start of the alphabet, as the second letter is from the end of the alphabet.

7 – 40
Starting with 14 and moving clockwise, add the two digits of each number together, and add this to the original number, to give the next value around.

8 – Q
In each row, add the numerical values of the left and central letters to give the value of the letter on the right.

9 – 5
The values in the segments of the upper middle circle equal the sum of the values in corresponding segments of the upper left and right hand circles, and the values in the segments of the lower middle circle equal the difference between values in corresponding segments of the lower left and right hand circles.

10 – M
In each diagram, start with the upper left box, and move anti-clockwise around the others. Letters advance through the alphabet in steps of 7 for the upper left diagram, 8 for the middle, then 9, then 10.

11 – 3
Starting at the top of the diagram, and moving down to the right, in diagonal lines, the sum of the digits in the first line equals 12. The sum of the digits in the next diagonal line equals 13, etc.

12 – 6
In each shape, multiply the top two numbers and the central number to give a two digit result, and write these two digits in the lower two circles.

13 – B
Starting at the top and working down, letters move through the alphabet in steps of 8 letters, then 9, then 10, etc.

14 – 37
As you move down the diagram, double each number and subtract 5 to give the next number.

15 – K
Split the diagram in half horizontally and vertically. Start in the top left square of each quarter, and move clockwise around the other squares in the quarter. In each quarter, letters advance through the alphabet in steps of 2 for the upper left quarter, 3 for the upper right, 4 for the lower right and 5 for the lower left.

16 – U
Start with the D on the outer left of the diagram, and move clockwise around the outer segments, then start on the N anti-clockwise around the inner segments. Letters advance through the alphabet in steps of 3, then 4, 5, and 6, repeating this sequence.

17 – A
Working in rows, from left to right, dots form straight sided shapes. The number of sides increases by 1 for each step to the right.

18 – 2
In each row of the grid, the numbers 0-9 appear once only.

19 – J
In each circle, the reverse alphabetical value of the lower letter equals the sum of the alphabetical values of the top 2 letters.

20 – B
Start at the top left and move down the left hand column, then move one place to the right and up the next column, etc. in a snakes and ladders pattern. Letters are written in alternate spaces, in steps of 7 letters at a time.

21 – 6
In each row of the diagram, the numerical value of the middle letter equals the sum of the left and right hand numbers, subtracting 3.

22 – 17
In each star, the number in the centre equals the difference between the sum of the even numbers and the sum of the odd numbers around the points of the star.

23 – (From left to right) U, J, Z
Starting in the top left, and working clockwise in a spiral, letters follow the alphabetic sequence, in steps of 2, 3, 4 and 5, then 2, 3, 4 and 5, etc towards the centre.

24 – N
Starting top left and moving to the right in a W shape, letters in corresponding segments in each circle follow sequences, skipping 0, 1, 2 and 3 letters at a time.

25 – R
The sum of the numerical values of letters in opposite segments of the circle is always 22.

26 – 26
Starting on the top left and moving to the right, then down one row and to the left, then down to the bottom row and to the right, numbers alternately add 8 then subtract 3.

27 – A
In each diagram, there are 2 lines of black dots, joining two sides together. The sides joined by the dots moves 1/4 turn clockwise as you move from left to right.

28 – 7
Starting with the numbers in the top circle, add the numbers from the corresponding segments of the left hand circle, to give the result in the lower circle.

29 – 6
Reading each line as a 3-digit number, the numbers follow the sequence of Square Numbers of 12, 13 and 14.

30 – 9
Starting top left and moving clockwise in a spiral, towards the centre, add the first two numbers, then subtract 1 to give the next number in the sequence.

31 – 99
Starting at the top, the first box represents 5x7, 6x8, 7x9, 8x10 and 9x11, each time the multiplications increase by 1.

SOLUTIONS

32 – H
Starting at the top and moving down, the sum of the numerical values of the letters in each oval follows the sequence 20, 22, 24, etc.

33 – 5
Take pairs of numbers at opposite ends of the diagram. Their total is always 10.

34 – M
Start with the top left square, and move clockwise around the others. The sum of the numerical values of the letters in each square equals 20 for the top left, 25 for the top right, 30 for the bottom right and 35 for the bottom left.

35 – 4
In each star, add the top number and lower two numbers to make a two digit total, and write this two digit number in the remaining left and right hand positions.

36 – From top to bottom,

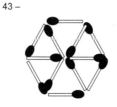

Starting top left, move towards the centre in a clockwise spiral. There are two sequences, on alternate circles, following this path. The first starts with one quarter shaded, with an extra quarter added at each turn. When the circle becomes full, a quarter segment is taken away each time. The second sequence follows the same pattern, but starts with a full circle.

37 – D
Start on the bottom left and move up to the top, then to the right one space and down to the bottom. Letters follow the alphabetic sequence alternately in steps of 6, then 8. Starting on the bottom right and moving up to the top, then left one space and down to the bottom, letters in this half follow the same pattern.

38 – 11
In each triangle, the central value equals the sum of the 2 even numbers from the outside corners of the triangle minus the odd number.

39 – N
Starting at the top left hand of every diagram, move around the outer circles in an anti-clockwise direction. Letters are written in alphabetic sequence, in steps given by the numerical value of the central letter.

40 – S
Starting with the top left segment and working to the bottom, letters move anticlockwise in steps of 4. Starting with the top right segment, letters move clockwise, in steps of 5.

41 – X
Starting top left, and moving clockwise around the diagram, in an hour glass shape, letters advance through the alphabet eight letters at a time.

42 – C
Starting top left, and working in rows, from top to bottom, letters move backwards through the alphabet, 6 letters at a time.

43 –

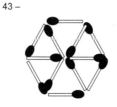

44 – 5
Start at the top of each triangle and move clockwise around its points. Add the first two numbers together and subtract 2 to give the next value round.

45 – E
Starting on the left, and moving to the right, letters are written in alphabetical order, moving forward 8 places, then back 2, then forward 7 places and back 3. Repeat this sequence to the end of the line.

46 – 8
In each triangle, multiply the lower 2 numbers together and subtract the upper number to give the value in the centre.

47 – 10
For each circle, add the left and right hand numbers together and put this total in the circle one place to the right.

48 – U
Starting with the top left square in each figure, and moving clockwise, letters advance by 4 places at a time, then 5, 6 and 7.

49 – 4
Splitting the diagram into quarters, each quarter represents the letter M, N, O and P, written in shaded blocks.

50 – D
Start with the watch on the left and move to the right. The time on the watches increases by 2 hours 3 minutes, then decreases by 1 hour 16 minutes, alternately.

51 – W
Start with A on the left hand side, and move in a clockwise spiral around the diagram. Letters advance through the alphabet in steps of 6.

52 – Z
Starting on the left and moving right, letters are written in alphabetical order, using every other letter written with only straight lines.

53 – E
In each grid, there are two shapes, made up of black circles. Working in rows, from left to right, both shapes increase in size by one circle each time.

54 – 2
Starting on the left, and moving right, each pair of numbers represents multiples of 9, starting with 36, subtracting 1 each time.

1 – 7
In each square, multiply the top and bottom numbers together to give a 2-digit result, and put the letters with the numerical values of each digit in the left and right hand spaces.

2 – M
In each column, add up each number and put the letter with this sum in the bottom circle.

3 – I
Start with the outer top left segment,

SOLUTIONS

and move around the circle clockwise, then move in to the middle segments and move anticlockwise. Following this path, letters advance through the alphabet in steps of 7 letters at a time.

4 – 0
In each row, the left hand number equals the total of the even valued letters in the middle box, and the right hand number equals the total of the odd valued letters in the middle box.

5 – 8
In each triangle, multiply the top and centre numbers, to give a 2-digit result, and write this result on the lower 2 points of each triangle.

6 – V
Starting with the diagram on the left, and moving 1 place to the right at each turn, letters in corresponding positions on each diagram move through the alphabet, skipping the same number of letters each time.

7 – 9
Multiply numbers in adjacent circles together, then subtract the original numbers, to give the value in the space in-between.

8 – S
In each grid, start in the top left and move down, then right one space and up, etc, in a snakes and ladders pattern. Letters advance through the alphabet in steps of 5 for the top left grid, 6 for the top right, 7 for the bottom left and 8 for the bottom right.

9 – 2
Working in rows, read the left and right hand numbers as a two digit number, and put the corresponding letter in the central square.

10 – 4
Reading each row as a 3-digit number, the rows follow the sequence of multiples of 12.

11 – E
Working from left to right, the shaded segment moves one place anticlockwise each turn, the star moves one place clockwise, while the black circles move one place, in opposite directions each turn.

12 – 1
In each star, calculate the difference between the 2 left hand and 2 right hand numbers. The value at the top of each star equals the product of these differences, and the value at the bottom of each star equals the difference between these 2 differences.

13 – F
In each shape, start at the bottom left and move up, then diagonally down to the right, and finally up the right hand column, in an N shape. Letters move through the alphabet in steps of 4, 5, 6, 7, 8, and 9.

14 – 6
In each figure, calculate the difference between the upper and lower left hand numbers, and the upper and lower right hand numbers and multiply these differences together to give the value at the top.

15 – 43
In each triangle shape, start at the left hand side of the longest row and move to the right, then on the next row and to the left, and finally to the third row. Add together the first two numbers and subtract 1 to give the next value around.

16 – 1
Taking the top left and top right circles as a source, segments in the central circle equal the sum of the numbers in corresponding segments of the source circles, segments in the lower left circle equal the product of the numbers, and the lower right equals the difference.

17 – C
On each watch, the minute value equals the hour value multiplied by 3.

18 – 2
Working from top to bottom, and reading each row as a 3-digit number, rows are arranged in order of the Square Numbers, from 11 to 15, with the digits reversed in each case.

19 – 6
Work through the diagram in horizontal rows. The sum of the numbers in each row is always 23.

20 – 6
Take values in corresponding positions of the outer 4 shapes, and put the results in the central shape, rotating the position of this result by 1/4 turn each time.

21 – F
Starting in the top left, and working clockwise in a spiral, to end up in the centre, letters move backwards through the alphabet, skipping 2 letters, then 3, 4, 5, etc.

22 – 11
Using the top two circles, add together numbers in corresponding segments, and put the results in the lower left hand circle. Calculate the difference between the top two circles, and put the results in the lower right hand circle.

23 – 5
In each star, the sum of the even numbers on the points, equals the sum of the odd points.

24 – Z
Start at the top, and work left to right in rows, top to bottom. Letters advance through the alphabet in steps of 10, 11, 12, 13, etc.

25 – 9
Calculate the sum of the numbers in corresponding positions of the outer 4 squares, subtract 5 form this result, and put it in the corresponding position of the middle square, 1/4 turn anticlockwise from the original.

26 – 3 of Spades
Divide the diagram in half, vertically. In each half, start at the top left card and move to the right, then down one row and to the left, and finally to the right, in a snakes and ladders pattern. The value of the cards in the left hand half increase alternately by 3 and 4, and the value of the cards in the right hand half increase alternately by 4 and 5. To calculate the suit of each card, start at the top left of the whole diagram and move down, then to the right one space and upwards, etc in a snakes and ladders pattern. Suits are written in order, following this path, starting with Hearts, then Clubs, Diamonds and Spades.

SOLUTIONS

27 – 9
The sum of the numbers in the left hand column equals the sum of the numbers in the right hand column.

28 – X
Starting top left, and working in columns, from left to right, letters advance through the alphabet in steps of 2, then 3, 4, 5, etc.

29 – P
In each diagram, the midpoint between the left and right hand pairs of numbers equals the letter in the centre.

30 – I
Start in the bottom left hand corner of the diagram and, moving around the whole diagram, work in a clockwise direction, around the outer squares. Letters are written in alphabetical order, in steps of 7 letters at a time. For the single square still remaining in each group of 4, add the numerical values of the other 3 letters in the square together to give a 2-digit number, and add these separate digits together, and put the letter with this numerical value in the central square.

31 – M
Start with the top row, second square from the right, and move down and to the right in diagonal lines, advancing across the diagram to the left. Letters are written in alphabetical order, in steps of 5 at a time.

32 – To the 2
Starting with the top left clock face and moving clockwise around the others, the minute hand moves back 2 places, then 4, 6 and 8, while the hour hand moves forward 2 places, then 4, 6 and 8.

33 – C
In each row, calculate the difference between the 2 numbers in the left hand column, and the 2 numbers in the right hand column. Multiply these differences together to give the numerical value of the letter in the centre.

34 – 1
Reading each line as a 3-digit number, add the top two lines together, and write the result on the bottom line.

35 – 6
Working in rows, starting top left subtract 2 to give the middle value, and 3 to give the right hand value, repeat on the next line, subtracting 4, then 5, and for the bottom line, subtract 6 then 7.

36 – E
In each diagram, add together the numerical values of the letters in the top two boxes, and subtract 5, to give the value of the letter in the lower box.

37 –

Contestant	Position	Style	Prize
Marc	3rd	French	Clock
Jane	2nd	Italian	Pots+pans
Sue	1st	Chinese	Hamper

38 – B
Start at the top, and move diagonally down and to the right. Letters advance through the alphabet in steps of 5 then 6. Continue this pattern, starting with the next circle down on the left, etc.

39 – S
Start with the letter in the top left, and move clockwise around the square. The numerical value of the letters follows the sequence of Prime Numbers, from 2 to 19.

40 – C
Starting top left, and working to the right along each row, letters follow the alphabetic sequence in steps of 6, 5 then 4. Repeat this sequence, top to bottom.

41 – 1212
Starting with 2 and moving clockwise, add 2 to each number, and multiply by 3 to give the next number.

42 – 25
Moving left to right, numbers increase by 7, then 6, 5 and 4.

43 – Z
Working in rows, from left to right, letters in the top row advance by 6 places at a time, letters in the middle row advance 8 places, and the bottom row advances 10 places.

44 – B

45 – A
Starting in the top left, and moving in rows, left to right, top to bottom, letters advance through the alphabet in steps of 6, 7 and 8.

46 – 5 years

47 – 5
Saw = 4
Sander = 3
Drill = 2

48 – 253
Working from top to bottom, numbers follow the sequence of Square Numbers, from 11 to 16, subtracting 3 each time.

49 – Q
Taking pairs of letters, from opposite segments of the circle, one letter is 10 places in the alphabet before the other.

50 – O
Start on the left of the middle row of letters, and move to the right, across all four diagrams. Letters advance through the alphabet in steps of 2, 3, 4, etc. In each separate diagram, letters also follow a sequence, moving from top to bottom, through the centre, with the value of the letters increasing by 2 each time for the left hand diagram, then 3, then 4, then 5 for the right hand diagram.

51 – 4
Split the left and right hand circles in half vertically. The letter with the numerical value of the sum of the digits in the left half of the left hand circle is placed in the top left segment of the central circle, and the letter with the numerical value of the sum of the digits in the right half of the left hand circle is placed in the top right segment of the central circle. Repeat this formula for the 2 halves of the right hand circle, putting the resulting letters in the lower segments of the central circle.

52 – J
Start on the top left of the left hand diagram, and move in horizontal lines, from left to right, top to bottom, across all 4 diagrams as a whole. Letters advance through the alphabet in steps of 7, then back 2, repeating this sequence all the way around.

SOLUTIONS

53 – 6
Start on the left and move to the right, taking pairs of dominoes. The difference between the spot total of the two dominoes in each pair follows the sequence 4, 6, 8, 10.

54 – 4
Starting on the left, and moving right, take the first 3 numbers in a diagonal line, and add 5 to each one, to give the values in the corresponding diagonal line to the right, subtract 4 from each of these numbers to give the values in the corresponding diagonal line on the far right.

55 –

Working in rows, start with the left hand circle, and add a new segment, in a clockwise direction, to give the next circle along. Also the colours of the segments in alternate circles are reversed.

LEVEL 16

1 – Y
Starting with the G and moving clockwise, letters advance through the alphabet in steps of 3 letters, then 4, then 5, etc.

2 – V
Starting on the top left of each outer square, and moving clockwise around the corners of the squares, letters advance through the alphabet in steps of 4 for the upper left square, 5 for the upper right, 6 for the lower right and 7 for the lower left. Additionally, the letters bounded by the central square take the inverse alphabetical value of the original letter.

3 – Anchor
Binoculars = 1
Anchor = 3
Buoy = 5

4 – 6
Working from top to bottom, reading each pair of numbers as a 2-digit value, values represent the reverse alphabetical value of letters of the alphabet, starting with A, written with 3 straight lines only.

5 – B
Working from left to right, one shaded segment remains still, while the other swaps back and forth, between opposite segments. The square moves clockwise, two segment at a time, and the black circle moves anticlockwise, two segments at a time.

6 – 11
Working in rows, add numbers in corresponding segments of the left and central circles together, and put the result in the opposite segment in the right hand circle.

7 – 1
Starting with the circle on the top left, and moving to the right, top row then bottom row, the sum of the numbers in each circle follows the sequence 12, 15, 18, 21, etc.

8 – B
Start on the top left, and work through the diagram in columns, from left to right. The sum of the numerical values of the letters in each column starts at 20, then increases by 1 as you move one column to the right.

9 – E
As you move to the right, the hour value decreases by 1, 2, 3 and 4, while the minute value increases by 5, 6, 7 and 8.

10 – Z
Starting on J and moving clockwise, letters advance 10 places forward, then 4 places back alternately.

11 – 14
Starting at the top left, and moving around the diagram clockwise, add the first two numbers together and add 1 to give the next value.

12 – S
Starting at the top left of the diagram, moving in a Z shape, letters advance through the alphabet in steps of 5.

13 – 4
Split the whole diagram in half, horizontally, to give two groups of 5 octagons. In each group, the central number in the top row equals the sum of the surrounding 4 numbers.

14 – 110
Starting on the left and moving right, double each number and add 2 to give the next number along.

15 – 4
Reading each pair of numbers as 2-digit values, the sum of the 4 numbers is given in the top space in the diagram.

16 – A
Working in rows, superimpose the left and central grids to give the pattern in the right grid. If crosses appear in the same position in both grids, they cancel out in the right hand grid.

17 – 12
In each circle, the number in the lower segment equals twice the difference between the numbers in the left and right hand segments.

18 – 5
Working through the diagram in rows, add the left and central numbers together and subtract 2 to give the right hand value.

19 – 2
Reading each row as a 3 or 2-digit number, subtract the central 2-digit value from the upper 3-digit value, to give the 3-digit result on the lower row.

20 – Y
Start with the top point of each star, and move clockwise around the other points. Letters advance through the alphabet in steps of 5 for the left hand star, 6 for the central star, and 7 for the right hand star.

21 – J
Starting with the letter in the top right segment of the top circle, and moving clockwise around the three circles, letters follow the alphabetic sequence, with the relative position of the letter revolving 1 place clockwise each turn. Follow the same sequence starting with the next segment clockwise on the top circle, but skip 1 letter each time. Repeat for the other segments, skipping an extra letter each time.

22 – A
Starting top left, work down to the bottom, then up the next column to the right, etc, letters are written in a repeating sequence, M, H, Z, A, L, Q, R, B, G following this pattern.

SOLUTIONS

23 – S
Starting with the top left segments, the letters move from the outer ring to the next segment in the inner ring, jumping 2 then 3 letters. The sequence that starts in the inner ring goes back 2 then 3 letters.

24 – 1
Add the numerical values of the upper two letters to give a 2-digit number, and put this in the upper central two boxes. Do the same for the lower two letters.

25 – Q
Working in columns, add the numerical value of the top and middle letters together to give the numerical value of the lower letter.

26 – 10
Starting with the left hand circle, add 4 to each number and rotate their positions 1 place clockwise to give the values in the upper right hand circle, then add 5 to each of these values and rotate their positions 1 place clockwise to give the values in the lower right hand circle.

27 – 30
Working in columns, divide the top value by 2 to give the middle value, and multiply this by 3 to give the bottom value.

28 – C
In each circle, the sum of the numerical values of the letters in the top two segments equals 18. And the sum of the lower 2 segments equals 22.

29 – 0
In each diagram, read the top two numbers as a 2-digit number, and subtract the central value, to give a 2-digit result, written in the lower two places.

30 – 10
In each circle, the value in the lower segment equals double the difference between the upper left and right hand values.

31 – 281
Working from top to bottom, numbers follow the sequence of multiples of 14, from 112 to 182, with each value being written back to front.

32 – M
Start with the letters in the top left circle, and move around the other circles in a clockwise direction. Letters advance through the alphabet 6 letters at a time, with the relative positions of each letter moving one place clockwise each time.

33 – 20
Working from top to bottom, the sum of the numbers in each row is put in the left hand box on the row below, and the difference between the two numbers in each row is put in the right hand box on the row below.

34 – C
Taking the numerical values of each letter, in each diagram, the central value equals the difference between the sum of the upper pair of values and the sum of the lower pair of values.

35 – 7
Add together corresponding segments in the upper two circles, and put the results on the segments on the lower left. Calculate the difference between values in the top two circles, and put the results in the lower right circle.

36 – 720 days before both watches told the same time, and 3,600 days before they both told the right time.

37 – 22
On each row of the diagram, the value in the centre of each row equals the sum of the other numbers in the row, subtracting 2.

38 – Y
Start at the top to the left hand triangle, and work across the whole diagram in horizontal lines from left to right, top to bottom. Letters are written in alphabetic sequence, skipping 3 letters each time.

39 – 3
In each diagram, the sum of the top two and middle digits equals the sum of the lower 2 digits.

40 – Q
Add together the numeric values of the top two letters and divide them by two. Write this answer in reverse numerical order, in the bottom box.

41 –

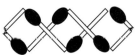

42 – 21
The numbers in each box correspond to the numerical values of the vowels in the alphabet.

43 – Z
In each star, start with the letter in the lower left hand point, and move around the other points in a clockwise direction. Letters advance through the alphabet in steps of 6 for the left hand star, 7 for the one in the centre, and 8 for the right hand star.

44 – N
Start on the left, and move to the right. Letters advance through the alphabet in steps of 2, then 3, then 4, etc.

45 – T
In each triangle, start with the bottom left letter, and move clockwise around the other points. Letters advance through the alphabet in steps given by the numerical value of the letter at the centre of the triangle.

46 – 6
In each circle, add together the left and right hand digits, and add 3 to give the value of the lower digit.

47 – 4, 12.

48 – 21
Starting at the top, the numbers represent multiples of 4, from 9 to 4, with the digits reversed in each case.

49 – D
Working in rows, left to right, top to bottom, letters follow the sequence of the first letter of the months of the year.

50 – 4
Splitting the diagram in half horizontally and vertically, each quarter contains the alphabet written in sequence, with the relative position of this sequence rotating 1/4 turn anti-clockwise as you move clockwise around the quarters.

SOLUTIONS

51 – 1
Start with the top left circle, and move around the others in a W shape. The sum of the numbers in each circle follows the sequence of 10, 12, 14, 16 and 18.

52 – Q
Start on the left and work to the right. There are two alternating sequences of letters – one starts with A and moves through the alphabet 5 letters at a time. The other starts on H and moves through the alphabet 3 letters at a time.

53 – From left to right, 31, 16, 39
Start at the top, following diagonal lines from the left hand edge, up to the right, numbers are arranged in the sequence of Prime Numbers, from 2 to 29, adding 1 after each repeat.

LEVEL 17

1 – A
Working in rows, if you superimpose the pattern of spots in the left and right hand grids you get the pattern in the central grid.

2 – B
As you move from left to right, add 1 to the value of each digit on the watch, and rotate the digits one place to the left.

3 – D
Working in rows from left to right, the • moves clockwise 2 squares at a time, around the edge of the grid. The X moves in a straight line from one side of the grid to the other, and back again. The # moves 1 place clockwise around the central 4 squares in each grid. Additionally, the gird revolves a quarter turn clockwise each time you move to the right.

4 – O
Working in rows, add up the digits in each row and put the letter with this numerical value in the centre of the row.

5 – 13
In each triangle, add up the lower 3 digits and divide by 3 to give the value at the apex of the triangle.

6 – V
Starting top left, and working anticlockwise, in a spiral towards the centre, letters move through the alphabet in steps of 3, 4, 5, etc.

7 – 48
Divide each circle in half, vertically. The top right segment equals the sum of the three segments to the left, the middle right equals the average of the three segments to the left, and the lower right equals their product.

8 – 1
The grid displays rotational symmetry, around 180° around its central point.

9 – 98
Starting with the lowest number and moving clockwise, add the separate digits of the first number together and add this to the original number, writing the result in the next segment along.

10 – 33
Add the first two numbers together and then subtract 4 to give the next number along.

11 – B
Working from top to bottom, replace each letter with its numerical value and read each pair of numbers as a 2-digit number. Numbers follow the sequence of multiples of 9, from 27 to 72.

12 – V
Start at the top, and work through the triangle in horizontal rows, from top to bottom, left to right. Letters move through the alphabet 5 letters at a time.

13 – (From top to bottom) B, D
Start at top right, and work in diagonal lines from the top, down to the right. Letters follow the alphabetic sequence, in steps of 3.

14 – A
Working from left to right, top row then bottom row, the sum of the numerical values in each circle follows the sequence of even numbers, from 8 to 16.

15 – 13
Working in rows, from left to right, double the left hand number to get the middle number, and add 3 to this to get the right hand number.

16 – Y
Start with the outer segment in the top left, and move anti-clockwise. Letters advance through the alphabet in steps of 6, then 7, then 8. Continue around the outer segments of the diagram, then move in an anti-clockwise direction around the inner segments.

17 – R
Working from top to bottom, letters move through the alphabet in steps of 2, then 3, then 2, etc.

18 – 2
Split the diagram into two halves vertically, consisting of 2 columns of 2 squares each, and read each 2 adjoining squares as a complete 2-digit number. Numbers follow the sequence of multiples of 7, subtracting 1 each time.

19 – T
Starting top left, and working clockwise, in a spiral, letters move through the alphabet in steps of 6, 5, 4, 3, 2 and 1, before repeating the sequence.

20 – 2
Working in rows, from top to bottom, and reading each row as a 3-digit number, the rows follow the sequence of multiples of 12, starting with 9.

21 – P
Working in rows, left to right and top to bottom, start with the top left letter in each circle, and move clockwise around it. In the first circle, letters follow the alphabetic sequence in steps of 5, the next is in steps of 6, then 7, 8, etc.

22 – 11
Working through the diagram in columns, add 4 to the top number to give the middle one, and add 6 to this number to give the lowest one.

23 – I
Starting with the top two segments, the sum of the numerical values of letters in adjoining segments equals 20.

24 – 4
Working in rows, starting with the central row, add the left and right hand digits together and put the result in the central space. Repeat for the upper and lower rows, but put the result in the opposite central space.

SOLUTIONS

25 – To the 4
Starting with the top clock face and moving clockwise around the others, the minute hand points to the value 3 less than that pointed to by the hour hand. Repeat for the other clock faces, subtracting 4, 5 and 6 from the hour hand values.

26 – Inner, then outer, G, B
Split the diagram in half horizontally, to give upper and lower sections. Starting with the upper section, move left to right across the large segments, then right to left across the small segments. Letters move through the alphabet in steps of 2, 3, 4, etc. Repeat this sequence for the lower half, starting with the large segment on the left.

27 – 9
Reading each horizontal line as a 3-digit number, the rows represent the cubes of 7, 8 and 9.

28 – E
Working from left to right across the 3 shapes, letters in corresponding positions in each shape follow sequences, skipping 1, 2, 3, 4 and 5 letters at a time, with their relative positions rotating 90° clockwise each time.

29 – U
Starting on the left, add 2, 3 and 4 to the value of the letters, and rotate their positions 1 segment clockwise to give the letters in the next circle to the right.

30 – 25
Starting on the left, halve the first number and add it to the second number to give the next one along. Repeat this sequence all the way to the right.

31 – 6
As you move down, numbers represent the reverse alphabetical values of the 5 vowels.

32 – V
Start with the top segment of the top left square, and move directly downwards. Each group of 4 letters follows the alphabetic sequence, in steps of 5 letters at a time. Taking other straight lines vertically and horizontally through the diagram, letters follow the same pattern.

33 – 93
Starting with the top segment, and moving clockwise, add the numbers in the first two segments together and subtract 7 to give the next number around.

34 – B
All the patterns are random, but the left hand column has 2 black squares per grid, the next has 4, then 6, and finally, the right hand column has 8 black squares per grid.

35 – 6
Starting with the numbers in the top row, left to right, multiply each one by 2 and write the results in the lower row, from right to left.

36 – U
Starting with the top left letter, and moving clockwise around the others, letters advance through the alphabet in steps given by the numerical value of the central letter (6).

37 – 8
Starting with the numbers in the top two circles, add numbers in the left hand segments of each circle, and put these values in the left hand segments of the lower left circle. Put the difference between segments in the right hand halves of the two top circles in the right hand half of the lower left circle. Repeat this pattern for the lower right circle, but putting the difference between numbers in the left hand half of the top two circles in the left hand half of the lower right circle, and the sum of the right hand half of the top two circles in the right hand half of the lower right circle.

38 – 33
Starting with numbers on the bottom row, add numbers in adjacent boxes together, and put the result in the box directly above. Continue in this way, up the triangle.

39 – U
Starting top left, and moving clockwise in a spiral towards the centre, letters follow the alphabetic sequence, skipping 8 letters each time.

40 – 4913
Starting from the top, and moving down, numbers follow the sequence of cubed numbers, from 12 to 17.

41 –

42 – 9
Reading each row as a 4-digit number, from top to bottom, rows follow the sequence of Cube Numbers from 16 to 19.

43 – F
In each group of 3 boxes, calculate the difference in numerical values between the top two letters, and add 1 to give the value of the letter in the lower box.

44 – J
Add the numerical values of the top two letters in each diagram, and write the letter with the corresponding reverse alphabetical value in the lower box.

45 – 10

46 – (From left to right) A, G
Using the numerical values of each letter, the sum of all rows and columns equals 25.

47 – U
Starting in the top left of the diagram, and working in columns, from top to bottom, letters follow the alphabetical sequence, advancing 2 letters, then 4, then 6, then 8, etc.

48 – 1
Split the diagram into 3 columns, each 2 spaces wide, and read each double space as a 2-digit number. Starting at the top of each column, add the 2 separate digits together, then add this to the whole 2-digit number, to give the result, written in the spaces underneath.

49 – A: 18   B: 72
In the first oval, all numbers are divisible by 8, and in the second, they are all divisible by 7.

SOLUTIONS

50 – 5
Working through the diagram in rows, find the difference between the left and right hand values, then add 2 to give the value in the central space.

51 – (From top to bottom) D, Z, U, Q
Split the diagram, horizontally through the centre. Letters in the top half start in the top left hand corner, and move in an anticlockwise spiral towards the centre, in steps of 4 letters at a time. Letters in the bottom half start in the bottom right hand corner, and move in a anticlockwise spiral towards the centre, in steps of 5 letters at a time.

LEVEL 18

1 – 2
In each square, multiply the top and bottom numbers together to give a 2-digit result, and write this result in the left and right hand spaces.

2 – 1
Working through the diagram in rows, the central value equals the sum of the other numbers in the row.

3 – 8
Multiply the 2 numbers in the outer segments together and add 1 to give the value in the inner segment opposite.

4 – 5
In each row, add together the numerical values of the 3 central letters to give a 2-digit sum, and put this 2-digit sum in the left and right hand boxes at the end of the rows.

5 – B
In each row, the first two grids are reflections of each other, around a vertical axis, and the second two grids are reflections of each other around a horizontal axis.

6 – B
Start at the top of the diagram, and move clockwise. Letters appear in alphabetical order, in steps of 10 letters at a time.

7 – 3
Split each grid into 2 halves, vertically, leaving 2 columns, each 2 squares

wide. Start with the top left pair and move down, then to the top right pair, and down again. Reading each pair as 2-digit values, the 2-digit values increase by 11, 12, 13, 14 and 15.

8 – 4
Split the large square into quarters, and start with the values in the top left corner. Add 1 to each number, and write the results in the top right quarter. Add 2, to give the results in the lower right quarter, and add 3 for the lower left.

9 – K
Split the diagram into quarters, of 3x3 squares. Starting in the top left of each square, and working clockwise in a spiral, towards the centre, letters follow the alphabetic sequence, 4 letters at a time.

10 – 7
Reading each row as a 4-digit number, the rows follow the sequence of the cubes of 10, 11, 12 and 13.

11 – 11
In each star, the number in the centre equals the difference between the sum of the numbers in the upwards triangle and the sum of the numbers in the downward triangle.

12 – H
In each diagram, add the numerical value of the upper right and left letters to the lower right and left letters, to give the letters in the centre of the columns. Calculate the difference between these middle letters to give the value of the letter right at the centre.

13 – 2
In each diagram, multiply the numbers shown on the arms together and add the number at the very top to give a 2-digit result, written in the lower 2 spaces.

14 – F
Start in the top left of the diagram and move to the right, then down one row and to the left, and finally to the right again. Letters are written in alphabetic order, in steps of 5 letters at a time.

15 – 8
Numbers in the lower left circle equal the sum of all the odd numbers in corresponding segments of the top

3 circles. Numbers in the lower right equal the sum of the even numbers.

16 – 5
In each star, add the top three numbers to give a two digit value, and write these two digits on the lower two points of the star.

17 – P
Working in rows, add the left and right hand numbers together, and put the letter with the reverse alphabetical value of this sum in the central box.

18 – C
Start with the A in the bottom left corner, and move in a clockwise spiral around the diagram towards the centre. Letters are written in alphabetic order, in steps of 6 letters at a time.

19 – 0
Use the top two diagrams as a source. Numbers in corresponding positions in the lower left diagram equal the sums of the numbers in the top two diagrams, numbers in the central diagram equal their product, and numbers in the lower right diagram equal their difference.

20 – From top to bottom, F, W, E
Start at top left, and work across the diagram in diagonal lines, starting on the left and moving up and to the right, letters are arranged in alphabetical order, skipping any letters written with curved lines.

21 – 6
Multiply the top two numbers of each circle together and add the digits together to get a single number.

22 – 4
The average of the numbers in each column is always 4.

23 – P
Start with the top left grid and move around the others in a clockwise spiral towards the centre. Letters follow alphabetic sequences, skipping 1, 2, 3 and 4 letters at a time, with their relative positions in each grid rotating 1/4 turn clockwise each time.

24 – Nine of Clubs
In each column of the diagram, add the top and bottom card values together and subtract 2 to give the value of the central card.

SOLUTIONS

25 – I
Working in rows, the central letter is always the vowel which appears in the alphabet, between the left and right hand letters.

26 – 1
Working in rows, top to bottom, and reading each row as a 3-digit number, they follow the sequence of multiples of 11, from 9 to 11.

27 – A
Square the numerical value of each large letter, and put the letter with the corresponding value in the smaller, central square in the opposite position.

28 – 5, 15
In each circle, numbers in alternate segments add up to 20.

29 – 9
Using the top two grids as a source, numbers in the lower left grid equal the sums of numbers in corresponding positions of the top two grids, subtracting 1 each time, and numbers in the lower right grid equal the differences between numbers in corresponding positions of the top two grids, adding 1 each time.

30 – 19
Divide the diagram in half, horizontally and vertically, to give 4 squares, each 3x3. In each square, add up the 4 outer numbers, and put the result in the space in the centre.

31 – To the 5
Start with the top left clock face and move clockwise around the others. The sum of the numbers pointed to by the hour and minute hand follows the sequence 3, 6, 9, 12 and 15.

32 – T
In each row, add together the numerical values of the pairs of letters to the left and right, then calculate their difference, putting the letter with this numerical value in the centre space.

33 – D
Working in rows, reflect the left and right hand grids around the vertical axis, and superimpose them to give the pattern in the central grid.

34 –

Reader	Book type	Hero	Book length
Anne	Romance	Max Morris	120 pgs
Beryl	Thriller	Lucy Carr	250 pgs
Frank	Biography	Pete Shear	400 pgs

35 – K
Start on the left hand side, and move clockwise around the diagram. Letters advance through the alphabet 9 letters at a time.

36 – 9
Take any group of 5 numbers along the side of the square, and their total is always 25.

37 – 13
Starting with the top row, take the left and centre circles and add together numbers in the corresponding segments, putting the results in the segments of the lower right circle, do the same with the lower left and centre circle, putting the results in the upper right circle.

38 – C
In each row, the sum of the numerical values of the left and right hand letters equals the numerical value of the central letter.

39 – From left to right, 2, 9
The numbers in every horizontal and vertical line add up to 25.

40 – B

41 – M
Working in rows, from top to bottom, the sum of the numerical values of the letters follows the sequence 16, 18, 20, 22, 24.

42 – Mark gets £50, Patrick gets £150 and Peter gets £300.

43 – From left to right, K, Λ, H
Start at the top left, and move clockwise, in a spiral, towards the centre. Letters are written in alphabetical order, in steps of 5, in alternate circles.

44 – 29
In each diagram, add up the 4 outer numbers then add 2 for the left hand group, 4 for the next, then 6, then 8, and put this result in the central circle.

45 – 1
Calculate the sums of the numbers in the left and right hand circles, to give 2-digit answers. Write the left hand answer in the top 2 segments of the central circle, and put the right hand answer in the bottom 2 segments of the central circle.

46 – 56
In each diagram, multiply the left hand number by the upper central number to give the central number one line down, and multiply the right hand number by the upper central number to give the lower central number.

47 – 4
Start on the left and move to the right, taking pairs of dominoes. The sum of each pair of dominoes follows the sequence 5, 10, 15 and 20.

48 – Flip the 9 over, to read 6, making the sum of both sets of numbers 21.

49 –

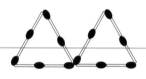

50 – 2, 4, 8, 16, 32 and 64.

51 – 3
Split the diagram in half, vertically, to give two columns of 2-digit numbers. The columns form, from top to bottom, left to right, multiples of 7, from 14 to 63.

LEVEL 19

1 – B
In each row, the left grid has one line of black dots, the central grid has 2 lines and the right grid has 3 lines.

2 – A
On each watch, the time shown contains two digits that are the same.

SOLUTIONS

3 – 4
Split the diagram into quarters, each one exactly the same.

4 – 9
Using the top row, double all the values in the left hand circle, and add the corresponding values in the middle and right hand circles, putting the results in the lower left hand circle, repeat the above sequence, but doubling the values in the centre circle, and putting the result in the lower centre circle, finish off by doubling the values in the upper right, and putting the results lower right.

5 – Z
Start on the top left of the diagram, and move from left to right, top row to bottom row. Letters advance through the alphabet in steps of 0, 7 then 0, before repeating this pattern.

6 – Q
Starting on the top left, and moving around the whole diagram in an anti-clockwise direction, outside then inside, letters advance through the alphabet 5 letters at a time.

7 – S
Starting on the left of the diagram, and working in columns from left to right, letters move through the alphabet 7 at a time.

8 – 6
Starting on the left, taking one number from corresponding segments in each circle, and reading this as a 3-digit number, the numbers follow the sequence of squares of 14, 15 and 16.

9 – 3
Split the circle in half vertically, and take pairs of digits from corresponding segments of the left and right hand halves of the circle. Reading these pairs of digits as 2-digit numbers, these numbers follow the sequence of multiples of 9, from 45 to 63.

10 – 5
As you go down, alternately subtract 8 to give the next number, then divide by 2. Repeat this pattern.

11 – 89
Working from top to bottom, numbers represent the sequence of Square Numbers, from 144 to 289, with the first digit left out.

12 – G
Start at the top of the triangle and move anti-clockwise around it. Letters move through the alphabet in steps of 3, 4, 5, 6, etc.

13
The circles spell out the names Joseph, Edward, Andrew and Robert.

14 – 3
In each square, add the top two numbers together to get a two digit number, and write this in the lower half of the square.

15 – 1
Working from left to right, along the top row and then the bottom, the sum of the numbers in each circle follows the sequence of Prime Numbers

16 – 8
In each row, the middle value equals the sum of the left and right hand values, adding 2 for the top row, 4 for the middle row, and 6 for the bottom row.

17 – D
Start with the H in the top left segment, and move clockwise around the shape, alternating between outer segment then inner segment. Letters advance through the alphabet 6 letters at a time.

18 – 38
Starting at the top, add 4 to the first number to get the second, then add 5, 6, 7, etc.

19 – 0
Working through the diagram in rows, the right hand value equals the sum of any odd numbers in the rest of the row.

20 – A
If you draw lines through the black dots in each grid, straight sided shapes are formed. Working from left to right, top row then bottom, the number of sides in each shape increases by 1 each time, from 3 to 8.

21 – F
Letters follow the alphabetic sequence in steps of 3. The sequence starts at the top of the left hand star, and moves to the same position on the next star to the right, etc. Then the next point clockwise of the star.

22 – 3
The sum of the numbers in each column of the diagram is always 21.

23 – L
Starting with H and moving anti-clockwise, letters advance through the alphabet in steps of 10, then 8, then 6, etc.

24 – 7
Add the number at each corner of the diagram to its 2 adjacent numbers. The total is always 15.

25 – To the 8
Start with the top clock face and move clockwise around the others. The sum of the numbers pointed to by the 2 hands follows the sequence 5, 10, 15, 20.

26 – C
Working in rows, if you superimpose the crosses in each grid, you get a perfectly symmetrical design each time.

27 – 17
As you move to the right, double the first number to give the next one, then subtract 5. Repeat this sequence.

28 – J
As you move down, add the number of straight lines in the first letter to the numerical value of that letter to give the next one down.

29 – F
Start with the A in the top left hand segment, and move in straight vertical lines, from top to bottom, left to right. Letters follow the alphabetic sequence, skipping 1 letter, then 2, then 3, etc.

30 – 518
As you move clockwise, subtract 3 from the first number and multiply by 2 to give the next one round.

31 – 1
Digits in the four corners of the diagram add up to 20, as do the digits in the middle of the four sides.

32 – 10
Moving clockwise around the triangle, and starting in any corner, the next number clockwise equals the sum of the two corner circles, from either side, and the number after that equals the difference of the two corner circles.

SOLUTIONS

33 – 15
Starting with the numbers in the segments in the top circle, multiply by 2, and subtract two to give the values in the left hand circle, and multiply by 3 and subtract 3 to give the values in the lower circle.

34 – 3
Taking each row as a 3-digit number, rows follow the sequence of cube numbers 5, 6 and 7.

35 – E
Start at the top left, and move around the diagram in a Z shape. The numerical value of the letters increases alternately by 6, then 3.

36 – E
Convert each letter to its numerical value, and split the diagram into rows, reading each row as a 2 or 3-digit value. The value represented by the middle line of the diagram equals the sum of the upper and lower values.

37 – 1
Numbers in the segments of the upper left hand circle equal the product of the numbers in corresponding segments of the lower 2 circles, and the numbers in the segments of the upper right hand circle equal the sum of the numbers in corresponding segments of the bottom two circles.

38 – 12
Working from the bottom row to the apex of the triangle, the sum of the values in each row follows the sequence 15, 14, 13, 12.

39 – 1
Split the diagram in half, vertically, to get two columns of 3-digit numbers. Starting top left, and working down, then top right, and down, the 3-digit numbers follow the sequence of Square Numbers from 10 to 21.

40 – It's possible for there to be none with all 4 characteristics.

41 – S
Start with the top left segment, and move to the right, across the top half of the 3 circles. Then move down to the lower half of the circles, and move left. Repeat this pattern for the lower circles. The letters follow the alphabetic sequence, 6 letters at a time.

42 – K
Working through the diagram in columns, from top to bottom, letters move through the alphabet in steps of 5 for the left hand column, 7 for the next one, then 9, then 11.

43 – O
In each diagram, add the numerical values of the top 2 letters together, divide this by 2 and subtract 2 to give the numerical value of the lower letter.

44 – S
Starting top left, and moving clockwise in a spiral, letters follow the alphabetic sequence, in steps of 2, 3, 4, etc.

45 – 2
Reading each line as a 3-digit number, from top to bottom, each represents the cubed values of 7, 8 and 9.

46 – I
In each horizontal line, add the numerical values of the left and right hand letters together, and put the letter with the reverse alphabetical value in the centre.

47 – 8
Reading each horizontal line as a 4-digit number, from top to bottom, each line represents the cubed values of 16, 17, 18 and 19.

48 – 6
Each row and column of the diagram adds up to 15.

49 – A
Split the diagram in half, horizontally and vertically, into quarters. Start in the top left cell of each quarter, and move around it in a clockwise spiral towards the centre. Letters are written in alternate segments, moving forward 7 letters at a time for the top left quarter, 6 letters for the top right, 5 letters for the lower right, and 4 letters for the lower left.

50 –   A: 319   B: 424
In the first oval, the sum of the separate digits of each 3-digit number is 9, and in the second oval, the sum of the separate digits is 7.

51 – C
The sum of the numerical values of the letters in each column of the diagram equals 29.

52 – V
Working in rows, left to right and top to bottom, the sequence follows letters written with only straight lines, skipping every other letter in this sequence.

53 – D
In each figure, the numerical value of the central letter equals the difference between the sum of the two left hand and right hand letters.

1 – U
The sum of the numerical values of the letters in opposite segments of the circle equals 26.

2 – J
Start with the letter J in the top left square, and move clockwise around the other squares. Letters follow the alphabetic sequence, skipping 4 letters at a time. Start with the X in the inner square in the top left, and move clockwise. These inner letters also follow the alphabetic sequence, skipping 5 letters at a time.

3 – 82
Start at the top and work down. Add the separate digits of the top number to the number itself to give the next one down, then subtract 12 to give the one after this. Continue with this alternating pattern.

4 – 4
From top to bottom, reading each pair of numbers as a 2-digit value, the numbers follow the sequence of Square Numbers, from 16 to 49, each written back to front.

5 – V
Starting with the top circle, letters move clockwise, around the outer circles, in steps of 4. Repeat this path, starting with the next circle down in the central column, with the letters moving in steps of 5. Move around the remaining circles in steps of 6.

6 – Q
Start at the top point on the left, moving right across the top of all 3 stars, then back to the left and across the middle points of each star, then

SOLUTIONS

across the lower points of each star. The letters follow the alphabetic sequence, skipping two letters at a time.

7 – 1
In each row of the diagram, the values in the central circle equal the sums of the digits in corresponding segments of the left and right hand circles.

8 – D
Split the diagram horizontally into 3 rows, each 2 circles high. Start with the top left circle in each row, and move one space to the right, alternating down and up. Letters advance through the alphabet 5 letters at a time for the upper double row, 6 letters at a time for the central row, and 7 letters at a time for the bottom row.

9 – D
Working in rows, from left to right, a new element is added to the grid at each step, with the grid rotating 90° clockwise each time.

10 – 2
Split the diagram into 3 vertical columns. The sum of the numbers in each column equal 17.

11 – X
Start at the top left and move to the right, then down one row and to the left, etc in a snakes and ladders pattern. Letters advance through the alphabet 9 letters at a time.

12 – 31
As you move to the right, double the previous number and subtract 4, then 3, then 2, then 1 to give the next number along.

13 – 7
Start anywhere on the diagram, and move clockwise, calculating the sum of every third circle. This always equals 15.

14 – E
Working from left to right, add 3 to each digit separately. If the minutes exceed 60, they return to 0, and the hours return to 1 o'clock if they exceed 12.

15 – 16
Starting top left and moving right, top row then bottom row, add 3 to the numbers in each segment, and rotate

their positions 1 place clockwise, to give the numbers in the next circle along. For the next circle, subtract 1 and rotate their positions 1 place clockwise, continue for the rest of the circles, adding 3 then subtracting 1 alternately.

16 – 5
In each circle, the digit is equal to the number of straight lines used to write the two letters in the same circle.

17 – 5
In each column of the diagram, the central value equals the average of the upper and lower numbers.

18 – B
Start with the J in the top left and move anti-clockwise around the shape in an hourglass shape. Letters advance through the alphabet in steps of 11 letters at a time.

19 – 14
In each star, the central value equals the sum of the top and lower two numbers, minus the left and right hand numbers.

20 – T, D
Starting with the top pair of letters, add their numerical values together to give the value of the left letter in the pair below. Calculate their difference to give the value of the right hand letter in the pair below.

21 – 6
In each square, the sum of the 3 outer numbers minus the central number is always 5.

22 – Outer ring=I,
Starting at the top left segment, the outer letters move clockwise, in steps of 6, and the inner letters move anticlockwise, in steps of 7.

23 – 19
In each circle, starting with the top left segment, and moving clockwise, numbers increase by the same amount each time, starting with 5 for the top left circle, then 6, 7 and 8 for the others.

24 – 1
Read each row of 3 numbers as a 3-digit number, and add the top row value to the middle row, to give the result written in the bottom row.

25 – O
Using the letters in the top right circle as a source, add 4 to the numerical values of each letter to give the letters in corresponding segments of the middle circle, and subtract 5 from the values to give the letters in corresponding segments of the bottom circle.

26 – 21
In each row, add the left and central numbers together, double it and add 1 to give the right hand value.

27 – E
Working in rows, the value of the central letter equals the sum of the left and right hand letters.

28 – A
Starting top left, and working to the right, along the row, then down one row and to the left, etc, letters follow the alphabet, in steps of 2, 3, 4 and 5, before repeating the sequence.

29 – 4
Starting with the top left and centre circles, add the values in corresponding segments in each circle, and put the results in the lower left circle. Do the same with the upper centre and right circles, putting the results in the lower right circle.

30 – F M R
Starting at the top and working down, add 5 to the numerical value of any even numbered letter, and add 7 to the numerical value of any odd numbered letter to give the letters in the space below.

31 – L
Starting with the letters in segments of the top left circle, add 3 to the numerical values of the letters, and write the results in the top right circle, with the relative positions of the letters moving 1/4 turn clockwise. Repeat this pattern, adding 4 to the values of the letters for the lower right circle, and 5 for the letters in the lower left circle, putting the results in the segments, 1/4 turn clockwise each time.

32 – 73, 48
Starting at the top, add the left and right hand numbers together and subtract 5 to give the lower left number. Add 2 to the left hand number to give the lower right hand number.

SOLUTIONS

33 – 1
In each diagram, multiply the left and right hand digits, and subtract the top and lower digits, to give the number in the centre.

34   7
In each circle, read the upper and lower two segments as two digit numbers, and add them together to get a two digit result. Put this result in the middle left and right hand segments.

35 – 28
As you move clockwise, numbers follow the sequence of Prime Numbers, subtracting 1 each time.

36 – U
Starting at the top and working in diagonal lines from top right to bottom left, letters alternately increase in value by 9, then decrease by 3.

37 – 80
In each triangle, the central value equals the product of the 3 outer numbers subtracting the sum of the 3 outer numbers.

38 – Q
In each diagram, start with the letter in the top left and move clockwise around the others. Letters advance through the alphabet in steps given by the numerical value of the central letter.

39 – 7
Start with the upper left and central circles, adding values in corresponding segments of the circles, and put the results in the lower right circle. Repeat this formula, using the upper right and central circles, putting the results in the lower left circle.

40 – G
Starting with the top left square, and moving around the others in a clockwise direction, letters in each segment follow the alphabetic sequence in steps of 2, 3, 4 and 5, with their relative positions in each square moving 1 place clockwise at each turn.

41 – U
Working in columns, add the numerical values of the top two numbers together, and put the resulting letter in their bottom box.

42 – N
The sum of the numerical values of the letters around each star is always 55.

43 – I
Starting on the left, and moving along the diagram to the right, letters move through the alphabet in steps of 5, then 3, then 7, repeating this sequence.

44 – 9
In each triangle, multiply the lower two numbers together and add the upper number to give the value in the centre.

45 – C
In each circle, multiply the inverse alphabetical value of the upper left hand letter by the regular alphabetical value of the upper right hand letter to give the value in the lower segment.

46 – W
Working from top to bottom in columns, letters follow the alphabetic sequence, skipping 5 letters then 7 letters.

47 – 6
Working top to bottom in pairs of columns, left hand then right hand, numbers follow the sequence of multiples of 7, with the digits reversed.

48 – E
As you move to the right, the two shaded segments rotate 1 place at a time in opposite directions, the circle moves 3 segments clockwise, while the cross moves 2 segments anticlockwise.

49 – 5
Splitting the diagram in half both horizontally and vertically, each quarter contains a pattern of black squares, representing the letters W, X, Y and Z.

50 – 3
Using the lower two circles as a source, the values in corresponding segments of the upper left circle equal the sums of the numbers in the lower two circles. The values in the upper central circle equal the products of the values in the lower two circles, and the upper right circle equals the difference between values in the lower two circles.

51 – 6
Starting on the extreme left and right hand of the row and working towards the centre, add the end digits together and subtract 3 to give the next value along to the left, and add 1 to give the next value along to the right. Repeat this sequence, working towards the centre.

52 – 4
In the top row, all diagrams are symmetrical around a vertical axis, in the middle row they are symmetrical around a horizontal axis, and in the bottom row, it's a diagonal axis.

53 – T
In each diagram, start on the top left and move clockwise, to end up in the centre. Letters follow the alphabetic sequence in steps of 6, 7, 8 and 9.